D1401875

PHYSICS

CONCEPTUAL

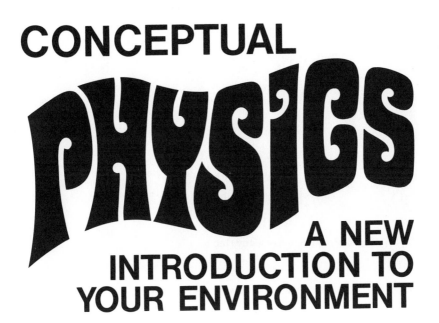

PHYSICS

A NEW INTRODUCTION TO YOUR ENVIRONMENT

Written & Illustrated
by:
PAUL G. HEWITT
City College of San Francisco

LITTLE, BROWN AND COMPANY

To Millie, Paul, Leslie, Jamie,
and the struggling student.

To the Student

Perhaps the most exciting discovery that you can make about the physical world is that all the diverse phenomena of nature are tied together by surprisingly few relationships. By no means apparent only in the laboratory or classroom, physical principles and relationships are evident in the everyday world around you: in the solid earth you stand on, the liquids you drink, the gases you breathe, the heat you feel, the light you see, the sounds you hear, and the radiation you tune in to. The purpose of this book is not to give you the rigorous preparation necessary for science majors, but to turn you on to a more perceptive view of physical reality by introducing you to the central ideas, principles, and relationships of physics and then relating them to your everyday environment.

You won't need a slide rule with this book. The concepts presented here are developed and supported without mathematics. You'll see some formulas from time to time, but these are used as a shorthand way of stating relationships—not as a way of building or proving them. You'll find that the questions within and at the end of each chapter deal with qualitative concepts and ideas rather than mathematical exercises. There are no computations—not even addition. But if you have a slide rule anyway, save it. You may find that physics is enjoyable and take a follow-up course. Then you can use your slide rule!

Paul Hewitt

San Francisco
January 1971

To the Instructor

This book seeks to reveal the excitement of physics by examining the phenomena of our everyday environment. It assumes that the student's personal knowledge of and curiosity about such things as the coldness of tile on bare feet, the sounds produced by the wavy grooves in a phonograph record, and the colors of gasoline on a wet street provide an effective basis for developing many of the principles and relationships in physics. It further assumes that physics is best communicated to the nonscience student conceptually rather than mathematically. This book therefore presents classical and modern physics qualitatively, with emphasis on the relevance of physics to the student's own experience.

I have resisted a strong temptation to be novel and have presented the topics in what I consider the most logical order—which results in an essentially traditional table of contents. After a brief chapter on science in general, the study of physics begins with mechanics. Starting with mechanics usually fails to stimulate student interest because of the numerous mathematical descriptions involved, but this difficulty is minimized with the qualitative approach used in this book. With the concepts of motion, force, energy, momentum, and the conservation principle well in hand, the student then is better equipped for further study. The properties of matter, following the section on mechanics, includes verbatim almost all of Chapter 1 of the first volume of *Lectures on Physics* by Richard P. Feynman. Field theory and electromagnetic induction are later presented as groundwork for electromagnetic radiation; hence the chapters on electricity and magnetism precede light. The electromagnetic and quantum nature of light precedes the behavior of light. A descriptive treatment of quantum mechanics, in turn, follows atomic spectra.

Mathematical derivations and systems and units of measurement are avoided in the main body of the text, appearing only in footnotes or the Appendix. Questions within and at the end of each chapter deal only with qualitative ideas and concepts and are noncomputational. Many of the questions are designed to prompt the application of physical principles to everyday situations. More than enough material is included for a one-semester course, which allows for a variety of course designs to fit the instructor's taste.

Be sure to see the Instructor's Manual for suggestions, teaching tips, and other helpful information.

Paul Hewitt

Acknowledgments

I am especially indebted to Walter Stream for his influence and extensive help in writing the manuscript. I thank Kai Lee for checking most of the manuscript for errors. I am also grateful to Jerry Hosken, Dave Wall, Dan St. John, Bernd Enders, Charles Ballentine, Marshall Johnson, and Annette Rappleyea for their helpful suggestions. I am most grateful to my students, too numerous to list, whose many comments and suggestions were paramount in developing this book, which is in large part a reflection of their participation.

I am grateful to Professor Richard P. Feynman, whose *Lectures on Physics*, Volumes I and II, were very influential in the writing of this book, for permission to include several sections of his Volume I verbatim (which appear in Chapter 9). I am grateful to Kenneth Ford, whose influential text, *Basic Physics,* served as a major reference. Thanks to Eric Rogers for his influence and permission to draw from illustrations (Figures 6.4 and 7.7) in his book, *Physics for the Inquiring Mind*; to Albert Baez for illustrations (Figures 18.1, 29.23, 29.25, and 35.10) from *The New College Physics—A Spiral Approach*; to Theodore Ashford for illustrations (Figures 14.9 and 16.7) from *From Atoms to Stars*.

Thanks also go to Ernie Brown for his artistic assistance on the cover and title page. The photomicrograph on the front and back covers is courtesy of Dr. Erwin Muller, Pennsylvania State University. For typing the manuscript through the several stages of development, I thank Lynette Fung, Liz Brachman, Barbara Buskey, Hilda Jannay, Bernice Johnson, Beverly Lum, Brenda Fung, and Lorraine Kahn.

A special note of appreciation is due Tom Sears, Science Editor of Little, Brown, for his very professional concern for the student's needs. I am also indebted to Judith Fillmore for copyediting the manuscript.

P.H.

Contents

PHYSICS

I think we must retain the belief that scientific knowledge is one of the glories of man. I will not maintain that knowledge can never do harm. I think such general propositions can almost always be refuted by well-chosen examples. What I will maintain —and maintain vigorously—is that knowledge is very much more often useful than harmful and that fear of knowledge is very much more often harmful than useful.

Bertrand Russell, 1872–1970

1
About Science

Science had its beginnings before recorded history when man first discovered reoccuring relationships in his environment. Through careful observations of these relationships he began to know nature, and because of nature's dependability, he found that he could make predictions which would give him some control over his environment.

Science got its greatest impetus in the sixteenth century when man began asking answerable questions about nature—when he began seeking relationships instead of final causes and testing ideas against experiment rather than only against logic. Where man once tried to influence natural events with magic and supernatural forces, he now had science to guide him. His advance, however, was slow because of the powerful opposition to scientific methods and ideas.

In about 1510 Copernicus suggested that the sun was stationary and that the earth revolved about the sun. He refuted the idea that the earth was the center of the universe. After years of hesitation, he published his findings and died before his book was circulated. His book was considered heretical and dangerous and was banned by the church for two hundred years. A century after Copernicus, the mathematician Bruno was burned at the stake—largely for supporting Copernicus, suggesting the sun to be a star, and suggesting that space was infinite. Galileo was imprisoned for popularizing the Copernican theory and for his other contributions to scientific thought. Yet a few centuries later Copernican advocates seemed harmless.

This happens age after age. In the early 1800s geologists met with violent condemnation for differing with the Genesis account of creation. Later in the same century, geology was safe but theories of evolution were condemned and the teaching of them forbidden. Perhaps this continues. "At every crossway on the road that leads to the future, each progressive spirit is opposed by a thousand men appointed to guard the past."* Every age has one or more groups of intellectual rebels who are persecuted, condemned, or suppressed at the time—but to a later age, they

---

*From "Our Social Duty" by Maeterlinck.

seem at least harmless, and often essential to the elevation of human conditions.

The Scientific Attitude   The enormous success of science has led to the general belief that scientists have developed and are employing a "method"—a method that is extremely effective in gaining, organizing, and applying new knowledge. Galileo, famous scientist of the 1600s, is usually credited with being the "Father of the Scientific Method." His method is essentially as follows:

1. Recognize a problem.
2. Guess an answer.
3. Predict the consequences of the guess.
4. Perform experiments to test predictions.
5. Formulate the simplest theory that organizes the three main ingredients: guess, prediction, experimental outcome.

Although this cookbook method has a certain appeal, it has not been the key to most of the breakthroughs and discoveries in science. Trial and error, experimentation without guessing, accidental discovery, and many methods account for the progress in science. Rather than a particular method, the success of science has more to do with an attitude common to scientists. This attitude is essentially one of inquiry, experimentation, and humility before the facts. If a scientist holds an idea to be true, and finds any counterevidence whatever, the idea is either modified or abandoned. In the scientific spirit the idea must be modified or abandoned in spite of the reputation of the person advocating it. As an example, the greatly respected Greek philosopher Aristotle said that falling bodies fall at a speed proportional to their weight. This false idea was held to be true for more than two thousand years because of Aristotle's compelling authority. In the scientific spirit, however, a single verifiable experiment to the contrary outweighs any authority, regardless of his reputation or the number of his followers and advocates.

The scientist must accept facts even when he would like them to be different. He must strive to distinguish between that which he sees and that which he wishes to see—for man's capacity for self-deception is vast. Man has traditionally tended to adopt general rules, beliefs, creeds, theories, and ideas without thoroughly questioning their validity, and to retain them long after they have been shown to be meaningless, false, or at least questionable. The most widespread assumptions are the least questioned. Most often, when an idea is adopted, particular attention is given to cases that seem to support it, while cases that seem to refute it are distorted, belittled, or ignored. We feel deeply that it is a sign of weakness to "change our minds." A competent scientist, however, must be an expert at changing his mind. This is because science seeks not to defend our beliefs, but to improve them. Better theories are made by those who are honest in the face of fact.

Away from his profession the scientist is inherently no more honest or ethical than other people. But in his profession he works in an arena that puts a high premium on honesty. The cardinal rule in science is that all claims must be testable—they must be capable, at least in principle, of being proved wrong. For example, if someone claims that a certain operation has a certain result, it must in principle be possible to perform an operation that will either confirm or contradict the claim. If confirmed, then the claim is regarded as useful and a stepping stone to further knowledge. None of us has the time, or energy, or expense to test every claim, so most of the time we must take somebody's word for a claim. We must, however, have some criterion for deciding whether one person's word is as good as another's, and whether one claim is as good as another. The criterion, again, is that the claim must be testable. To reduce the likelihood of error, the scientist accepts the word only of those whose ideas, theories, and findings are testable—if not in practice then at least in principle. Speculations that cannot be tested are regarded as "unscientific." This has the long-run effect of *compelling* honesty—findings widely publicized among fellow scientists are generally subjected to further testing. Mistakes (and lies) are bound, sooner or later, to be found out; wishful thinking is bound to be exposed. The honesty so important to the progress of science thus becomes a matter of self-interest to the scientist. There is relatively little bluffing in a game where all bets are called. In fields of study where right and wrong are not so easily established, the pressure to be honest is considerably less.

The Difference Between Science and Technology

Many people are confused about what constitutes "science." Some of the antagonism toward science arises from the feeling that modern science is too materialistic and opposed to humanism. But when most people talk about "science" they are really talking about "technology"—which is responsible for many of the good and many of the bad things around today.

Science is a method of answering theoretical questions; technology is a method of solving practical problems (and often creating new problems out of the "solutions"). Science has to do with discovering the true facts and relationships between observable phenomena in nature, and with establishing theories that serve to organize these facts and relationships; technology has to do with tools, techniques, and procedures for implementing the findings of science. This distinction between science and technology is not clear to most people, who are easily convinced that all implementations of science constitute "progress." The purveyors of technology are often able to prevent or stop debate on issues having to do with encroaching technology with the statement, "You can't stop progress." But progress in science and progress in technology are entirely different.

Progress in science excludes the human factor. And this is justly so. The scientist, who seeks to comprehend the universe and know the truth with the highest degree of accuracy and certainty, cannot pay heed to his own or other people's likes or dislikes, or to popular ideas about the fitness of things. What scientists discover may shock or anger people—as did Darwin's theory of evolution. But even an unpleasant truth is more than likely to be useful; besides we have the option of refusing to believe it! But hardly so with technology; we do not have the option of refusing to hear the sonic boom produced by a supersonic aircraft flying overhead; we do not have the option of refusing to breathe polluted air; and we do not have the option of living in a nonatomic age. Unlike science, progress in technology *must* be measured in terms of the human factor. Technology can have no legitimate purpose but to serve man—man in general, not merely some men; and future generations, not merely those who presently wish to gain advantage for themselves. Technology must be humanistic if it is to lead to a better world.

The future of science and technology need not be as bleak as that depicted in Huxley's *Brave New World*, or as harsh as the totalitarianism of Orwell's *1984*. Humanistically oriented, science and technology can alleviate the needless scarcity in the world and make energy, food, and material goods plentiful. In a world of scarcity men have always fought with one another. A world of peace and prosperity has always been a dream rather than a reality, for such a world is hard to come by on a planet hampered by scarcity. Wise applications of science, however, can create a world of material abundance for all men. In a world of abundance, the psyche of man may well be altered—man's relationship to man may then be one of cooperation rather than competition. In such an environment, can a loving world become a reality?

Physics—The Basic Science

Science first branches into the study of living things and non-living things: the life sciences and the physical sciences. Life science branches into such areas as biology, zoology, and botany. Physical science diverges into such areas as astronomy, chemistry, and physics. But physics is more than a part of the physical sciences. Physics is the most fundamental and all-inclusive of the sciences, both life and physical. Physics, essentially the study of matter and energy, is at the root of every field of science, and underlies all phenomena. Physics is the present-day equivalent of what used to be called *natural philosophy*, from which most of present-day science arose.

The following chapters represent the findings of those who answered the compelling call to adventure—the expedition in search of the hows and whys of the physical world. Their findings are our legacy. In these chapters we will attempt to develop a conceptual understanding of this legacy as it relates to the phenomena of motion, force, energy, matter, sound, electricity, magnetism, light, and the atom and its nucleus. The analysis of these topics makes up that which we call physics, the knowledge of which opens new doors of perception. Our environment is far richer when we are aware of the beauty and harmony of the laws by which all physical phenomena are governed.

Suggested Reading

Baker, Adolph, *Modern Physics and Antiphysics*, Reading, Mass., Addison-Wesley, 1970. This is an interesting paperback which, in addition to treating modern physics, explores current attitudes concerning the relevance of physics today.

Photo by Frank Zagarino.

PART I

Mechanics

2

The Study of Motion

More than two thousand years ago the ancient Greek scientists were familiar with some of the ideas in physics that we study today. They had a very good understanding of levers, simple machines, and floating bodies, and a fairly good understanding of some of the properties of light. But they were confused about motion. Probably the first to seriously study motion was Aristotle, the most outstanding philosopher-scientist in ancient Greece. Aristotle attempted to clarify motion by classification.

Aristotle on Motion

Aristotle divided motion into two main classes: *natural motion* and *violent motion*. We shall briefly consider each.

Natural motion was thought to proceed from the "nature" of bodies. In Aristotle's view every body in the universe had a proper place, determined by this "nature"; and any body not in its proper place would "strive" to get there. Being of the earth, an unsupported lump of clay properly fell to the ground; being of the air, an unimpeded puff of smoke properly rose; being a mixture of earth and air, but predominantly earth, a feather properly fell to the ground but not as rapidly as a pure lump of clay. Larger bodies were expected to strive harder—hence, bodies in the same medium were thought to fall with speeds proportional to their weights: the heavier a body, the faster it fell.

Natural motion could be either straight up or straight down, as in the case of all things on earth; or they could be circular, as in the case of celestial objects. Unlike up and down motion, circular motion could be perceived as without beginning or end, repeating itself without deviation. Thus Aristotle asserted that celestial bodies were perfect spheres made of a perfect and unchanging substance which he called "ether" (the only celestial body in which any kind of change or imperfection could be detected was the moon—but the moon, after all, was nearest the earth and suffered some contamination from the corrupted earth).

Violent motion, Aristotle's other class of motion, resulted from pushing or pulling forces. Violent motion was imposed motion.

9

A person pushing a cart or lifting a heavy weight imposed it, as did someone hurling a stone or winning a tug-of-war. The wind imposed it on ships. Flood waters imposed it on boulders and tree trunks. The essential thing about violent motion was that it was externally caused and was imparted to objects—they moved not of themselves, but were pushed or pulled.

The concept of violent motion had its difficulties, for the pushes and pulls responsible for it were not always evident. For example, a bowstring moved an arrow until the arrow left the bow; after that, further explanation of the arrow's motion seemed to require some other pushing agent. It was imagined, therefore, that a parting of the air by the moving arrow resulted in a squeezing effect on the rear of the arrow as the air rushed back to prevent a vacuum from forming. In this way the arrow was propelled through the air as a bar of soap is propelled in the bathtub when you squeeze one end of it.

To sum up, Aristotle taught that all motions resulted either from the nature of the moving object or from a sustained push or pull. Provided only that a body was in its proper place, it would not move unless subjected to a force. Except for the celestial bodies, the normal state was one of rest.

Aristotle's views were generally thought beyond question for nearly two thousand years. Implicit in the thinking of ancient, medieval, and early Renaissance man was the notion that the normal state of bodies was one of rest. Since it was evident to most thinkers up to the sixteenth century that the earth must be in its proper place—and since a force capable of moving the earth was inconceivable, it seemed quite clear that the earth does not move.

It was in this climate that the astronomer Copernicus formulated his theory of the moving earth. Copernicus reasoned from his astronomical observations that the earth traveled around the sun. For years he worked without making his thoughts public. This was for two reasons. The first was that he feared persecution —a theory so completely different from common opinion would surely be taken as an attack on established order. The second reason was that he had grave doubts about it himself—he could not reconcile the idea of a moving earth with the prevailing ideas of motion. Finally, in the last days of his life, at the urging of close friends he sent his *De Revolutionibus* to the printer. The first copy of this famous exposition reached him on the day he died, May 24, 1543.

Most of us know about the reaction of the medieval church to the idea that the earth traveled around the sun. Because Aristotle's views had become so formidable a part of church doctrine, to contradict them was to question the church itself. For many church leaders the idea of a moving earth threatened not only their authority, but the very foundations of faith and civilization. Their fears were well founded. For better or for worse this new idea was to overturn their conception of the cosmos.

Galileo and the Leaning Tower

It was Galileo, the foremost scientist of the sixteenth century, who gave credence to the Copernican view of a moving earth. He accomplished this by discrediting the Aristotelian ideas about motion. Although not the first to point out difficulties in Aristotle's views, Galileo was the first to provide conclusive refutation through observation and experiment.

Aristotle's falling-body hypothesis was easily demolished by Galileo. He is said to have dropped objects of various weights from the top of the Leaning Tower of Pisa and compared their falls. Contrary to Aristotle's assertion, he found that a stone twice as heavy as another did not fall twice as fast. Except for the small effects of air resistance, Galileo found that objects of various weights, when released at the same time, fell together. On one occasion, Galileo is alleged to have attracted a large crowd to witness the dropping of a light object and a heavy object from the top of the tower. It is said that many observers of this demonstration who saw the objects hit the ground together scoffed at the young Galileo and continued to hold fast to their Aristotelian teachings.

Galileo's Inclined Planes

After destroying the falling-body theory, Galileo went further and flatly denied the basic principle of Aristotle: that a body requires a push or pull to keep it moving. According to Galileo, if there is no interference with a moving body, it will keep moving in a straight line forever—no push, pull, or force of any kind is necessary.

He tested this theory of motion by experimenting with the motion of various objects on inclined planes. He noted that balls rolling on downward sloping planes picked up in speed while balls rolling on upward sloping planes lost speed, Figure 2.1. From this he reasoned that balls rolling along a horizontal plane would neither speed up nor slow down. In practice, of course, such a rolling ball would slow down. But the ball would finally come to rest not because of its "nature," but because of friction.

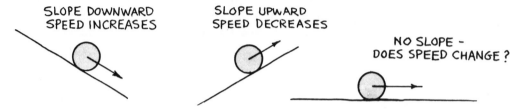

Fig. 2.1   Motion of a ball on various planes.

This idea was supported by Galileo's observation of motion along smoother surfaces: when there was less friction, the motion of bodies persisted for a longer time—the less the friction, the more the motion approached constant speed. He reasoned that in the absence of friction or other opposing forces, a body would go on forever.

This assertion was supported by a different experiment and another line of reasoning. Galileo placed two of his inclined planes facing each other, Figure 2.2. He observed that a ball released from a position of rest at the top of a downward sloping

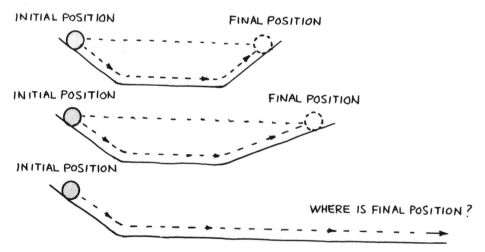

Fig. 2.2   A ball rolling down an incline on the left tends to roll up to its initial height on the right. The ball must roll a farther distance as the angle of the incline on the right is reduced.

plane rolled down and then up the slope of the upward sloping plane until it almost reached its initial height. He reasoned that only friction prevented it from rising to exactly the same height, for the smoother the planes, the more nearly the ball rose to the same height. Then he reduced the angle of the upward sloping plane. Again the ball rose to the same height, but it went farther. Additional reductions of the angle yielded similar results—to reach the same height the ball had to go farther each time. He then asked the question, "If I have a long horizontal plane, how far must the ball go to reach the same height?" The obvious answer is, "Forever—it will never reach its initial height."*

Galileo made a still deeper analysis. Because the downward motion of the ball from the first plane is the same for all cases, the speed of the ball when it begins moving up the second plane is the same for all cases. If it moves up a steep slope it loses its speed rather rapidly. On a lesser slope it loses its speed more slowly and rolls for a longer time. The less the upward slope, the more slowly it loses its speed. In the extreme case where there is no slope at all—that is, when the plank is horizontal—the ball should not lose any speed. In the absence of retarding forces the ball should move forever without slowing down. This tendency of an object to maintain its state of motion he called *inertia*.

Galileo's concept of inertia discredited the Aristotelian theory of motion. It could then be seen that no force was required to keep the earth in motion. The way was open for Isaac Newton to synthesize a new vision of the universe. Before we go on to Newton, however, we should acquaint ourselves with some of the terms that Galileo introduced to describe motion.

Description of Motion

In Aristotle's description of motion the *distance* of an object from its proper place was of fundamental importance. Galileo broke with the traditional concept and realized that *time* was the important missing ingredient in describing motion. Both distance and time underlie the three ideas needed to describe motion; namely *speed*, *velocity*, and *acceleration*.

Speed

The most basic property of a moving body is *speed*. By virtue of its motion, a body travels a certain distance in a given time. An automobile, for example, travels so many miles per hour.

---

*From Galileo's "Dialogues Concerning the Two New Sciences."

Speed is simply the ratio of distance traveled per time. That is,

$$\text{Speed} = \frac{\text{distance}}{\text{time}}$$

For example, if we drive a distance of 60 miles in a time of 1 hour, we say our speed is 60 miles per hour. More precisely, we would call this our *average* speed, for the speed of our car during the trip usually undergoes some variation. If there is no variation we can refer to our motion as *constant* speed, where *equal distances* are covered in *equal intervals* of time.

The speed that a body has at any one instant is called *instantaneous* speed. It is the speed registered by the speedometer of a car. When we say the speed of a car at a particular instant is 40 miles per hour, we are specifying its instantaneous speed and we mean that if the car continued moving at that rate for an hour it would go 40 miles. The instantaneous speed, or speed at any instant, is often very different from the average speed.

We can look at speed in still another way. Speed is a *rate*, describing how rapidly distance is covered as time goes by. To say that we are traveling 40 miles per hour is not to say that we shall go 40 miles in the next hour. We can certainly travel at 40 miles per hour for distances less than 40 miles. This speed is possible if we travel for small or large distances or for short or long time intervals. Speed is the rate at which distance is covered.

Velocity

When we describe speed and the *direction* of motion, we are specifying *velocity*. In saying a body travels at a rate of 40 miles per hour, we have specified its speed. But when we say a body travels 40 miles per hour to the north, we have specified its velocity. Constant velocity implies constant speed and constant direction—that is, motion is along a straight line. To say that a body moves with constant velocity is to say that it moves with unvarying speed in a straight-line direction. But constant speed may or may not mean constant velocity. For example, a body moving in a circle with a constant speed of 30 miles per hour does *not* have constant velocity, because the direction of motion is changing every instant.

Acceleration

We can change the state of motion of a body by changing its speed, by changing its direction of motion, or by changing both its speed *and* direction. Any of these changes is a change in velocity. We define the change per second of velocity as acceleration.

$$\text{Acceleration} = \frac{\text{change of velocity}}{\text{time}}$$

We are all familiar with acceleration in an automobile. In driving we call it "pick-up" or "get-away"; we experience it when we tend to lurch toward the rear of the car. Suppose we are driving and in one second we steadily increase our velocity from 30 miles per hour to 35 miles per hour, and then to 40 miles per hour in the next second, to 45 in the next second, and so on. We increase our velocity by 5 miles per hour each second. This change in velocity is what we mean by acceleration. In this case we would be undergoing an acceleration of 5 miles per hour per second. Notice that acceleration is not the total change in velocity; it is the *rate of change*, or *change per second*.

The term *acceleration* applies to decreases as well as increases in velocity. For example, we say that the brakes of a car produce large retarding accelerations; that is, the decrease per second in the velocity of a car is large. This is sometimes called *deceleration* or *negative acceleration*. We experience deceleration when we tend to lurch toward the front of the car.

Suppose we were driving around a curve at a constant speed of 30 miles per hour. Although in this case there would be no change in speed, there would be a change in direction and, therefore, a change in velocity. This change in velocity is acceleration, which we would feel as we tended to lurch toward the outer part of the curve. We distinguish between speed and velocity for this reason, and define acceleration as the rate at which velocity changes, thereby encompassing both the cases of change in speed and direction.

Acceleration of Falling Bodies

It was Galileo who first introduced the idea of acceleration. He developed it in describing the motion of falling bodies. Although he had invented the pendulum clock, he could not measure time intervals short enough to accurately measure the velocity of rapidly falling objects. He overcame this difficulty by doing most of his experimental work with inclined planes. This technique enabled him to "slow down" the accelerated motion of rolling balls so that he could more accurately measure the relationships between distance and time.

Galileo verified his guess that the velocity of balls rolling down the inclines increased uniformly with time. He found that the balls picked up the same amount of speed in each successive time interval—that is, the balls rolled with uniform acceleration. For example, if we express velocity and time in modern units, a ball rolling down a plane inclined at a certain small angle might be found to pick up a velocity of 2 feet per second for each second it rolls. It accelerates 2 feet per second each second. Its instantaneous velocity at 1-second intervals, increasing by this amount, is then 0, 2, 4, 6, 8, 10, and so forth, feet per second. We can see that the velocity of the ball at any given time after being released from rest is simply equal to its acceleration multiplied by the time.*

$$\text{Velocity acquired} = \text{acceleration} \times \text{time}$$

If we substitute the acceleration of the ball in this relationship, we can see that at the end of 1 second the ball is traveling at 2 feet per second; at the end of 2 seconds it is traveling at 4 feet per second; at the end of 10 seconds it would be traveling 20 feet per second, and so on. The velocity at any time is simply equal to the acceleration multiplied by the number of seconds it has been moving.

If the incline of the plane is made steeper, the acceleration increases and the ball rolls faster according to the same relationship. The ball attains its maximum acceleration when the incline is tipped vertically—this is the acceleration of free fall. The following table shows what may be observed when air resistance has little or no effect on a falling object.

Time of Fall (in seconds)	Velocity Acquired (in feet per second)
0	0
1	32
2	64
3	96
4	128
5	160

*Note that this relationship follows from the definition of acceleration. From $a = v/t$, simple algebraic rearrangement gives $v = at$.

The column at the right gives the velocity at the end of the first, second, third, fourth, and fifth seconds. The most important thing to note in these figures is the way the velocity changes. *During each second of fall the body gains a velocity of 32 feet per second.* This gain per second is the acceleration. The acceleration of a body falling under conditions where air resistance is negligible is approximately equal to 32 feet per second per second.*

Note from the table that the velocity acquired by a falling body is equal to the acceleration multiplied by the time of fall. We can express the velocity of a falling body in shorthand notation as

$$v = 32t$$

Here v is the velocity of fall expressed in feet per second when the number of seconds of fall is substituted for t. A more detailed analysis of this with numerical examples can be found in Appendix II at the end of this book.

Galileo verified a second reasoned guess with his inclined planes. He reasoned that the distance a uniformly accelerating object travels is proportional to the square of the time. His deduction and an algebraic derivation of this relationship can also be found in Appendix II. We will state here only the results. The distance traveled by a uniformly accelerating body starting from rest is

$$\text{Distance traveled} = \tfrac{1}{2} \text{ (acceleration} \times \text{time} \times \text{time)}$$

We can express this relationship for the case of a freely falling body in shorthand notation as†

$$d = 16t^2$$

---

*Note the repetition of "per second." From the nature of the meaning of the word *acceleration*, the unit of time enters *twice*—once for the unit of velocity, and again for the interval of time in which the velocity is changing. Instead of stating the acceleration of freely falling objects to be "32 feet per second per second," we can shorten this to "32 feet per second²" or, in briefest notation, "32 ft/sec²," read "32 feet per second squared."

†d = average velocity × time

$$d = \frac{\text{beginning velocity} + \text{final velocity}}{2} \times \text{time}$$

$$d = \frac{0 + 32t}{2} \times t$$

$d = 16t^2$ (See Appendix II for further explanation.)

where d is the distance in feet when the time of fall in seconds is substituted for t and squared. Compare this formula with the following table.

Time of Fall (in seconds)	Distance Fallen (in feet)
0	0
1	16
2	64
3	144
4	256
5	400

Note that an object falls a distance of only 16 feet during the first second of fall, although its velocity at 1 second is 32 feet per second. This is often confusing, for we may think that the object should fall a distance of 32 feet. But for it to fall 32 feet in its 1 second of fall it would have to fall at an average velocity of 32 feet per second for the *entire* second. It starts its fall at 0 feet per second and its velocity is 32 feet per second only in the last instant of the 1-second interval. Its average velocity during this interval is the average of its beginning and final velocities, 0 and 32 feet per second. This is 16 feet per second, which over a time interval of 1 second gives a distance of 16 feet. As the object continues to fall in succeeding seconds, it will fall through ever-increasing distances because its velocity is continuously increasing.

It is a common observation that all bodies do not fall with equal accelerations. A leaf, a feather, or a sheet of paper, for example, may flutter to the ground slowly. That the air is the factor responsible for these different accelerations can be shown very nicely with a closed glass tube containing a light and heavy object, a feather and a coin, for example. In the presence of air the feather and coin fall with quite unequal accelerations. But if the air in the tube is evacuated by means of a vacuum pump, and the tube is quickly inverted, the feather and coin fall with the same acceleration, Figure 2.3. Although air resistance appreciably alters the motion of falling feathers and the like, the motion of heavier objects like stones and baseballs is not appreciably affected by the air. The relationships $v = 32t$ and $d = 16t^2$ can be used to a very good approximation for most objects falling in air.

Fig. 2.3 A feather and a coin fall at equal speeds in a vacuum.

$$\text{SPEED} = \frac{\text{DISTANCE}}{\text{TIME}}$$

TIME = 1 HOUR

SAN FRANCISCO

LIVERMORE

$$\text{SPEED} = \frac{60\text{ MI}}{1\text{ HR}} = 60 \text{ }^{MI}\!/_{HR}$$

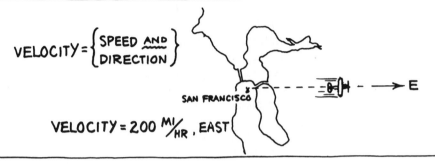

$$\text{VELOCITY} = \left\{ \begin{array}{l} \text{SPEED AND} \\ \text{DIRECTION} \end{array} \right\}$$

SAN FRANCISCO

E

$$\text{VELOCITY} = 2.00 \text{ }^{MI}\!/_{HR}\text{ , EAST}$$

ACCELERATION

$$\left\{ \begin{array}{l} \text{RATE OF} \\ \text{CHANGE IN} \\ \text{VELOCITY} \end{array} \right\} \text{ DUE TO } \left\{ \begin{array}{l} \text{CHANGE IN SPEED} \\ \text{AND}/_{OR}\text{ DIRECTION} \end{array} \right\}$$

30 $^{MI}\!/_{HR}$ 60 $^{MI}\!/_{HR}$ 0 $^{MI}\!/_{HR}$

CHANGE IN SPEED BUT
NOT DIRECTION

30 $^{MI}\!/_{HR}$ 30 $^{MI}\!/_{HR}$

CHANGE IN DIRECTION
BUT NOT SPEED

CHANGE IN SPEED
AND DIRECTION

$$\text{ACCELERATION} = \frac{\text{CHANGE IN VELOCITY}}{\text{TIME}}$$

TIME = 0 SEC. VELOCITY = 0

TIME = 1 SEC. VELOCITY = 32 $^{FT}\!/_{SEC}$

TIME = 2 SEC. VELOCITY = 64 $^{FT}\!/_{SEC}$

$$\text{ACCELERATION} = \frac{64 \text{ }^{FT}\!/_{SEC}}{2 \text{ SEC}}$$

$$a = 32 \frac{^{FT}\!/_{SEC}}{SEC}$$

$$a = 32 \text{ }^{FT}\!/_{SEC}\text{ SEC}$$

$$a = 32 \text{ }^{FT}\!/_{SEC^2}$$

Fig. 2.4   Motion analysis.

Much of the confusion that arises in analyzing the motion of falling objects comes about because it is easy to get "how fast" mixed up with "how far." When we wish to specify how fast something is falling, we are talking about velocity, which is expressed as $v = 32t$. When we wish to specify how far something falls, we are talking about distance, which is expressed as $d = 16t^2$. Velocity (how fast) and distance (how far) are entirely different from each other.

The most confusing concept, and probably the most difficult encountered in this book, is "how quickly does how fast change" —acceleration. What makes acceleration so complex is that it is *a rate of a rate*. It is often confused with velocity, which is itself a rate. Acceleration is not velocity, nor is it even a change in velocity; it is the rate at which velocity itself changes.

Please remember that it took mankind nearly two thousand years from the time of Aristotle to reach a clear understanding of motion, so be patient with yourself if you find that you require a few hours to achieve as much!

Questions

1. A ball is rolled across the top of a billiard table and slowly rolls to a stop. How would Aristotle interpret this observation? How would Galileo interpret it?

2. If the speedometer of a car indicates a constant speed of 30 miles per hour, can you say that the car is *not* accelerating? Why not?

3. Distinguish between uniform velocity and uniform acceleration.

4. Compare the accelerations of a car and a bicycle for the case where the car increases its speed from 60 to 65 miles per hour in the same time that the bicyclist goes from rest to 5 miles per hour.

5. Perform one of the very rare numerical exercises asked for in this book and extend the tables on pages 16 and 18 from 0 to 5 seconds to 0 to 10 seconds.

3
Newton's Laws of Motion

Newton's First Law of Motion

In the year that Galileo died, Isaac Newton was born. Twenty-three years later Newton had developed his famous laws of motion. These laws, the final attainment of a long scientific revolution, were to complete the overthrow of the Aristotelian ideas that had dominated the thinking of the best minds for two thousand years. We will consider these laws in order—the first, sometimes called "the law of inertia," we quote from Newton's *Principia*:

Law 1. *Every body continues in its state of rest, or of uniform motion in a straight line, unless it is compelled to change that state by forces impressed upon it.*

The key word in this law is *continues*: a body *continues* to do whatever it happens to be doing unless it is acted upon by a force. If it is at rest it *continues* in a state of rest. If it is moving it *continues* to move without turning or changing its speed. In short, the law says that a body does not accelerate of itself; acceleration must be imposed against the tendency of a body to retain its state of motion. This neatly summarizes our discussion of the previous chapter: recall that this tendency of a body to resist a change in motion was what Galileo called *inertia*.

Every body possesses inertia, and how much depends on the amount of matter the body contains—the more matter, the more inertia. In speaking of how much matter a body contains, we use the term *mass*. The greater the mass of a body, the greater its inertia. Mass is a measure of the inertia of a body.

It is easy to confuse the two ideas of *mass* and *weight*. This is because mass and weight are directly proportional to each other. That is, if the mass of an object is doubled, its weight is also doubled. If the mass of an object is halved, its weight is halved. But there is a distinction between the two. We can define each as follows:

Mass: *The quantity of matter in a body. More specifically, it is the measurement of the inertia or sluggishness that a body, in the absence of friction, exhibits in response to any effort made to start it, stop it, or change in any way its state of motion.*

Weight: *The force of gravitational attraction upon a body.*

In the United States we commonly describe the quantity of matter in an object by its gravitational pull to the earth, or its weight. This is usually expressed in pounds. In most of the world, however, the measure of matter is commonly expressed in mass units, the gram or the kilogram.* At the surface of the earth, the mass of a 1-kilogram brick weighs 2.2 pounds. Away from the earth's surface, where gravity is less, a 1-kilogram brick weighs less. On the moon, for example, where gravity is only a sixth as strong as earth gravity, 1 kilogram of mass weighs about 0.36 pounds. But the mass of the brick is the same everywhere. The brick offers the same resistance to speeding up, regardless of whether or not the earth, moon, or anything at all is attracting it. For example, in a space capsule located at a region between the

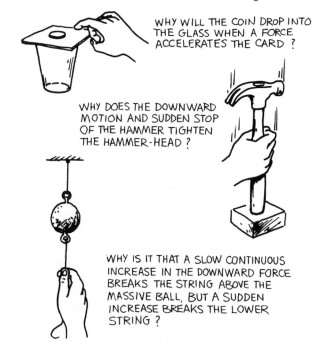

WHY WILL THE COIN DROP INTO THE GLASS WHEN A FORCE ACCELERATES THE CARD ?

WHY DOES THE DOWNWARD MOTION AND SUDDEN STOP OF THE HAMMER TIGHTEN THE HAMMER-HEAD ?

WHY IS IT THAT A SLOW CONTINUOUS INCREASE IN THE DOWNWARD FORCE BREAKS THE STRING ABOVE THE MASSIVE BALL, BUT A SUDDEN INCREASE BREAKS THE LOWER STRING ?

Fig. 3.1

---

*The system of measurement common in America is called the "engineering system," in which the unit of mass is called the *slug* and the unit of force is called the *pound*. Most other parts of the world use the "metric system," in which the unit of mass is the *gram* or *kilogram* and the unit of force is correspondingly called the *dyne* or *newton*. See Appendix I at the back of the book for more about systems of measurements.

earth and the moon where gravities cancel one another, a brick still has mass. If placed on a scale it wouldn't weigh anything, but its resistance to a change in motion is the same as on earth. Just as much force would have to be exerted by an astronaut in the space capsule to shake the brick back and forth as would be required to shake it back and forth while standing on earth. Except for friction effects, it would be just as hard to push a Cadillac across a level surface on the moon as on earth. How hard it is to get an object moving is one thing and how much it weighs is something else. Mass and weight are different from one another.

It is also easy to confuse mass and volume. Perhaps this is because when we think of a massive object, we think of a big object—that is, a voluminous object that occupies much space. But an object may be massive—a lead storage battery, for example—without occupying much space at all. Or this confusion might be supported because mass and volume are often proportional to each other, at least for the same material. Two kilograms of sugar, for example, will fill a bag of twice the volume as one kilogram of sugar. But this does not mean that mass *is* volume. Because two kilograms of sugar have twice the sweetening power as one kilogram, we don't say that mass *is* sweetening power. Two loaves of bread may have the same mass but quite unequal volumes. You can always compress a loaf of bread and change its volume, but the mass doesn't change—it contains the same amount of matter. So you see that mass is neither weight nor volume.

Although Galileo introduced the idea of inertia, Newton grasped its significance. The law of inertia defines natural motion and tells us what kinds of motion require further explanation. According to Aristotle, the forward motion of an arrow through the air required an explanation. For him, this type of motion was externally caused, because the arrow's state was one of rest. Newton's first law states instead that the behavior of the arrow is natural; constant motion along a straight line requires no explanation. Aristotle and his followers accepted circular motion in the heavens as the natural course of events. The law of inertia makes clear that, in the absence of outside influences, the planets would not move in the divine circles envisioned by the ancients, but in straight-line paths off into space. For Newton, the curved motion of the moon and planets *did* require an explanation. We shall see later that his search for this explanation led to the law of gravity.

Newton's Second Law Every day we see bodies that do not continue in a constant state of motion—things initially at rest later may move; moving objects follow paths that are not straight lines; objects in motion stop. Most of the motion we observe is accelerated motion, and is the result of an impressed force. The relationship of acceleration to force and inertia is given in Newton's second law. It states:

Law 2. *The acceleration of a body is directly proportional to the net force acting on the body and inversely proportional to the mass of the body.*

In symbol notation this can be summarized as

$$a \sim \frac{F}{m}$$

We shall use the wiggly line, $\sim$, as a symbol meaning "is proportional to." We say that acceleration a is directly proportional to the force F, and inversely proportional to the mass m. By this we mean that if F increases, a increases; but if m increases, a decreases. With appropriate units of F, m, and a, the proportionality may be expressed as an exact equation:

$$a = \frac{F}{m}$$

A body is accelerated in the direction of the force acting on it. Applied in the direction of the body's motion, a force will increase the body's speed. Applied in the opposite direction, it will decrease the speed of the body. Applied at right angles, it will deflect the body. Any other direction of application will result in a combination of speed change and deflection. *The acceleration of a body is always in the direction of the impressed force.*

A force, in the simplest sense, is a push or a pull. Its source may be gravitational, electrical, magnetic, or simply muscular effort. In the second law Newton gives a more precise idea of force by relating it to the acceleration it produces. He says in effect that *force is anything that can accelerate a body.* Furthermore, he says the larger the force, the more acceleration it produces—for a given body, twice the force results in twice the acceleration; three times the force, three times the acceleration, and so forth. Acceleration is directly proportional to the applied force.

The body's mass has the opposite effect. The more massive the body, the less its acceleration—for the same force, twice the mass results in half the acceleration; three times the mass, one-third the acceleration. Increasing the mass decreases the acceleration. For example, if we put identical Ford engines in both a Cadillac and a Volkswagen, we would expect quite different accelerations even though the driving force in each car was the same. The Cadillac with its greater mass has a greater resistance to a change in velocity than does the Volkswagen. Consequently, the Cadillac requires a more powerful engine to achieve comparable accelerations. To attain the same acceleration, a larger mass requires a correspondingly larger force. We say acceleration is inversely proportional to mass.

The acceleration of a body then depends *both* on the size of the impressed force and on the mass of the body.

Net Force

Newton's second law tells us that if we wish to accelerate a body, we must exert a force on it; the greater the force, the greater will be the acceleration. But what happens when more than one force acts on a body? For example, if you and a friend pull in the same direction with equal forces on an object, the object will have twice the acceleration as if you pulled alone. If, however, you each pulled with equal force but in opposite directions, the object would not accelerate. Because they are oppositely directed, the forces on the object cancel one another.

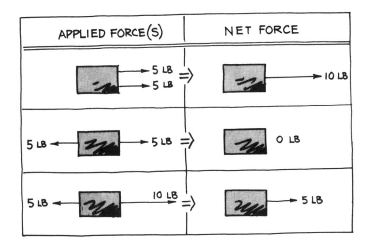

Fig. 3.2   Net force.

One of the forces can be considered to be the negative of the other and they add algebraically to zero.

When forces are applied to an object in the same or opposite directions, the acceleration of the object is found to be proportional to the algebraic sum of the forces. That is, if the forces are in the same direction, they are simply added; if in the opposite direction, they are subtracted. For example, if you pull on an object with a force of 20 pounds and your friend pulls in the opposite direction with a force of 15 pounds, the resulting acceleration is the same as if you pulled alone with a force of 5 pounds. The resulting 5 pounds is the *net force*. It is the *net* force that accelerates objects.

If two or more forces are pulling at some angle to one another so they are neither in the same nor opposite directions, they add geometrically. We will consider this more complicated case later in Chapter 5.

This idea of the net force must be taken into account even when a single force is applied, because forces other than the *applied* force may act on the object. Usually these are friction forces. Friction arises from the irregularities in the surfaces of sliding objects. The irregularities act as obstructions to motion. Even very smooth surfaces have irregular surfaces on the microscopic level. There are many points of contact where the atoms cling together. As sliding continues the atoms snap apart or are torn from one surface by the other. In fluids also, there is friction, since a body moving through it must push aside some of the fluid.

The direction of the frictional force is always in a direction opposing motion. Thus if an object is to move at constant velocity, a force equal to the opposing force of friction must be applied. The two forces will exactly cancel one another. We say the net force is zero, hence the acceleration is zero. But zero acceleration does not mean zero velocity. Zero acceleration means that the object will maintain the velocity it happens to have, neither speeding up nor slowing down.

So we see that no force, other than that to overcome friction, is necessary to maintain the motion of a body. A force is necessary *only to change* the state of motion, that is, to *accelerate* it. This is understandable to anybody who has pushed an automobile by hand. A considerable force is necessary to get the car moving from a position of rest. This is because the car must be "accelerated" from rest to a state of motion. But once it is moving, one has only to push with enough force to counterbalance friction. Then the net force on the car is zero and it rolls at constant speed.

Newton's Third Law of Motion

Whenever we exert a force on a body, the body exerts an equal force on us. This important property of forces is called "Newton's third law"—the law of action and reaction.

Law 3. *To every action force there is an equal and opposite reaction force.*

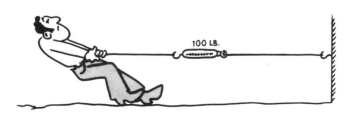

Forces always occur in pairs. There is never only a single force in any situation. For example, a weightlifter pushes up on a barbell while the barbell pushes down on the weightlifter. The force he exerts up is matched to the weight of the barbell directed downward. We can call the upward exertion the *action force*, and the downward weight of the barbell the *reaction force*. Or if we pull on a spring with a force of 25 pounds, the spring stretches and pulls on us with the same force. If we increase the pull to 30 pounds, the spring stretches further until it develops a force of 30 pounds and pulls back on us with that force.

We can never push or pull on something without that something pushing or pulling back on us. If we push against a wall, the wall pushes back on us. If we fasten a hook to a wall so we can pull on the wall, the wall in turn pulls on us—and with an equal but oppositely directed force. It is easy to acknowledge that we push or pull on the wall, but not so easy to see that the wall in turn pushes or pulls on us.

To get a different view of this, suppose we apply a pulling force on the wall by means of a rope. We can measure our applied force by means of a spring scale, Figure 3.4. If we pull on the rope with a force of say 100 pounds, then a tension of 100 pounds is set up all along the rope as our force is transmitted through the rope and spring scale to the wall. Again, it is easy to acknowledge that the rope is pulling on the wall, but not so easy to realize that the wall is pulling on the rope. If the wall didn't pull back on the rope, the rope would accelerate. But the rope doesn't accelerate because, although we pull on one end of the rope, the wall pulls equally hard on the other end. The forces at the ends of the rope cancel one another, producing a zero net force on the rope as a whole. The equal pulls of 100 pounds at each end

Fig. 3.3 Action-reaction. The action force is the upward push of the athlete on the barbell; the reaction force is the weight of the barbell pushing down on the athlete.

Fig. 3.4 A tug-of-war with a hook on the wall.

set up a tension of 100 pounds *within* the rope, which is read on the spring scale. Note that there is a distinction between the net force acting *on* the rope (which would accelerate the rope) and the tension force *within* the rope.

To better understand that the wall pulls on the rope just as hard as we do, lets look at this another way. Suppose we untie the rope from the wall and place the end in the hands of a strong man instead—and suppose the strong man holds the rope as rigidly as the wall. When we pull again with a force of 100 pounds, wouldn't the strong man have to pull equally as hard in the opposite direction just to "hold the rope still" while we pulled on it, Figure 3.5? And isn't the tension in the rope as read on the spring scale the same as before? Think about this. In this case it is easy to see that the rope is being pulled at both ends. But the strong man who "holds the rope" is doing just as the wall was doing when it "held the rope." Both the strong man and the wall pull on the rope. So you see, when you pull on an object, the object really does pull back!

In many instances, Newton's third law is far from obvious. For example, what are the action and reaction forces in the case of a body falling in a vacuum? You might say the weight of the body is the action force, but can you identify the reaction force? It should be mentioned that Newton himself had some difficulty in applying his third law to certain problems. The difficulty arises when one misses an important but subtle distinction between action forces and reaction forces. It is the distinction between forces acting "on the body" and forces acting "by the body." In the case of the person pulling on a spring, the action force is the person pulling *on* the spring. Reaction is the force *by* the spring which acts on the person. In the case of the falling body, the weight or downward force, the *action*, is *by* the earth *on* the body. The upward force, the *reaction*, is *by* the body *on* the earth. So the earth pulls on the body—action; the body pulls on the earth—reaction. The two forces—action and reaction—never act on the *same body*.

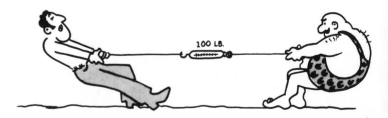

100 LB.

Fig. 3.5 A tug-of-war with a strong man.

The idea of a falling body pulling on the earth may seem puzzling. The pull of the earth on the body is less puzzling because the acceleration of 32 ft/sec^2 is quite noticeable. The same force acting on the huge mass of the earth, however, produces an acceleration so small it cannot be measured. But it is there. A less extreme example might make this clearer. When a rifle is fired, the force acting on the bullet is exactly equal to the reaction force acting on the rifle; hence the rifle kicks. Considering the forces to be equal, one might expect the kick to be considerably more than it is. But in analyzing changes in motion, Newton's second law reminds us that we must also consider the masses involved. Suppose we let F represent both the action and reaction force, m the mass of the bullet, and M the mass of the more massive rifle. Then the accelerations of the bullet and the rifle are found by taking the ratio of force to mass. The acceleration of the bullet is given by

$$\frac{F}{m} = a$$

while the acceleration of the recoiling rifle is

$$\frac{F}{M} = a$$

and we see why the change in motion of the bullet is so huge compared to the change of motion of the rifle. A given force divided by a small mass produces a large acceleration, while the same force divided by a large mass produces a small acceleration. We have used different size symbols to indicate the differences in relative masses and resulting accelerations. If we used similar exaggerated symbols to represent the acceleration of the earth when reacting to a falling body, the symbol m for the earth's mass should be larger than the page. This huge quantity divided into the force F, the weight of the falling body, would result in a microscopic a to represent the acceleration of the earth toward the falling body.

We see Newton's third law at work everywhere. In walking we push against the floor, and the floor pushes back on us. The tires of a car push against the pavement, and the pavement pushes back on the car. It is the reaction forces, those acting in the direction of our resulting accelerations, that account for our motion in these cases. These forces depend on friction; a person or car on ice, for example, may not be able to exert

ACTION: TIRE PUSHES ON ROAD   REACTION: ROAD PUSHES ON TIRE

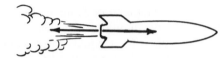

ACTION: ROCKET PUSHES ON GAS

REACTION: GAS PUSHES ON ROCKET

ACTION: MAN PULLS ON SPRING   REACTION: SPRING PULLS ON MAN

ACTION: EARTH PULLS ON BALL

REACTION: BALL PULLS ON EARTH

Fig. 3.6 Action and re-action forces. Note that when action is *A exerts force on B*, the reaction is then simply *B exerts force on A*.

the action force to produce the needed reaction force by the ice. In the case of swimming, we push the water backward, and the water pushes us forward. An airplane pushes the air backward and the air in turn pushes the airplane forward. A rocket in the vacuum of space pushes exhaust gases backward and the exhaust gases in turn push the rocket forward. In these and countless other instances forces always occur in pairs, each of which is equal and opposite to the other. Thus we cannot touch without being touched.

Questions

1. Give an accurate explanation of the process of freeing a coat from dust by shaking it.

2. Why do you fall forward when a moving train decelerates to a stop and fall backward when a train accelerates from rest? What happens if the train rounds a curve at constant speed?

3. If the spool is pulled to the right, which way will it roll? (Try it and see!)

FORCE

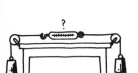

4. A rocket out in space becomes easier and easier to accelerate as it travels along. Why? (*Hint*: About 90 per cent of the mass of a newly launched rocket is fuel.)

5. Why can you exert greater force on the pedals of a bicycle if you pull up on the handlebars?

6. Two 10-pound weights are attached to a spring scale as shown. Does the scale read 0, 10, 20 pounds, or give some other reading? (*Hint*: Would it read any differently if one of the ropes was tied to the wall instead of to the hanging 10-lb weight?)

7. Why does a car burn more gasoline in the city than in the country?

Newton's Laws and Falling Bodies

Galileo gave no reason why bodies fall with equal accelerations. We shall see that Newton's second law provides the explanation. Falling bodies accelerate toward the earth because of the force of attraction between these bodies and the earth. This is the force of gravity, which we will discuss in detail later. We call the gravitational force that acts on a body the *weight* of the body.

A heavier body is attracted to the earth with more force than a light body. A 10-pound object, for example, is attracted to the earth with a force of 10 pounds. A 5-pound object is attracted to the earth with only half as much force. Why then, as Aristotle supposed, doesn't the 10-pound object fall twice as fast? The answer is that the acceleration of a body depends not only on the force, but on the mass as well. A 10-pound body has twice as much mass as a 5-pound body—which is to say, a 10-pound body has twice the resistance to a change in motion as a 5-pound body. Twice the force acting on twice the inertia produces the same acceleration as half the force acting on half the inertia.

Consider, for example, the falling bricks in Figure 3.7. The two bricks tied together have twice the weight, and therefore twice the accelerating force toward the earth as the single brick. But the two-brick package has twice the mass and hence twice the resistance to acceleration. Twice as much mass requires twice the force to accelerate it the same as the single brick. Twice as much force divided by twice as much mass gives the same acceleration as half as much force divided by half as much mass. Both accelerate equally.

This is true for any difference in weight. A boulder one hundred times more massive than a pebble falls at the same rate as the pebble because although the force on the boulder (its

$$\frac{F}{m} = a \qquad \frac{2F}{2m} = a$$

Fig. 3.7 The ratio of weight (*F*) to mass (*m*) is the same for all bodies in the same locality; hence their accelerations are the same in the absence of air resistance.

weight) is a hundred times greater than the force (or weight) of the pebble, its mass (resistance to a change in motion) is a hundred times that of the pebble. The greater force is needed to offset the equally greater mass.

Objects falling in a vacuum is one thing, but what of the practical cases of objects falling in air? Although a feather and a stone will fall equally in a vacuum, they fall quite differently in the presence of air. How do Newton's laws apply to objects falling in air? The answer is that Newton's laws apply exactly the same for all falling bodies, whether they are in air or in a vacuum. The results, of course, are quite different in the two cases. The important thing to keep in mind is the idea of *net force*. In a vacuum the net force is the weight, because it is the only force acting on a falling object. In the presence of air, the net force is the difference between the weight and the force of air resistance.*

The force of air resistance acting on a falling body depends on two things. First, it depends on the size of the falling object; that is, on the amount of air the object must plow through in falling. Second, it depends on the speed of the falling object— the faster the speed, the greater the number of air molecules an object encounters per second, and the greater the force of molecular impact. Air resistance depends on the size and the speed of a falling object.

A feather dropped in the air accelerates very briefly and then "floats" to the ground at constant velocity. This happens because the air resistance acting up against the feather just cancels out the weight. So the net force on the feather is zero and no acceleration takes place. Since the feather is so light and has a relatively large surface area, it doesn't have to fall very fast before the air resistance equals its weight. The same idea applies to all objects falling in air. As a falling object gains speed the force of air resistance builds up until it equals the weight of the falling object. When the force of air resistance equals the weight of the falling object, the *net* force becomes zero and the object no longer accelerates—it falls at a constant speed. Acceleration terminates, and we say the object has reached its *terminal velocity*. For a feather, terminal velocity is approximately a few inches per second, whereas for a skydiver it is about 140 miles per hour. A

---

*In mathematical notation, $a = (F_{net}/m) = (WT - R)/m$, where WT is the weight and R is the air resistance. Note that when $R = WT$, the $a = 0$; then the object falls at *constant* velocity.

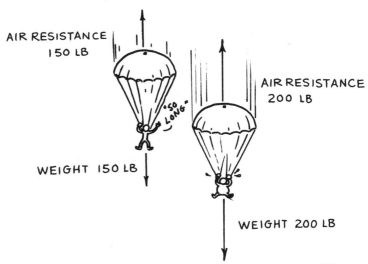

AIR RESISTANCE
150 LB

AIR RESISTANCE
200 LB

"SO LONG"

WEIGHT 150 LB

WEIGHT 200 LB

Fig. 3.8 The heavier parachutist must fall faster than the lighter parachutist for air resistance to cancel his heavier weight.

skydiver varies his terminal velocity by varying his position of fall. Head or feet first, he encounters less air resistance and attains maximum terminal velocity. Minimum terminal velocity is attained by spreading himself out like a flying squirrel.

Consider a two-hundred-pound and a hundred-and-fifty-pound parachutist jumping together from the same altitude. For simplicity, suppose that their chutes are initially opened and are the same size. The same size chute would mean that at equal speeds, the air resistance would be the same on each. Who gets to the ground first, the heavy man or the lighter man? The answer would be that the man having the greatest terminal velocity would get to the ground first. At first we might think that because the chutes are the same, the terminal velocities for each man would be the same and, therefore, both would reach the ground together. This is not true, however, because air resistance also depends on speed. The 200-pound man will reach his terminal velocity when air resistance against his chute builds up to 200 pounds. But the 150-pound man will reach his terminal velocity when air resistance acting against his chute builds up to only 150 pounds. The 150-pound man will reach his terminal velocity first, while the heavier man accelerates to a speed corresponding to 200 pounds of air resistance. Terminal velocity for the heavier man will be greater than terminal velocity for the lighter man because the heavier man must fall fast enough for air resistance to build up to his greater weight. The result is that the heavier man will reach the ground first.

A baseball will fall faster in air than a tennis ball for the same reasons as stated for the parachutists. The difference in the rates of fall is not as pronounced, but the difference is there. The principle is obvious for an exaggerated case, say the falling of a bird's feather and an iron feather of the same size. Acceleration terminates when air resistance builds up to the weight of the falling object.

In Summary

An object at rest tends to remain at rest; an object in motion tends to remain in motion at constant speed along a straight-line path. This tendency of objects to resist a change in motion is called *inertia*. Mass is a measure of inertia. Objects will change their states of motion only in the presence of a net force.

When a net force is impressed upon an object it will accelerate. The acceleration is directly proportional to the net force and inversely proportional to the mass. Symbolically,

$$a \sim \frac{F_{net}}{m}$$

Acceleration is always in the direction of the net force. When objects fall in a vacuum the net force is simply the weight and the acceleration is g. (We use the symbol g rather than a to denote that acceleration results from gravity alone.) When objects fall in air the net force is equal to the weight minus the force of air resistance, and the acceleration is less than g. When the force of air resistance equals the weight of a falling object, acceleration terminates and the object falls at constant velocity.

For every applied force there is an opposite and equal reaction force. Forces therefore always occur in pairs. Action force and reaction force act on different bodies. Action force acts *on* a body and reaction force acts *by* that body; so the action and reaction forces never cancel out.

Suggested Reading

Andrade, E. N., *Sir Isaac Newton—His Life and Work* (Science Study Series), Garden City, N. Y., Doubleday (Anchor), 1954.

Questions

1. Clearly distinguish between *mass, weight,* and *volume.*
2. If a projectile were moving in free space at such a distance from all bodies that gravitation was insensible, in what path would it move?
3. Each of the chain of bones forming your spine is separated from its neighbors by disks of elastic tissue. What happens, then,

when you jump heavily on your feet from an elevated position? Can you think of a reason why a person is a little taller in the morning than at night?

4. If we find a body which we know to be acted upon by a force, but which is not moving, what inference can we draw?

5. What kind of motion does a constant net force produce on a body of constant mass?

6. Why is it more difficult to push a stalled car from a position of rest than it is to keep it in motion once it is rolling?

7. Neglecting the effects of friction, which will roll down a hill faster—a Cadillac or a Volkswagen? Explain.

8. Do you find it easier to walk on a carpeted floor than one having a polished smooth surface? Why is this so?

9. As you stand on a floor, does the floor exert an upward force against your feet? How much force does it exert? Why are you not moved upward by this force?

10. When Galileo dropped two balls from the top of the Leaning Tower of Pisa, air resistance was *not* really negligible. Assuming both balls were the same size, yet one much heavier than the other, which ball struck the ground first? Why?

4
Nonlinear Motion

When a net force is applied along a body's direction of motion, the body travels in a straight line, and we describe its motion as *linear*. When a net force acts in any other direction, the body travels in a curve, and we describe its motion as *nonlinear*. A ball thrown into the air, a rock whirling around in a circular path at the end of a string, a car rounding a curve, the earth and the planets orbiting the sun—these are all examples of nonlinear motion. We will begin our study of nonlinear motion by considering the familiar case of an object thrown into the air—projectile motion.

Projectile Motion

A projectile is any body that is projected by some force and continues in motion by its own inertia. In the absence of gravity the motion of a projectile would be simple enough; it would be linear and uniform. But gravity complicates its otherwise simple motion. Because of the force of gravity, a projectile undergoes acceleration and its motion is different from instant to instant. Its motion is complicated. In order to understand this complicated motion of a projectile, we will separate it into its horizontal motion and its vertical motion.* We will study each of these components of motion individually and then combine our findings.

Let's consider a simple projectile: a ball rolled off the edge of a horizontal table. To consider only the horizontal motion, we will do a simple thought experiment. We will do the impossible stunt of "turning off" gravitation and then investigate the motion of the ball. A neat way to record its motion would be with the use of a strobe light and a camera. We could darken the room, set the camera lens open for a time exposure, and set the strobe light so that it blinks at short, equally spaced intervals of time. This would allow us to photograph the position of the ball at different times on the same photographic plate. Our picture

---

*A rational way to understand any complicated problem is to separate the problem into its component parts and investigate each individually. If the parts can be understood then the task of understanding the whole is clearer.

would look something like that of Figure 4.1a. The motion is seen to be linear and uniform, because no forces accelerate the ball, either vertically or horizontally.

To investigate vertical motion we will turn gravitation back on and take a picture of the ball as it drops from a position of

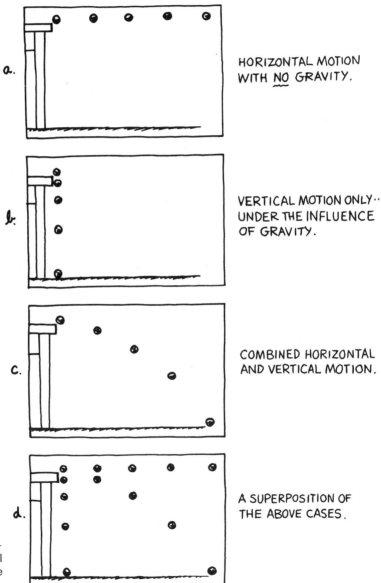

a. HORIZONTAL MOTION WITH NO GRAVITY.

b. VERTICAL MOTION ONLY·· UNDER THE INFLUENCE OF GRAVITY.

c. COMBINED HORIZONTAL AND VERTICAL MOTION.

d. A SUPERPOSITION OF THE ABOVE CASES.

Fig. 4.1 Simulated photographs of a moving ball illuminated with a strobe light.

rest at the edge of the table top. This time it has no horizontal velocity and drops straight down. Our photograph, Figure 4.1*b*, shows that the ball covers successively greater distances in equal intervals of time, which is to be expected because the ball is accelerating. It is accelerating straight downward because there is a gravitational force acting straight downward.

So we find that horizontal motion is uniform, and the projectile covers equal horizontal distance in equal times. Vertical motion is accelerated and the projectile travels successively greater distances in equal time intervals. We performed the first part of our experiment with gravitation "turned off." Suppose we repeat this first part, rolling the ball off the edge of the table, but this time in the presence of gravity. A photograph of this reveals that the curved motion of the ball is a combination of the horizontal and vertical motions, Figure 4.1*c*. During the five flashes of the strobe light the ball has traveled just as far horizontally as it did with no gravity. This is understandable when it is realized that the force of gravity acts only vertically. Gravitation does not act horizontally, so there is no acceleration horizontally. Horizontal motion is unaffected by gravity. Only the vertical part of the motion changes. We can also see that regardless of whether the ball is dropped from rest or moving horizontally, it falls the same vertical distance in the same interval of time. We know this because in each case the strobe light flashed five times before the ball reached the floor. So gravitation pulls on objects whether they are moving or not. We conclude that while the ball is moving sideways it is falling, and the combination of these two motions produces a curved path. This is made clearer if we superimpose the three pictures so we can view all three experiments at once, Figure 4.1*d*. An actual strobe-light photograph of two balls released simultaneously is shown in Figure 4.2. A projectile accelerating vertically while moving at a constant horizontal speed traces out a path called a *parabola*.

Consider a projectile hurled upward, Figure 4.3. If no forces acted on the projectile, then according to the law of inertia it would follow a straight-line path as shown by the dashed line. But the force of gravity causes the projectile to accelerate away from a linear path. At every succeeding instant the projectile tends to follow a linear path (dotted lines), but the force of gravity (arrows) pulls it into a curved path. The figure shows the positions of the projectile along its trajectory at equal intervals of time. Inspection will show that the projectile travels equal *horizontal* distances in equal intervals of time. This is because

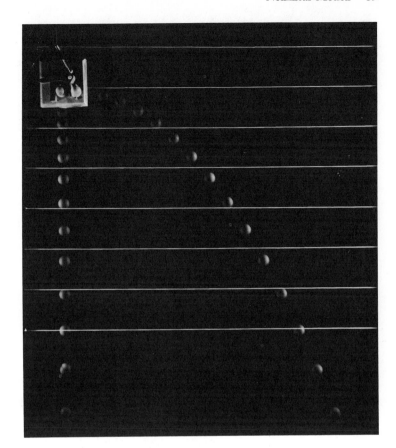

Fig. 4.2 A strobe photograph of two golf balls released simultaneously from a mechanism that allows one ball to drop freely while the other is projected horizontally. (From *College Physics*, Physical Science Study Committee, Raytheon Education Co., 1968.)

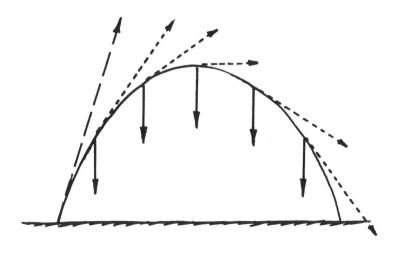

Fig. 4.3 The projectile tends to go in a straight path (dotted lines) but is pulled into a parabola by gravity.

there is no horizontal force and hence no acceleration in the horizontal direction. Acceleration acts only in a vertical direction. The combination of nonaccelerated horizontal motion and accelerated vertical motion results in a parabolic trajectory.*

If the effects of air resistance are negligible, every object projected into the air follows the path of a parabola. In practical cases, air resistance may be considered negligible only for slowly moving objects with high densities, like a rock or solid ball. For high-speed projectiles such as bullets or cannon shells, the air resistance continually slows the projectiles down and the path departs from a parabola, Figure 4.4.

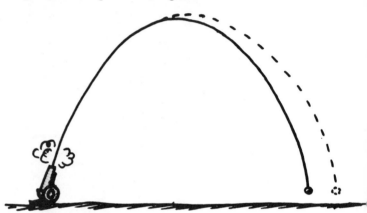

Fig. 4.4 In the presence of air resistance a high-speed projectile falls short of a parabolic path.

The vertical height and horizontal range of a projectile depends on both the initial velocity and angle of projection of the projectile. The paths of several projectiles all having the same initial velocity but different projection angles are shown in Figure 4.5.

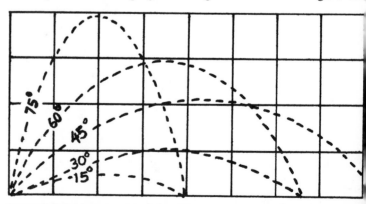

Fig. 4.5 The range of a projectile shot at the same speed at different projection angles.

*Any path followed by a projectile is called a *trajectory*.

The figure neglects the effects of air resistance, so the paths are all parabolas. The maximum height is obtained when the projection is straight up and the maximum horizontal distance when the angle of projection is 45 degrees. Note from Figure 4.5 that the same horizontal distance, or range, can be obtained from two different projection angles. This is true of all pairs of angles that add up to 90 degrees. An object thrown into the air at an angle of 30 degrees, for example, will land just as far downrange as if it were thrown at the same speed at an angle of 60 degrees. For the steeper angle, of course, the object remains in the air for a longer time.

In the absence of air resistance, a projectile will rise to its maximum height in the same time it takes to fall from that height to the ground. This is because its deceleration by gravitation while going up is the same as its acceleration by gravitation while coming down. The speed it loses while going up is therefore the same as the speed it gains while coming down. So the projectile arrives at the ground with the same speed it had when it was projected from the ground, only in the opposite direction.

Circular Motion

A baseball thrown into the air is under the influence of a constant force directed vertically beneath it. At any point along its trajectory, the direction of the force of gravity is parallel to the direction of the gravitational force at any other point. The path of such a projectile is a parabola. If instead a projectile were under the influence of a constant net force directed perpendicular to its direction of motion, its path would be a circular arc. In this case the direction of the force at any position would be directed to a single point located at the radial center of the arc. Both cases are shown in Figure 4.6. The broken lines repre-

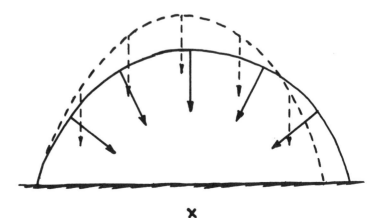

Fig. 4.6 A projectile follows a parabolic path when the force acting on it is straight down. If instead the force acts sideways to its direction of motion and is directed to a single point (X), its path is circular.

X

sent the parabolic path traced when the force accelerating the projectile is always vertical and directed to the horizontal plane beneath; the solid line represents the circular path traced if the force accelerating the projectile were instead directed toward a single point at position X. We find that all objects which move in circular paths are pushed or pulled toward a single point with a constant force.

Fig. 4.7 The force acting on the whirling can is toward the center.

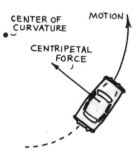

Fig. 4.8 When a car goes around a curve there must be a force pushing the car toward the center of the curve.

Centripetal Force

Any force that causes an object to follow a circular path is called a *centripetal force*. Centripetal means "center-seeking," or "toward the center." If we whirl a tin can on the end of a string, we find that we must keep pulling on the string, Figure 4.7. The centripetal force is transmitted by the string which pulls the can into a circular path. Gravity and electricity can be transmitted across empty space to produce centripetal forces. The moon, for example, is held in an almost circular orbit by gravitational force directed toward the center of the earth. The orbiting electrons in atoms experience an electrical force toward the central nuclei.

When an automobile goes around a corner, the friction between the tires and the road is the centripetal force holding the car in a curved path, Figure 4.8. If this friction is not large enough, the car refuses to make the curve and the wheels slide sideways; we say the car "skids," Figure 4.9.

Centrifugal Force

Consider again the case of the whirling can on the end of a string. The string exerts a force, called the centripetal force, on the can. By Newton's third law, the reaction to this force is an outward pull on the string, equal and opposite to the force the string exerts on the can. This outward force is called the *centrifugal force*. Centrifugal means "center-fleeing," or "away from the center." The two forces, centripetal and centrifugal, are numerically equal;* they act, however, not only in opposite directions, but on different things—one acting on the can, the other on the string.

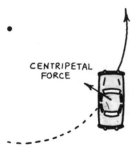

Fig. 4.9 A car skids on a curve when the centripetal force (friction of road on tires) is not great enough.

---

*Both centrifugal and centripetal forces depend on the mass and speed of the circularly moving body and its radius of curvature. The exact relationship is $F = mv^2/r$.

In the case of an automobile going around a curve, the force supplied by the road through the friction between the road and tires is the centripetal force. The reaction to this force, the centrifugal force, is the force the wheels exert on the road, pushing on the road in a direction away from the center of the curve, Figure 4.10. Note that only *centripetal force acts on the car*, moving it toward the center of curvature. *Centrifugal force acts on the road*, as evidenced by gravel that is noticeably pushed toward the outside of the curve.

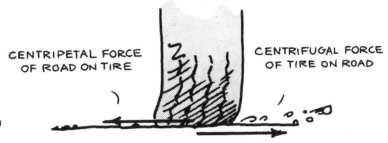

CENTRIPETAL FORCE
OF ROAD ON TIRE

CENTRIFUGAL FORCE
OF TIRE ON ROAD

Fig. 4.10 A tire making a turn toward the left.

In ordinary speech, people do not distinguish between centripetal and centrifugal forces, but apply the name *centrifugal* to both. They may call the force that the string exerts on the whirling can and also the force that the can exerts on the string a centrifugal force; or they may say that a centrifugal force pulls outward on the can. For example, if the string holding the whirling can breaks, Figure 4.11, it is commonly stated that a centrifugal force pulls the can from its circular path. But the fact is that when the string breaks the can goes off in a straight line path because *no* force acts on it. This idea is confusing and merits more explanation.

If you are riding in a car that suddenly stops short, you pitch against the dashboard. In doing so you would not be likely to say that a force pushed you forward. You hit the dashboard because of the absence of a force, that which seat belts would have provided. You hit the dashboard because no force was supplied to stop you along with the car. By the same token, if you are in a car that rounds a sharp corner, you pitch outward against the door of the car. There is no force pushing you against the door, for you hit the door because there was *no* centripetal force holding you in circular motion (that which seat belts and harness would have provided). In the absence of this force, you tend to go in a straight line while the car door curves and crosses

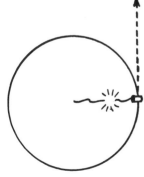

Fig. 4.11 When the string breaks, the whirling can moves in a straight line tangent to its circular path.

your straight-line path and intercepts you. There is no centrifugal or centripetal force banging you against the car door. Yet it is common to say that you hit the door because of centrifugal force.

When we swing a tin can into a circular path by a string, there is no force pulling the can outward. There is no centrifugal force acting on the can. There is only an inward force, the centripetal

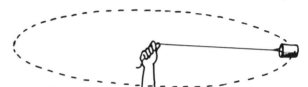

Fig. 4.12   The only force that acts *on* the whirling can (neglecting gravity) is directed *toward* the center of circular motion. This is called *centripetal force.* No outward force acts on the can.

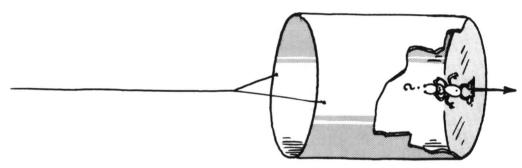

From the point of view of a bug inside the whirling can there exists a force directed *away from* the center of circular motion. He calls this *centrifugal force,* which is as real to him as gravity.

Fig. 4.13   The centripetal force (adhesion of mud on the spinning tire) is not great enough to hold the mud on the tire, so it is thrown off in straight-line directions.

force, the inward pull of the string, acting on the can. By Newton's third law, we can say the can pulls back on the string and there is, therefore, a centrifugal force acting on the string— but not on the can. No centrifugal force acts on the can. Now suppose there is a bug inside the whirling can, Figure 4.12. The bug inside the can would feel himself being forced to the far side of the can's path, and to him, inside the can, there seems to be an outward force. He feels a force pushing him outward away from the center of the swinging system, and he calls this center-fleeing force a centrifugal force. From his point of view or frame of reference, the force seems real. But when viewed from outside the rotating system, the only real force acting on the bug is that of the can pushing against his feet—the centripetal force that holds him in a circular path. To the person who lurches against the car door when the car rounds a corner, the outward "centrifugal force" seems real. But from the point of view of an observer

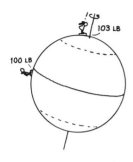

Fig. 4.14 Because of the earth's spin, the weight of a person traveling away from a pole (the axis of daily rotation) gradually diminishes and is least at the equator.

outside the rotating system, such forces are fictitious. They don't exist. The "centrifugal force effect" is attributed not to any force, but to inertia—the tendency of bodies to follow straight-line paths.

Rotational Inertia

Just as an object at rest tends to stay at rest and an object in motion tends to remain moving in a straight line, there is a law of inertia for rotating systems. It is simply that a rotating object tends to remain rotating about its axis of rotation. Once an object is set spinning about an axis of rotation, it tends to remain spinning about that axis. A football, for example, is given a spin about its long axis when it is thrown. Once spinning, it will remain spinning about its long axis, exposing the ball to the least amount of air resistance. Similarly, a bullet is set spinning by spiral bores in the barrel of a gun. The spinning motion offers

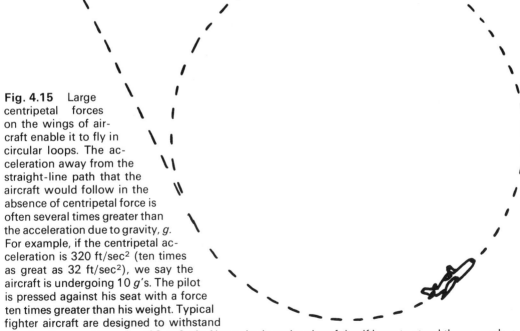

Fig. 4.15 Large centripetal forces on the wings of aircraft enable it to fly in circular loops. The acceleration away from the straight-line path that the aircraft would follow in the absence of centripetal force is often several times greater than the acceleration due to gravity, g. For example, if the centripetal acceleration is 320 ft/sec² (ten times as great as 32 ft/sec²), we say the aircraft is undergoing 10 g's. The pilot is pressed against his seat with a force ten times greater than his weight. Typical fighter aircraft are designed to withstand accelerations on the order of 8 or 9 g's. Not only does the aircraft itself have to stand these accelerations, but so do all the objects in the aircraft, including the organs of the pilot's body. When an aircraft is performing an 8-g turn, for example, the force required to hold the blood in the pilot's brain must be eight times the ordinary force provided by the heart. Without it, blood may rush out of the pilot's brain and result in his "blacking out." Considerable research has been done to develop techniques that allow pilots to undergo several g's without losing consciousness.

stability against slight disturbances that otherwise could set it tumbling in a haphazard manner, thereby increasing air resistance. Once spinning, the flywheel of an automobile engine tends to remain spinning, ensuring rotation of the crankshaft between the applied explosive forces in the combustion chambers.

The rotational inertia of an object, of course, depends on the massiveness of the object. A massive grindwheel has more rotational inertia than a wooden spool of thread. But more important is the location of the mass with respect to the axis of rotation. The greater the distance between the bulk of an object's mass and its axis of rotation, the greater the rotational inertia. Industrial flywheels, for example, are constructed such that most of their mass is concentrated along the rim. Once spinning, they

Fig. 4.16 The tendency of the pole to resist rotation aids the acrobat.

have a greater tendency to remain spinning than if their mass were concentrated nearer the axis of rotation. It follows that the greater the rotational inertia of an object, the harder it is to set that object into rotational motion. This fact is employed by a circus tightrope walker when he carries a long pole to enable balancing. Much of the mass of the pole is far from the axis of rotation, its midpoint. The pole, therefore, has considerable rotational inertia. If the tightrope walker starts to topple over, a tight grip on the pole would require that the pole rotate. But the rotational inertia of the pole resists this, giving the tightrope walker a sufficient margin of time to readjust his position of balance.

Fig. 4.17 A solid cylinder rolls down an incline faster than a ring, whether or not they have the same mass or outer diameter. A ring has greater rotational inertia compared to its own weight.

Because of rotational inertia, a solid cylinder starting from rest will roll down an incline faster than a ring or hoop. The ring has its mass concentrated farthest from its axis of rotation and therefore is harder to start rolling. A ring has a greater tendency to resist a change in its state of rotation. Any solid cylinder will beat any ring on the same incline. This doesn't seem plausible at first thought, but remember that any two objects, regardless of mass, will fall together when dropped. They will also slide together when released on an inclined plane. When rotation is introduced, the object with the larger rotational inertia *compared to its own weight* greater resists a change in its motion. Hence any disk will roll faster than any ring on the same incline.

Summary of Terms

Linear motion. Motion along a straight-line path.

Nonlinear motion. Any motion not along a straight-line path.

Projectile. Any body that is projected by some force and continues in motion by its own inertia.

Parabola. The curved path followed by a projectile in the absence of air resistance.

Centripetal force. A center-seeking force that causes an object to follow a circular path.

Centrifugal force. The reaction to centripetal force, which is an outward force.

Rotational inertia. That property of a body to resist any change in its state of rotation—if at rest it tends to remain at rest; if rotating it tends to remain rotating and will continue to do so unless interrupted.

Questions

1. At the instant a horizontally held rifle is fired over a level range, a bullet held at the side of the rifle is released and allowed to drop to the ground. Which bullet, the one fired downrange or the one dropped from a position of rest, strikes the ground first?

2. In the absence of air resistance, if a ball is thrown vertically upward with a certain initial speed, upon returning to its original level it will have the same speed. When air resistance *is* a factor affecting the ball, will the ball fall to the ground faster, the same, or slower than if there were no air resistance? Why?

3. If a ball is thrown vertically into the air in the presence of air resistance, would you expect the time during which it rises to be longer or shorter than the time during which it falls?

4. Suppose you are on a ledge in the dark and wish to estimate how high above ground the ledge is. So you drop a stone over the edge and hear it strike the ground in one second. How high is the ledge above the ground? Could you estimate the height of the ledge with the stone if you weren't close enough to the edge to be able to drop the stone straight down? If so, how and why? If not, why not?

5. The boy on the tower throws a ball 50 feet downrange as shown. What is his pitching speed?

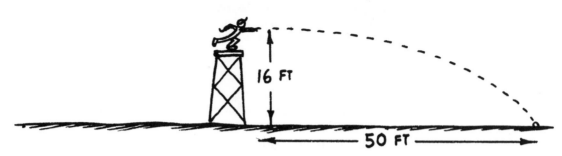

6. The effects of gravity are not felt by occupants in an orbiting space vehicle. Gravity is simulated, however, if the space vehicle is rotating about an axis like a wheel. Explain.

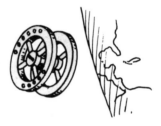

7. There is no centrifugal force acting on the empty whirling can as shown in Figure 4.12. But when a bug is placed in the can, there *is* a centrifugal force acting on the can. Identify this force.

8. A motorcyclist is able to ride on the vertical wall of a bowl-shaped track as shown. His weight is counteracted by the friction of the wall on the tires (vertical arrow). Is it centripetal or centrifugal force that acts on the motorcycle? On the wall?

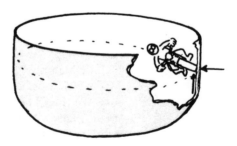

9. If you should buy a quantity of gold in Mexico and weigh it carefully on a spring balance, would the same quantity of gold weigh more, less, or the same if weighed on the same spring balance in Alaska? Explain.

10. Why is it that a horizontally held fly rod greatly aids an angler in maintaining his balance on a thin tree trunk or a rounded log?

5
Vectors, Torque, and Mechanical Equilibrium

Many quantities in physics, such as mass, time, and volume, can be completely specified by their *magnitudes*, or sizes. They do not involve any idea of direction. Such quantities are called *scalars*. They obey the ordinary laws of addition, subtraction, multiplication, and division. If 5 quarts of water are poured into a pail which initially has 3 quarts of water in it, the resulting volume is 8 quarts. If a 10-gram mass is removed from the pan of a balance containing 50 grams, the resulting mass on the pan is 40 grams. These are illustrations of the addition and subtraction of *scalar quantities*.

Some quantities, such as forces and velocities, require both magnitude and direction for a complete description. For example, if we are told that two forces of 10 pounds each are acting on an object, we can specify the resulting force only if we know the directions of the two forces. Or if we are told that a boat is traveling 10 miles per hour in a river that is flowing at 3 miles per hour, we can specify the resulting velocity of the boat only if we also know the relative directions of the stream flow and the orientation of the boat. Physical quantities that must be specified by both *magnitude* and *direction* are called *vector quantities*.

Vectors   *Vector Representation of Force*

A given force can be represented by means of an arrow, or *vector*. The length of the arrow, drawn to some suitable scale, indicates the magnitude of the force, while the direction in which the force acts is shown by the arrowhead. The point of application is represented by the tail of the arrow.

Figure 5.1 shows two forces acting on a cart. The man applies a force of 30 pounds and the donkey applies a force of 50 pounds. The forces are shown by vectors. The scale used lets $\frac{1}{4}$ inch represent 10 pounds. Hence the 30-pound force is represented by a vector $\frac{3}{4}$ inch long, and the 50-pound force by a vector $\frac{5}{4}$ inch long. The cart is represented by the dot. When the two forces act in the same direction, the resulting pull is equal to the sum of the individual forces and acts in the same direction. The cart

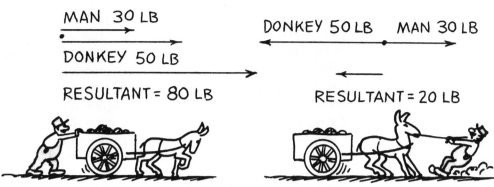

Fig. 5.1   Force vectors drawn to a scale of $\frac{1}{4}$ inch = 10 pounds.

moves as if both forces were replaced by a single force of 80 pounds. This single force is called the *resultant* of the two forces. When the two forces act in opposite directions, the resultant is equal to the difference between them, and acts in the direction of the larger force.

Because the vectors in Figure 5.1 are along the same direction, the resultant can be found by addition or subtraction. Vector quantities in different directions, however, cannot generally be added, subtracted, multiplied, or divided by the methods of ordinary arithmetic; they must be treated by geometric addition.

Geometric Addition of Forces

When forces act at an angle to each other, a simple geometrical technique can be used to find the magnitude and direction of the resultant force. We construct a *parallelogram* of force vectors*. Consider the barge being towed by the horses in Figure 5.2. We

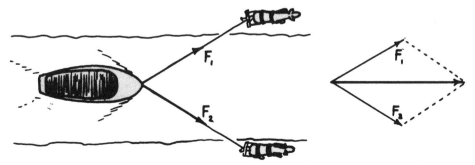

Fig. 5.2   The barge moves under the action of the resultant of the two forces, F_1 and F_2. Its direction is along the diagonal of the constructed parallelogram of which F_1 and F_2 are sides.

*A parallelogram is a four-sided plane figure having the opposite sides parallel and equal.

can see that the barge will not move in the direction of either of the forces exerted by the horses, but rather in the direction of their resultant. The resultant is found by using the following rule:

The resultant of any two forces acting at the same point may be represented by the diagonal of a parallelogram constructed with the two force vectors as sides.

We can apply this rule to a pair of forces that act on a common point and find the resultant as follows, Figure 5.3: Draw two vectors making the same angle to each other as that between the given forces. Choose a suitable scale and measure the length of the vectors so that each will correspond in magnitude to each of the given forces. Using the arrows as sides, construct a parallelogram. From the point of application of the given forces, draw the diagonal of the parallelogram. This diagonal represents the magnitude and direction of the resultant force. Find its magnitude by measuring the length of the diagonal and referring to the scale. The angle may be measured with a protractor.

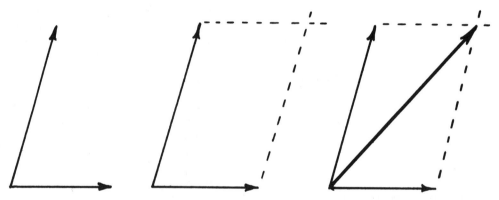

Fig. 5.3 Construction of the resultant of two vectors. *Step I:* Draw vector to scale. *Step II:* Construct parallelogram. *Step III:* Diagonal is resultant.

Exercise   1. By the parallelogram method construct the resultant of the 3-pound and 4-pound forces represented by the vectors shown. They are drawn to scale where $\frac{1}{2}$ inch = 1 pound. Measure your resultant with a ruler and compare it to the correct answers given at the bottom of the page.*

---

*1: 5 lb, 6 lb, 4 lb. 2: Minimum when they are directly opposite each other, $4 - 3 = 1$ lb; maximum when they are in the same direction, $4 + 3 = 7$ lb.

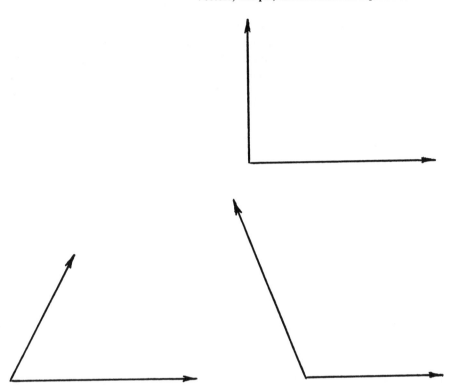

2. What are the minimum and maximum resultants possible for a 3-pound and 4-pound force acting on the same object?

The principle of forces combining according to the parallelo-gram rule is an experimental fact. It can be shown to be correct by suspending a block by two spring scales. Suppose the block weighs 10 pounds. If it is to hang at rest, the 10 pounds of down-ward force by gravity must be counteracted by an upward force of 10 pounds. This upward force must be supplied by the scales. Whatever the readings on each scale, the resultant of the com-bined readings must have a magnitude of 10 pounds and must act vertically upward, in a direction opposite to the pull of gravity. If the springs pull with an upward resultant of less than 10 pounds, the block will not be supported and will accelerate downward; if they pull with an upward resultant of more than 10 pounds, the block will accelerate upward. If the block is to hang at rest, the resultant force of the two spring scales must be equal and opposite to the force of gravity on the block.

When the block is supported by both scales vertically above it, each scale reads 5 pounds. The resultant of the two 5-pound forces is 10 pounds, and the block hangs at rest. When the scales are held at some angle to each other, their readings increase such that their resultant will be 10 pounds. This is illustrated in Figure 5.4. Note that as the angle between the scales is increased, the scale readings increase. We know the

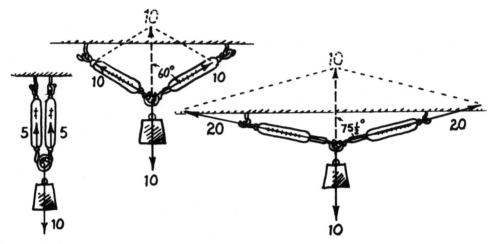

Fig. 5.4   As the angle increases the scale readings increase so that the resultant (dotted-line vector) will be 10 pounds, which is required to support the 10-pound weight.

diagonal of the parallelogram described by the scale positions must be 10 units long in each case to support the weight of the block. As the angle between the sides of the parallelogram increases, the magnitudes of the sides must also increase if the diagonal remains constant.

Questions   1. If the children on the swings are of equal weight, which swing is most likely to break?

2. Two pictures of equal weight are hung in a gallery as shown. In which of the two arrangements is the wire most likely to break?

3. Why can't a tightly strung clothesline support the weight of a small child attempting to hang from it?

4. In which position is the tension the least in the weightlifter's arms?

5. Why do electric power lines sometimes break when just a few pounds of ice form on them in winter?

6. The strong man cannot pull hard enough to make the chain straight. Why not?

7. Why are the main supporting cables of suspension bridges designed to sag so?

Velocity Parallelogram

Velocity is also a vector quantity because it involves both magnitude and direction. For example, if an airplane that normally flies at 80 miles per hour flies in the direction of a strong 60-mile-per-hour wind, its resultant velocity is 80 + 60 = 140 miles per hour. We simply add the two velocities because they are in the same direction. If the plane flies against the wind, its velocity relative to the ground is only 80 − 60 = 20 miles per hour. We subtract the velocity of the wind from the velocity of the plane because they are in opposite directions. This is simple enough, but what if the plane flies in a direction at some angle with respect to the wind? In such a case we find its resultant velocity by using the parallelogram method. Consider, for example, an airplane flying crosswind. Suppose it is heading due north at the rate of 80 miles per hour and is being blown eastward at the rate of 60 miles per hour. What is the resultant velocity of the plane?

To find the solution we can construct two vectors, one for the velocity of the airplane and one for the velocity of the wind. In Figure 5.5, we have chosen a scale of $\frac{1}{2}$ inch to represent

Fig. 5.5 An 80-mile-per-hour airplane flying in a 60-mile-per-hour crosswind has a resultant velocity of 100 miles per hour.

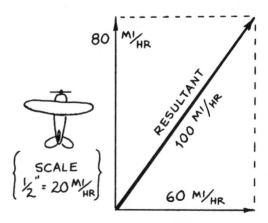

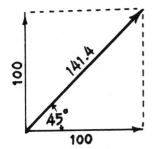

Fig. 5.6 The diagonal of a square is $\sqrt{2}$ the length of one of its sides.

20 miles per hour. The diagonal of the constructed parallelogram measures $2\frac{1}{2}$ inches, which represents 100 miles per hour.*

There is one special case of the parallelogram that often occurs. When two vectors that are equal in magnitude and at right angles to one another are to be added, the parallelogram becomes a square. Since it is a property of a square that the length of a diagonal is $\sqrt{2}$, or 1.414 times one of the sides, the resultant of two equal vectors acting at right angles to each other is $\sqrt{2}$ times one of the vectors. For example, the resultant of two equal vectors of magnitude 100 acting at right angles to each other is 141.4.

Vectors and Projectile Motion

The parabolic trajectory of a projectile can be better understood with vectors. The path of a projectile is the result of constant horizontal motion superimposed with vertically accelerated motion. We can represent horizontal motion at all points on the path of a projectile by vectors of constant length, and vertical motion by vectors whose length varies with velocity in the vertical direction, Figure 5.7. At any point, the resultant of vertical and horizontal motion lies tangent to the parabolic curve.

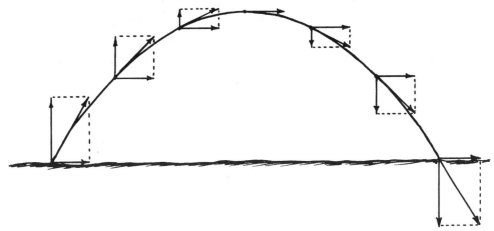

Fig. 5.7   The parabola is the result of combining horizontal and vertical components of motion. Note that the length of the vector representing horizontal motion is constant at all points. Only the vertical component of motion changes because of the vertical acceleration due to gravitation.

---

*When the vectors are at right angles to each other, their resultant can be found by a well-known theorem of geometry which states that the square of the hypotenuse of a right-angle triangle is equal to the sum of the squares of the other two sides. Note that two right triangles are present in the parallelogram (rectangle in this case) in Figure 5.5. From either one of the triangles we get:

$$(\text{Resultant})^2 = 60^2 + 80^2$$
$$= 3600 + 6400$$
$$= 10{,}000 \text{ (The square root of 10,000 is 100 as expected.)}$$

Resolution of Vectors

We have seen that two vectors acting on the same body may be replaced by a single vector (the resultant), which produces the same effect upon the body as the combined effects of the given vectors. On the other hand, any single vector may be regarded as the resultant of two vectors, each of which acts on the body in some direction other than that of the given vector. These two vectors are known as the *components* of the given vector that they replace. The process of determining the components of a vector is called *resolution*.

A man pushing a lawnmower applies a force that pushes the machine forward and also against the ground. In Figure 5.8,

Fig. 5.8 The applied force on the lawnmower, **AB**, may be resolved into a horizontal component, **AC**, and a vertical component, **AD**.

AB represents the force applied by the man. We can separate this force into components. The line **AD** represents the downward component, which is the downward push against the ground, and **AC**, the forward component, which is the force that moves the lawnmower.

We can find the magnitude of these components by drawing a rectangle with **AB** as the diagonal. According to the parallelogram method, force **AB** is the resultant of the forces **AC** and **AD**. Hence the two components **AC** and **AD** acting together are equivalent to the force **AB**. That is, the motion of the lawnmower is the same whether we assume that the man exerts two forces, **AC** and **AD**, or only one force, **AB**.

The rule for finding the components of any vector is relatively simple. A line **AB** (Figure 5.9) representing the force, velocity, or

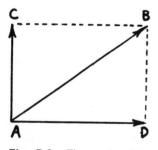

Fig. 5.9   The vector **AB** has component vectors **AC** and **AD**.

whatever vector is in question, is drawn to scale in the proper direction. A rectangle *ACBD* is then drawn, enclosing the vector **AB** in such a way that **AB** is a diagonal and the sides of the rectangle lie along the direction of the desired components. The components of the vector **AB** are then represented in direction and magnitude by the lines **AC** and **AD**.

Exercise   With ruler, draw the horizontal and vertical components to the two vectors shown. Measure the components and compare your findings with the answers given at the bottom of the page.*

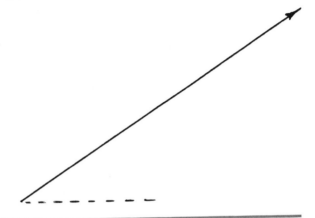

Applications of Vector Resolution

A barrel can be rolled up an inclined plane with a force less than that required to lift it. Why this is so can be understood by considering the components of its weight. We can represent the weight of a barrel on an incline as a vector that can be

Fig. 5.10 It is easier to roll the barrel up the incline than it is to lift it vertically. Why?

---

*In inches: First vector—horizontal component 1½; vertical component 2. Second vector—horizontal component 3; vertical component 2.

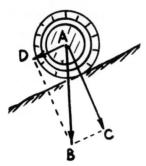

Fig. 5.11 The weight of the barrel is represented by vector **AB**. The barrel accelerates down the plane because of component **AD**.

separated into components, Figure 5.11. The vector **AB** represents the weight of the barrel; the vector **AC** the component of force that is equal to the force the barrel exerts against the incline; the vector **AD** represents the component of the weight parallel to the incline. When the barrel pushes down on the incline, the incline pushes back with a force exactly equal but opposite to component **AC**. Therefore the component **AC** is neutralized and has no tendency to produce motion. It is the component **AD** that accelerates the barrel down the incline. If we wish to prevent the barrel from rolling down the incline, we must apply a force equal and opposite to the force **AD**. If we wish to roll the barrel up the incline, we must push with an initial force somewhat greater than **AD** to accelerate it from rest, but once it is moving a force equal and opposite to **AD** is all that is required to maintain constant velocity. We can see from Figure 5.11 that the vector **AD** is shorter than the vector

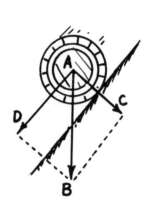

Fig. 5.12 Component **AD** increases as the angle of incline increases.

AB; hence the force necessary to roll the barrel up the incline is less than the force necessary to lift the barrel vertically. Note that the steeper the incline, the greater is the magnitude of **AD**, Figure 5.12. We would have to push harder to roll a barrel up a steep incline; similarly, if we let the barrel roll down a steeper incline the greater component **AD** causes a greater acceleration. When the incline is tipped 90 degrees (vertical), the component **AD** equals the weight of **AB** and the barrel reaches its maximum acceleration, 32 feet per second each second.

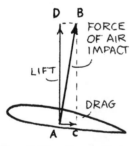

Fig. 5.13 Cross-section view of an airplane wing showing the lift and drag components.

When moving air strikes the underside of an airplane wing, the forces of air impact against the wing may be represented by a single vector perpendicular to the plane of the wing, Figure 5.13. We represent the force vector as acting midway

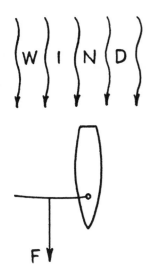

Fig. 5.14

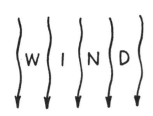

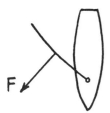

Fig. 5.15

along the lower wing surface, where the dot is, and pointing above the wing to show the direction of the resulting wind impact force. This force can be broken up into two components, one horizontal and the other vertical. The vertical component, **AD**, is called *lift*. The horizontal component, **AC**, is called *drag*. If the aircraft is to fly at constant velocity at constant altitude, then lift must equal the weight of the aircraft and the thrust of the plane's engines must equal drag. The magnitude of lift (and drag) can be altered by changing the speed of the airplane or by changing the angle (called angle of attack) between the wing and the horizontal.

The wing need not have the curved surfaces shown in Figure 5.13. (Those toy balsa-wood airplanes you may have flown a few years ago had flat surfaces.) We will learn in Chapter 13 that the curved surface of the wing produces an "airfoil" which produces additional lifting force.

The Sailboat

Sailors have always known that a sailboat can sail downwind, that is, in the direction of the wind. Sailors have not always known, however, that a sailboat can sail upwind, that is, against the wind. To understand how this is possible, consider first the case of a sailboat sailing downwind.

Figure 5.14 shows a sailboat sailing downwind. The force of wind impact against the sail accelerates the boat. Even if the drag of the water and all other resistance forces are negligible the maximum speed of the boat is the wind speed. This is because the wind will not make impact against the sail if the boat is moving as fast as the wind. The sail would simply sag. If there is no force then there is no acceleration. The force vector in Figure 5.14 *decreases* as the boat travels faster. The force vector is maximum when the boat is at rest and the full impact of the wind fills the sail, and minimum when the boat travels as fast as the wind. If the boat is somehow propelled to a speed faster than the wind (by way of an outboard motor, for example), then air resistance against the front side of the sail will produce an oppositely directed force vector. This will slow the boat down. Hence the boat, when driven only by the wind, cannot exceed wind speed.

If the sail is oriented at an angle as shown in Figure 5.15, the boat will move forward, but with less acceleration. There are two reasons for this:

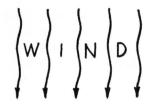

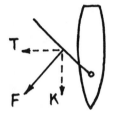

Fig. 5.16

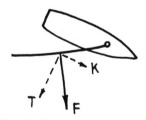

Fig. 5.17

1. The force on the sail is less because the sail does not intercept as much wind in this angular position.

2. The direction of the wind impact force on the sail is not in the direction of the boat's motion, but is perpendicular to the surface of the sail. Generally speaking, whenever any fluid (liquid or gas) interacts with a smooth surface, the force of interaction is perpendicular to the smooth surface.* The boat does not move in the same direction as the perpendicular force on the sail, but is constrained to move in a forward (or backward) direction by a deep, finlike keel beneath the water.

We can better understand the motion of the boat by resolving the force of wind impact, **F**, into perpendicular components. The important component is that which is parallel to the keel, which we label **K**, and the other component is perpendicular to the keel and is labeled **T**. It is the component **K**, as shown in Figure 5.16, that is responsible for the forward motion of the boat. Component **T** is a useless force that tends to tip the boat over and move it sideways. This component force is offset by the heavy, deep keel. Again, maximum speed of the boat can be no greater than wind speed.

If a sailcraft sails in a direction other than exactly downwind, Figure 5.17, and has its sail properly oriented, it can exceed wind speed. In the case of a sailboat cutting across the wind, the wind may continue to make impact with the sail even after the boat exceeds wind speed. A surfer, in a similar way, exceeds the velocity of the propelling wave by angling his surfboard across the wave. Greater angles to the propelling medium (wind for the boat, water wave for the surfboard) result in greater speeds. A sailcraft can sail faster cutting across the wind than it can sailing downwind.

As strange as it may first seem, maximum speed is attained by cutting into (against) the wind; that is, by angling the sailcraft in a direction upwind! Although a sailboat cannot sail *directly* upwind, it can reach a destination upwind by angling back and forth in zigzag fashion. This is called *tacking*. Suppose the boat and sail are as shown in Figure 5.18. Component **K** will push the

---

*If the force were not perpendicular, there would be a component along or parallel to the surface. But a component parallel to the smooth surface has nothing to push against and therefore does not physically exist. Only the component that is perpendicular to the surface exists.

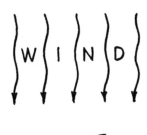

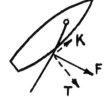

Fig. 5.18

boat along in a forward direction, angling into the wind. In the position shown the boat can sail faster than the speed of the wind. This is because as the boat travels faster, the impact of wind is *increased*. This is similar to running in a rain that comes down at an angle. When you run into the direction of the downpour, the drops strike you harder and more frequently; but when you run away from the direction of the downpour, the drops don't strike you as hard or as frequently. In the same way, a boat sailing upwind experiences greater wind-impact force, while a boat sailing downwind experiences a decreased wind-impact force. When the boat is directed at an angle upwind, the force of wind impact can accelerate the boat to speeds much faster than wind speed. The boat reaches its terminal speed when opposing forces cancel the force of wind impact. The opposing forces consist mainly of water resistance against the hull of the boat. The hulls of racing boats are shaped to minimize this resistive force, which is the principal deterrent to high speeds.

Iceboats, sailcraft equipped with runners for traveling on ice, encounter no water resistance and can travel at several times the speed of the wind when they tack upwind. Although ice friction is nearly absent, an iceboat does not accelerate without limit. The terminal velocity of a sailcraft is determined not only by opposing friction forces, but by the change in relative wind direction. We will discuss this idea after the following exercise, which should be worked out first.

Exercise   1. Three sailboats are oriented to the wind at different positions as shown in Figure 5.19. The dotted lines show the directions parallel and perpendicular to the keels of the boats. The wind-impact force vectors are indicated for each. These vectors

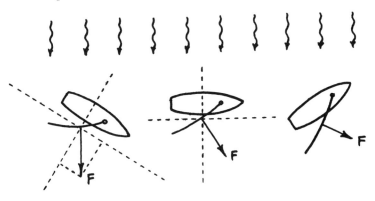

Fig. 5.19

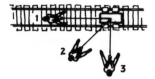

Fig. 5.20

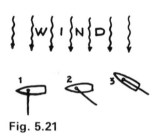

Fig. 5.21

comprise the diagonals to the parallelograms, which happen to be rectangles here, that will determine the relative sizes of the components **K** and **T**. The rectangle for boat (1) is drawn. *You* draw the component vectors **K** and **T** for boat (1). Then for boat (2), draw the appropriate rectangle and then the component vectors **K** and **T**. Do the same for boat (3) after you decide the appropriate directions for the dotted lines.

2. Figure 5.20 shows the top view of a small railway car being pulled by constant forces in three directions. Greatest acceleration will result if it is pulled from position (1). The car will accelerate if pulled from position (2), but not as much as from position (1) because the component of force along the track becomes less as the angle between track and rope is increased. Pulling from position (3) will not move the car at all, as there is no component of force along the track direction.

With the foregoing example in mind, and the fact that the force of wind impact upon sails acts perpendicularly to sails, discuss the relative motions of the boats shown in Figure 5.21.

Two of the boats are *not* propelled in a forward direction by the wind. Which two? Why?

Relative wind.   The force of air impact against a sail depends not only on the magnitude and direction of the wind, but also on the magnitude and direction of the sailcraft. Even on a day when the wind is not blowing, a moving body experiences a "wind" due to motion through the air (on a windless day stick your head out the window of a 60-mile-per-hour car and you'll feel a 60-mile-per-hour wind). The resultant wind due to both the velocity of air moving across the earth's surface and the velocity of the sailcraft is called the *relative wind*. We can make use of vectors to determine the magnitude and direction of the relative wind.

Thus far we have used vectors to represent the *force* of wind impact. We will now use vectors to represent the *velocity* of the wind. Consider the boat sailing crosswind in Figure 5.22. We suppose the wind has a particular specified velocity and represent this with the downward pointing *velocity* vector. We further suppose that the boat has been propelled to a speed equal to that of the wind, so there is an apparent wind represented by the horizontal *velocity* vector. When we construct the resultant of these two vectors (you might refer to Figure 5.6), we find that the relative wind makes an angle of 45 degrees with the keel of

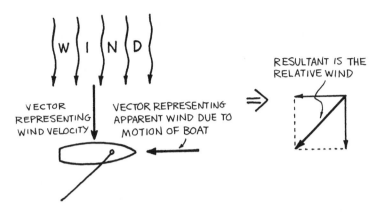

RESULTANT IS THE
RELATIVE WIND

VECTOR
REPRESENTING
WIND VELOCITY

VECTOR REPRESENTING
APPARENT WIND DUE TO
MOTION OF BOAT

Fig. 5.22 The relative wind is the resultant of the moving air and the moving boat.

the boat. If the sail is set at the same 45-degree angle, the relative wind will blow by the sail rather than into it. There will be no force of air impact against the sail and the boat will be propelled no faster—even in the absence of water (or ice) resistance, it will have reached its terminal speed. To sail faster the sail should be pulled in to a smaller angle so that the relative wind will again make impact with its back surface.

Illustrative Problem

Suppose a sailcraft tacks at a 45-degree angle upwind. Neglecting water friction, at what angle must its sail be oriented so that it may approach a terminal velocity that is twice wind speed?

Solution. First draw a diagram of the sailcraft heading 45 degrees upwind, Figure 5.23.

Second, draw a vector of arbitrary length to represent the velocity of the wind, Figure 5.24. To simplify construction, draw it so that its tail is at the mast of the craft. The direction of this vector should be along the direction of the wind.

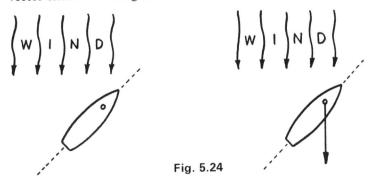

Fig. 5.23   **Fig. 5.24**

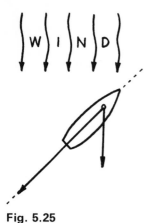

Fig. 5.25

Third, since the craft is to travel at twice wind speed, it will intercept a "wind" twice as great as the natural wind, which will be directed against the motion of the craft. We represent this by a vector twice as long and in the direction shown in Figure 5.25, again placing the tail of the vector at the mast of the craft.

Next, we find the resultant of these two vectors by the parallelogram method, Figure 5.26. This resultant represents the relative wind. We can measure its angle with a protractor.

In this case the angle is $14\frac{1}{2}$ degrees and is indicated by the shading, Figure 5.27. It is the maximum angle the sail can have for a sailing velocity equal to twice wind speed. To sail faster in the same direction, the sail must be pulled farther into the shaded region where it will again intercept the impact of the relative wind.

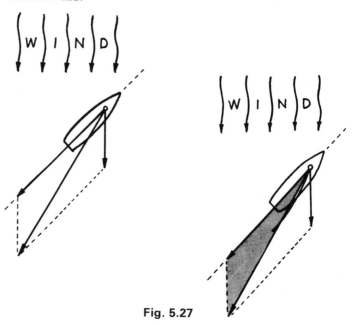

Fig. 5.26

Fig. 5.27

Exercise   Consider the boats shown in Figure 5.28. Boat *A* is sailing crosswind and boat *B* is tacking upwind. Show by vectors that in the absence of resistive forces, the terminal speed of boat *A* is *twice* wind speed, and the terminal speed of boat *B* is *three times* wind speed.

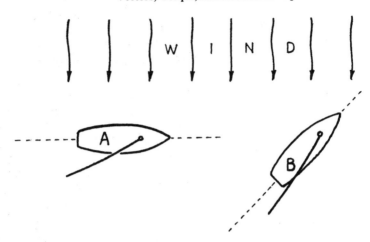

Fig. 5.28

To summarize—so long as there is an unbalanced component of force along the direction of the boat's keel, the boat will accelerate to greater speeds. Terminal speed is reached when the net force becomes zero. This occurs when: (1) resistance or friction forces which oppose motion cancel the driving wind-impact force; or (2) when the relative wind is directed along the surface of the sail such that no air impact occurs. Finally, note the distinction between force vectors and velocity vectors. When we discuss the force of wind impact and its components, we make use of force vectors. When we discuss the terminal speed of the craft, we make use of velocity vectors to determine the direction (and magnitude) of the relative wind. It is easy to get these vectors confused.

Only the simplest case of a flat sail has been treated here. Sails are not flat, but are curved when under wind impact. This curvature is as important to sailcraft as curved wing surfaces are to aircraft. Wind passing over the curved sail produces an additional and important force which will be discussed in detail in Chapter 13.

Question   Why does vertically falling rain make slanted streaks on the side windows of a moving automobile? If the streaks make an angle of 45 degrees, what does this tell you about the relative speeds of the car and the falling rain?

Torque

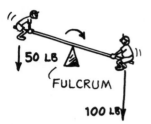

Fig. 5.29 The torque produced by the heavier boy is greater than the torque produced by the lighter boy, so the seesaw rotates.

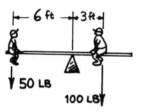

Fig. 5.30 No rotation is produced when the torques balance each other.

Often forces are applied in such a way that rotational motion is produced. Consider two boys who weigh 50 and 100 pounds sitting on opposite ends of a 12-foot seesaw, Figure 5.29. We know that the seesaw will not remain horizontal; the 100-pound boy will move downward, and the 50-pound boy upward. The weight of the 100-pound boy produces a clockwise rotation about the fulcrum, while the weight of the 50-pound boy tends to produce a counterclockwise rotation. When the two boys are at the ends of the seesaw, the two rotational tendencies do not balance each other, and there is a resulting clockwise rotation. We know from experience that the boys can balance on the seesaw if the heavier boy sits closer to the fulcrum. We see that the tendency to produce rotation depends not only on the force acting, but also on a *distance*.

A simple experiment shows that if the 50-pound boy sits 6 feet from the fulcrum and the 100-pound boy sits 3 feet from the fulcrum, the seesaw will balance. Note that $50 \times 6 = 100 \times 3$. Evidently the tendency to produce rotation depends on the product of force and distance. The 50-pound boy counterbalances the heavier boy because his greater distance from the fulcrum gives him more *leverage*. He has a greater lever-arm distance.

The product of force and lever arm (50 pounds × 6 feet for the lighter boy on the seesaw and 100 pounds × 3 feet for the heavier boy) is called *torque* (rhymes with "fork").

$$\text{Torque} = \text{force} \times \text{lever-arm distance}$$

The lever-arm distance is defined as the perpendicular distance from the force vector to the fulcrum or pivot point. If a seesaw is to balance, the torque tending to produce clockwise rotation must be balanced by the torque tending to produce counterclockwise rotation.

If we wish to turn a stubborn bolt with a wrench, we apply a force to the end of the wrench to produce a torque. If the bolt

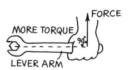

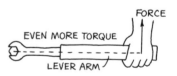

Fig. 5.31 Although the magnitudes of the force are the same in each case, the torques are different.

is particularly stubborn, we can increase the torque by exerting more force, or we can put a pipe over the handle of the wrench and increase the lever arm. Maximum torque is produced when the force is applied perpendicular to the handle.*

Whenever an unbalanced torque is applied to an object, the object is set into rotation. Torques produce rotational motion.

Center of Mass and Center of Gravity

If the net force on an object is zero, that is, if all the forces acting on an object balance out, and if there are no unbalanced torques acting on it, we say the object is in a state of equilibrium. No change in the object's state of motion is taking place. There are different states of equilibrium, however, for not all balanced objects behave in the same way. Take a cone, for example. Suppose we balance it very carefully on its tip. What happens if we push on it even very slightly? It falls over. But we have no trouble at all balancing the cone on its base, for it tends to return to its balanced position if it is tipped. It has to be pushed far over before it falls. Yet in either case the cone was balanced before it was pushed. In the first case we say the cone was in *unstable equilibrium*, and in the second case it was in *stable equilibrium*. If we lay the cone on its side and then push it, it will simply roll, with no tendency to go to a new position or return to its initial position. A cone lying on its side is in a position of *neutral equilibrium*.

The kind of equilibrium an object has is determined by the position of its *center of mass*. For a given body, the center of mass is the average position of all the particles of mass that constitute the body. For example, a symmetrical object like a ball can be thought as having all its mass concentrated at its center; by contrast, an irregularly shaped body such as a baseball bat has more of its mass toward one end. The center of mass of a baseball bat therefore is toward the heavier end. A cone has its center of mass exactly one-third of the way up from its base.

Center of gravity is a term more popularly used to express center of mass. The center of gravity is simply the average position of weight distribution. Since weight and mass are proportional to each other, center of gravity and center of mass refer to

---

*See Appendix III for a more thorough treatment of torques.

the same point of a body.* The physicist prefers to use the more general term *center of mass,* for a body has a center of mass whether or not it is under the influence of gravity. We shall, however, use either term to express this concept, and favor the term *center of gravity* because of its wider familiarity.

We can see from Figure 5.32 that the states of equilibrium for an object depend on whether its center of gravity is raised or lowered when the object is tipped. If the center of gravity is

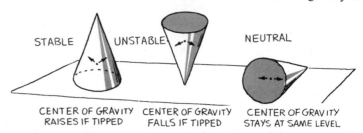

STABLE   UNSTABLE   NEUTRAL

CENTER OF GRAVITY   CENTER OF GRAVITY   CENTER OF GRAVITY
RAISES IF TIPPED   FALLS IF TIPPED   STAYS AT SAME LEVEL

Fig. 5.32   States of equi-librium.

raised, the object is in stable equilibrium. When such an object is tipped and then released, its weight acting downward at its center of gravity causes it to fall back to its original position. If the center of gravity of an object is lowered when it is tipped, the object is in unstable equilibrium. When such an object is disturbed it falls over. If tipping or displacing an object neither raises nor lowers its center of gravity, the object is in neutral equilibrium. A ball resting on a level surface, for example, is in neutral equilibrium. When disturbed, its center of gravity is neither raised nor lowered—the ball is in equilibrium in any new position.

Locating the Center of Gravity

The center of gravity of a uniform object such as a yardstick is at its midpoint, for the stick acts as though its entire weight were concentrated there. Supporting that single point supports the stick as a whole. Balancing an object provides a simple method of locating its center of gravity. In Figure 5.33, the many small arrows are force vectors that represent the pull of gravity all along the yardstick. All these vectors can be combined with the resultant vector acting through the center of gravity. The entire weight of the stick may be thought of as acting at this

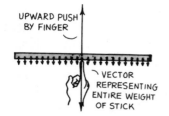

UPWARD PUSH
BY FINGER

VECTOR
REPRESENTING
ENTIRE WEIGHT
OF STICK

Fig. 5.33 The weight vectors for all parts of the stick act as a single resul-tant vector at the center of gravity.

---

*For very large bodies, such as the moon, where the farthest part is in a region of weaker gravitation than the nearest part, the center of gravity is not located at the center of mass.

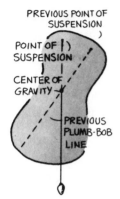

single point. Hence we can balance the stick by applying a single upward force in a direction that passes through this point.

The center of gravity of any freely suspended object lies directly beneath (or at) the point of suspension, Figure 5.34. If a vertical line is drawn through the point of suspension, the center of gravity lies somewhere along that line. To determine exactly where it lies along the line, we have only to suspend the object from some other point and draw a second vertical line through that point of suspension. The center of gravity lies where the two lines intersect.

The center of mass of an object may be a point where no mass exists. For example, the center of mass in the case of a ring and hollow sphere is at the geometrical centers where no matter exists. Similarly, the center of mass of a boomerang is outside the physical structure, and not within the material making up the boomerang, Figure 5.35.

If we drop a line straight down from the center of gravity of a body of any shape and it falls inside the base of the body, it is in stable equilibrium; if it falls outside the base it is unstable. Why doesn't the famous Leaning Tower of Pisa topple over? As we can see in Figure 5.36, a line from the center of gravity of the tower falls inside its base—and so the Leaning Tower has stood for several centuries.

To reduce the likelihood of tipping, it is usually advisable to design objects with a wide base and low center of gravity. The

Fig. 5.34 Finding the center of gravity for an irregularly shaped object.

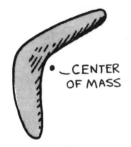

Fig. 5.35 The center of mass can be outside the mass of a body.

Fig. 5.36 The center of gravity of the Leaning Tower of Pisa lies above a point of support and therefore is in stable equilibrium.

wider the base, the higher the center of gravity must be raised before the object will tip over, Figure 5.37.

When you stand erect (or lie flat) your center of gravity is within your body. Why is the center of gravity lower in an average woman than in an average man of the same height? Is your center of gravity always at the same point in your body? Is it always inside your body? What happens to it when you bend over?

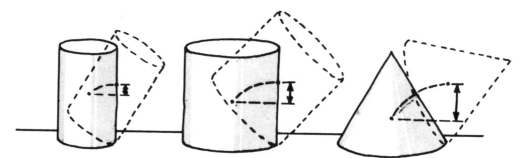

Fig. 5.37   The vertical distance that the center of gravity is raised in tipping determines stability. An object with a wide base and low center of gravity is most stable.

Center of Gravity and Trajectory Motion

If a baseball is thrown spinning into the air, it follows a smooth parabolic trajectory. If a baseball bat is thrown spinning into the air, its path is not smooth. Its motion is wobbly. But the center of mass *does* follow a smooth parabolic trajectory while other parts of the spinning bat wobble about this point.

The multiple-flash photograph shows a wrench sliding across a smooth horizontal surface. Its center of mass, indicated by the dark mark, follows a straight-line path while the motion of every other part of the wrench is more complicated. Since there is no net external force acting on the wrench, its center of mass moves equal distances in equal time intervals.

Fig. 5.38   The center of mass of the spinning wrench follows a straight-line path. (From *College Physics*, Physical Science Study Committee, Raytheon Education Co., 1968.)

The center of mass of the solar system lies within the massive sun, but not at its geometrical center. As a result the sun wobbles about this point as the planets orbit. Astronomers detect similar wobbles in the nearest stars, which is evidence that our sun is not the only star with a system of planets!

Fig. 5.39 An athlete can jump in such a way as to clear the bar while his center of gravity passes *beneath* the bar. Dick Fosbury accomplishes this with his unusual style. (Photo by Associated Press.)

Summary of Terms

Scalar quantity. A quantity that may be specified by magnitude and without regard to direction. Examples are mass, volume, speed, and temperature.

Vector quantity. A quantity that has both magnitude and direction. Examples are force, velocity, acceleration, and torque.

Vector. An arrow drawn to scale used to represent a vector quantity.

Fig. 5.40   (Photo by Jim Conley.)

Resultant. The geometric sum of two or more vectors. Example:

Component. The parts into which a vector can be separated, which have a smaller magnitude and act in a different direction than the vector:

Resolution. A method of separating a vector into its component parts.

Torque. The product of force and lever-arm distance, which tends to produce rotation.

Center of gravity. The average position of weight or the single point associated with a body where the force of gravity can be considered to act.

Center of mass. The average position of mass or the single point associated with a body where all its mass can be considered to be concentrated.

Equilibrium. The state of a body when not acted upon by a net force or net torque. A body in equilibrium may be at rest or moving at uniform velocity; that is, it is not accelerating.

Questions

1. Is it necessary that weights be placed in the middle of the pans of an equal-arm balance for accurate measurements? Why not?

2. Why is it easier to carry the same amount of water in two buckets, one in each hand, than in a single bucket?

3. The drawing shows a boy playing "solitary seesaw." Explain how this is accomplished.

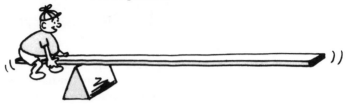

4. Using the ideas of torque and center of gravity, explain why a ball rolls down a hill.

5. Can you stand with the back of your heels against a wall and bend over to touch your toes without falling over? Try it and see! Explain.

6. How can the three bricks be stacked so that the top brick has maximum horizontal displacement from the bottom brick? For example, stacking them like the dotted lines suggest would be unstable and the bricks would topple over.

7. Where is the center of mass of a doughnut?

8. Explain why a long drooping pole aids a tightrope walker.

9. The centers of gravity of three trucks parked on a hill are shown by the X's. Which truck(s) will tip over?

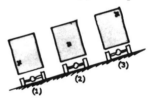

10. The three balancing acts on the tightrope are in equilibrium. Which is stable, unstable, and neutral?

6
Work, Power, and Energy

Perhaps the most central idea underlying all of science is the concept of energy. It is the combination of energy and matter that makes up the universe: matter is the substance and energy is the mover of the substance. Matter has always been an easy notion to grasp. Matter is stuff; it has mass and occupies space; it can be seen, felt, and smelled. Energy, on the other hand, is more abstract. One cannot see, feel, taste, or smell energy. In fact, we can't really say what energy *is*—at least not in the sense that we can say what matter is. Energy is an intangible "something" that takes several familiar forms. It can, for example, appear as the energy of motion. It can appear as the form of heat and light. It can appear on an atomic or molecular scale as chemical energy. It can appear in the flow of electric current. On the nuclear scale it can appear in one of the most awesome forms—as nuclear energy. We are at the dawn of an age where men will soon have control of inexhaustible amounts of energy. This control of energy can bring promise for a peaceful future or it can be the means of the world's destruction. In this critical time it is imperative that we understand more about this prime mover. We will begin by introducing a related concept—work.

Work

When we lift a load against the earth's gravity, *work* is done. The higher we lift the load or the heavier the load, the more work is done. In every case where work is done two things enter: (1) the exertion of a *force* and (2) the *movement* of something by that force. We say:

Work is defined and measured by the product of the net force exerted and the distance through which that force moves.

Work = force × distance moved in the direction of the force, or simply,

$$W = F \times d$$

If we lift two loads a story high, we do twice as much work as lifting one load, because the weight or *force* is twice as great. Similarly, if we lift a load two stories we do twice as much work because the *distance* is twice as great. To compare the work of

77

carrying a load upstairs to that of pushing it across the floor, we measure the force and the distance in each case and multiply the two; we then compare the two products.

Note that our definition of work involves both a force *and* a distance. We may push against a wall for hours, and get really tired, but if the wall does not move—that is, if the distance the force moves is zero—we have done no work on the wall. Work may be done on the muscles by stretching and contracting, which is force × distance on a biological scale, but this work is not done on the wall.

The units of measurement in which work is expressed contain units of distance and units of force. We usually express work in foot-pounds.*

Power   Note that the definition of work says nothing about the time during which work is done. The same amount of work is done in carrying a load up a flight of stairs whether we walk up or run up. So why is it that we are more tired after running up that flight in a few seconds than in walking up in a few minutes? To distinguish between such cases we introduce the time rate of doing work, which we call *power*. Power is simply equal to work divided by time:

$$\text{Power} = \frac{\text{work}}{\text{time}}$$

An engine of much power can do work rapidly. For example, the engines of several kinds of cars will provide the work necessary to drive the cars to the top of a steep hill. But different engines will do the same task in different times. An engine that will drive a car up the hill in a short interval of time develops more power than an engine that requires longer time to do the same amount of work.

---

*In the metric system, a common unit of work is the dyne-centimeter, called the *erg*. It is the work done when a force of 1 dyne is exerted through a distance of 1 centimeter. Lifting a mosquito through a height equal to the thickness of your finger requires about 1 erg of work. Another metric unit of work is the newton-meter, called the *joule* (rhymes with "pool"). One joule of work is done when a force of 1 newton is exerted 1 meter. 10,000,000 (10^7) ergs equal 1 joule. A unit of work used in the submicroscopic world is the *electron volt* (eV). One eV is about one millionth of one millionth of an erg (1.6×10^{-12} erg, to be exact). If you're not familiar with the numerical shorthand notation used here (1.6×10^{-12}), you may want to read the section on "Scientific Notation" in Appendix I at the back of the book.

Power can be expressed in the units of foot-pounds per second, but is usually expressed in horsepower. This unit was first defined in the latter part of the eighteenth century by James Watt, developer of the steam engine. When Watt tried to sell steam engines to British coal mines, the question arose as to how many horses one of his new engines would replace. He had some workhorses walk around and around a wheel used to raise a heavy weight out of a deep well and found that each horse averaged about 550 foot-pounds of work per second. He called this unit the horsepower, and used it to rate his engines. Hence, today we say that 1 horsepower is equivalent to 550 foot-pounds per second (or 33,000 foot-pounds per minute).*

Energy

Work is done in lifting the heavy ram of a pile driver, and as a consequence the ram acquires the property of being able to do work when it falls. When work is done in winding a spring mechanism, the spring acquires the ability to do work and is able to run a clock, ring a bell, or sound an alarm. In each case, something has been acquired. When work is done on an object something is given to the object which, in many cases, enables it to do work. This "something" that enables a body to do work is called *energy*. It appears in many forms, which we will discuss in subsequent chapters. We shall give attention here to two forms of mechanical energy—potential energy and kinetic energy.

Potential Energy

An object may store energy by virtue of its position. Such stored energy is called *potential energy*, for in the stored state an object has the potential for doing work. A stretched or compressed spring, for example, has potential energy. When a B-B gun is cocked, energy is stored in the spring. A stretched rubber band has potential energy because of its position, for if it is part of a slingshot it is capable of doing work.

The chemical energy in fuels is potential energy, for it is actually energy of position when looked at from a microscopic point of view. This energy is available when the positions of electrical charges within and between molecules is altered, that is, when a chemical change takes place. Potential energy is pos-

---

*In the metric system power is measured in joules per second or *watts* (in honor of James Watt). One watt of power is expended when 1 joule of work is done each second. One kilowatt equals 1000 watts. One horsepower equals 745.7 watts.

sessed by any substance that can do work through chemical action. The energy of coal, gas, electric batteries, foods, and the like is potential energy.

Potential energy may be due to an elevated position of a body. Water in an elevated reservoir and the heavy ram of a pile driver when lifted have energy because of position. The energy of elevated positions is usually called *gravitational potential energy*.

Kinetic Energy

If we push on an object we can set it in motion. More specifically, if we do work on an object, we can change the energy of motion of that object. If an object is in motion, by virtue of that motion it is capable of doing work. We call energy of motion *kinetic energy*. The kinetic energy of an object is equal to half its mass multiplied by its velocity squared.

$$\text{Kinetic energy} = \tfrac{1}{2}mv^2$$

It can be shown that*

$$\text{Force} \times \text{distance} = \text{kinetic energy}$$

or, in shorthand notation,

$$Fd = \tfrac{1}{2}mv^2$$

Accident investigators are well aware that an automobile traveling at 60 miles per hour has four times as much kinetic energy as an automobile traveling at 30 miles per hour. This means that a car traveling at 60 miles per hour will skid four times as far when its brakes are locked as a car traveling at 30 miles per hour. This is because the velocity is squared for kinetic energy.

Kinetic energy underlies various forms of energy that appear to be more different from one another than they actually are. Heat, for example, is really the kinetic energy of tiny molecules of which matter is composed. If the kinetic energy of molecules is made to vary in rhythmic patterns, we have sound. Electricity involves the kinetic energies of electrons; and even light energy originates from the vibratory motion of electrons within the atom. Whatever phase of energy we study, we find that an understanding of mechanical energy is fundamental to an understanding of the other forms.

---

*If we multiply both sides of Newton's second law, $F = ma$, by d we get $Fd = mad$; since $d = \tfrac{1}{2}at^2$ we can say $Fd = ma(\tfrac{1}{2}at^2) = \tfrac{1}{2}m(at)^2$, and substituting $v = at$, we get $Fd = \tfrac{1}{2}mv^2$.

The Conservation of Energy

Recall from Chapter 2 Galileo's inclined-plane experiments, in which he rolled balls down inclines. Galileo found that when a ball was released and allowed to roll from a particular point on an incline and up another, it never reached a level higher than its origin, Figure 6-1.

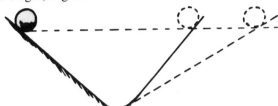

Fig. 6.1 The released ball will roll to its original height.

The same effect can be demonstrated with a pendulum. An extended pendulum bob released from a position of rest will rise no higher than its starting level when it swings to the other side. The bob swings back and forth beneath this level. This is true even if the string is obstructed by a peg, as shown in Figure 6.2. When the ball or pendulum bob in Figures 6.1 and 6.2 is at the starting level, it has potential energy. When released, potential energy diminishes as the height diminishes and the energy is converted to energy of motion. At the lowest part of the inclined plane or swing, the ball or bob has minimum potential energy and maximum kinetic energy. At this point the potential energy has been converted into kinetic energy. In the ideal case where friction is negligible, the kinetic energy gained is exactly equal to the potential energy lost. The transfer of energy continues as the kinetic energy is transformed again into potential energy when the ball or bob reaches its original height. The process continues as potential energy changes to kinetic energy and then back to potential energy and so on in a cycle, Figure 6.3.

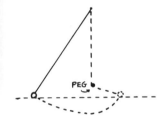

Fig. 6.2 The pendulum bob will swing to its original height—whether or not the peg is present.

We find in practice that the swinging pendulum bob or the rolling ball doesn't quite reach its original level. Some of the energy is expended in overcoming friction. The less friction there is, however, the closer the bob or ball comes to its starting level. But energy is not lost, even in the presence of friction. Careful exam-

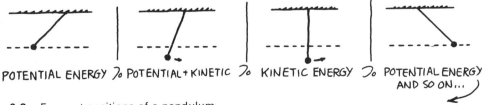

POTENTIAL ENERGY ⟩₀ POTENTIAL+KINETIC ⟩₀ KINETIC ENERGY ⟩₀ POTENTIAL ENERGY AND SO ON...

Fig. 6.3 Energy transitions of a pendulum.

ination would show that air molecules and the molecules in the swinging string or the inclined plane have gained kinetic energy — exactly the amount lost by the swinging bob or rolling ball. We call molecular kinetic energy heat. In any case, no energy is lost; it is simply transformed from one form to another.

The study of the various forms of energy and of the transformation of one form of energy into another has led to one of the great generalizations in physics, known as the law of *conservation of energy:*

Energy cannot be created or destroyed; it may be transformed from one form into another, but the total amount of energy never changes.

As an example of the transformations that energy may undergo, consider radiant energy coming to the earth from the sun. Part of this energy from the sun goes into evaporating water from the surface of the ocean. The water vapor forms into clouds and eventually returns to the earth as rain that may be trapped behind a dam. By virtue of its position the water has energy that may drive a turbine where it will be converted to electrical energy. Electrical energy is distributed to houses where it is used to light, heat, cook, or operate gadgetry. Energy is transformed from one form to another.

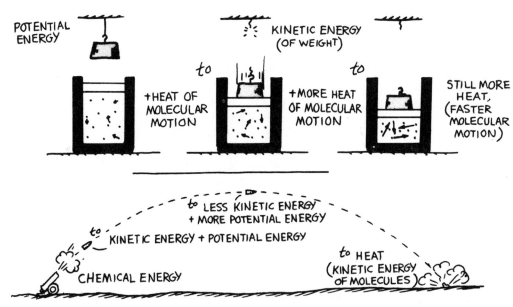

Fig. 6.4   Energy changes.

Throughout all these transformations, the total energy remains constant. During transformation, however, some energy is dissipated in the form of heat. For example, all the energy supplied to an electric motor is not transformed to mechanical energy. The motor becomes warm in the process and dissipates energy in the form of heat. This is wasted energy. The amount of *usable* energy therefore decreases with each transformation. The same is true of energy transfer in the food chain.

Energy comes into biological systems by first being bound in green plants by the complicated and not yet fully understood process of photosynthesis. The chemical energy of the plants is passed to plant-eating animals, then to the animals that eat the plant-eaters, and so on. At each stage some energy is dissipated in the form of heat.* An interesting consequence of this is that there is more life at the lower end of the food chain than at the upper end. For example, there are more tons of grass than there are tons of grass-eating insects, a greater tonnage of insects than there are birds, more birds than there are bird-eating animals, and so on. The amount of usable energy decreases with each stage. But when the dissipated energy is taken into account, the total energy remains constant. None mysteriously disappears.

Early in the twentieth century, Albert Einstein found that mass itself could be converted into energy. Likewise, energy can be converted to mass. We can think of mass energy as "energy of being," matter possessing energy by virtue of existing. A material particle can be regarded as a highly concentrated and localized packet of energy. The amount of this energy is proportional to the mass of the particle, as described by Einstein's most famous equation

$$E = mc^2$$

The energy of being E and the mass m of a particle are related by the quantity c, which is the speed of light. How this comes about will be discussed in Chapter 33 when we treat the Special Theory of Relativity.

---

*Unlike the dissipation of energy, things like DDT become concentrated in the food-chain process. For example, there is some concentration of DDT in the grass, more in the grasshopper that eats and concentrates DDT from the grass, more still in the little fish that eats the grasshopper, and more still in the bigger fish that eats the small fish, and so on. The biggest concentrations therefore show up at the end of the food chain. Pelicans, because of this, are rapidly approaching extinction. Next?

Most of our energy comes from the sun which ultimately comes from the conversion of mass in the sun to energy. The thermonuclear reaction producing this energy is called *fusion*, where hydrogen atoms are fused together to form helium. When this process can be controlled here on earth, the energy that can be obtained from fusing the hydrogen atoms in 10 quarts of water per second will equal all the electrical power now being generated in the United States. Physicists and technologists are presently working on ways in which this can be done.

Machines—An Application of Energy Conservation

Work is done on a machine and simultaneously work is done by a machine. If the heat energy created by frictional forces is sufficiently small, the work output will, in good approximation, be equal to the input work. We can say,

$$\text{Work input} = \text{work output}$$

or since work = force × distance,

$$(F \times d)_{\text{input}} = (F \times d)_{\text{output}}$$

The simplest machine is the lever. By applying a small force through a relatively large distance, we can exert a large force through a relatively small distance. Although the output force can be many times greater than the input force, the energy or work output can be no greater than the input energy.

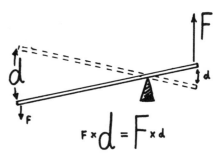

Fig. 6.5   The lever.

A child uses the principle of the lever in jacking up the front end of an automobile. By exerting a small force through a large distance she is able to provide a large force acting through a small distance. Consider the example illustrated in Figure 6.6. Every time she pushes the jack handle down 25 inches, the car

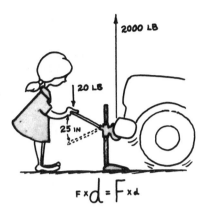

Fig. 6.6 Applied force × applied distance = output force × output distance.

rises only a hundredth as far, but with one hundred times as much force.

A block and tackle, or system of pulleys, is a simple machine that multiplies force at the expense of distance. One can exert a relatively small force through a large distance and lift a heavy weight through a relatively short distance. With the ideal pulley system such as that shown in Figure 6.7, the man pulls 10 feet of rope with a force of 25 pounds and lifts 250 pounds a vertical distance of 1 foot. The energy the man expends in pulling the rope is numerically equal to the increased potential energy of the 250-pound block.

Any machine that multiplies force does so at the expense of distance. Likewise, any device that multiplies distance does so at the expense of force. No machine or device can put out more energy than is put into it. No machine can create energy; it can only transform it from one form to another.

Energy Quanta

For a long time physicists thought of energy as being continuous—that the energy emitted or absorbed by a body could have any value between some minimum amount and some maximum amount. Since there is an infinity of numbers between any two numbers,* it was assumed there could be infinitely small gradations of energy. It turns out that energy is emitted or absorbed in discrete packets, or *quanta*. The energy of a light

Fig. 6.7 Applied force × applied distance = output force × output distance.

*There are infinitely many numbers between 1 and 2 if we express them in decimals to an infinite number of decimal places.

pulse, for example, is some whole-number multiple of quanta, just as the weight of a pile of pennies is some whole-number multiple of the weight of a single penny. The mechanics of atoms requires that we acknowledge that energy is granular, that it occurs as multiples of a smallest unit or quantum of energy. The branch of mechanics that deals with such phenomena is called *quantum mechanics*. At the atomic scale this becomes very important, but in the mechanics of the nonmicroscopic world we can think of energy as being continuous without getting into trouble. We introduce energy quanta here only as a matter of interest, and will study it further in Chapters 26 and 32.

Summary of Terms

Work. The product of the net force exerted and the distance through which the force moves:

$$W = F \times d$$

Power. The time rate of work:

$$\text{Power} = \frac{\text{work}}{\text{time}}$$

Energy. The quality of an object that enables it to do work.

Potential energy. The stored energy that a body possesses because of its position with respect to other bodies.

Kinetic energy. Energy of motion; more specifically,

$$\text{Kinetic energy} = \tfrac{1}{2}mv^2$$

Conservation of energy. Energy cannot be created or destroyed; it may be transformed from one form into another, but the total amount of energy never changes.

Conservation of energy and machines. The work output of any machine cannot exceed the work input. In an ideal machine, where no energy is transformed into heat,

$$\text{Work input} = \text{work output}$$

$$(F \times d)_{\text{input}} = (F \times d)_{\text{output}}$$

Suggested Reading

Rogers, Eric, *Physics for the Inquiring Mind*, Princeton, N.J., Princeton University Press, 1960. Part III of this enjoyable textbook treats energy in detail.

Scientific American, September, 1971. The entire issue is about energy and power.

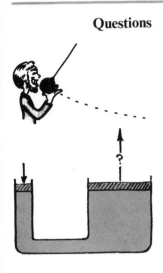

Questions   1. What makes a swinging pendulum finally come to rest? Where does the energy go in this case?

2. A physics instructor demonstrates energy conservation by releasing a heavy pendulum bob as shown in the sketch and allowing it to swing to and fro. What would happen if in his exuberance he gave the bob a slight shove as it left his nose? Why?

3. In the hydraulic machine shown, it is observed that when the small piston is pushed down 10 inches, the large piston is raised 1 inch. If the small piston is pushed down with a force of 1 pound, how much force is the large piston capable of raising?

4. Discuss the design of the roller coaster shown in the sketch and the conservation of energy.

5. When a rifle with a long barrel is fired, the force of expanding gases acts on the bullet for a longer distance. What effect does this have on the velocity of the emerging bullet?

6. Suppose in the preceding problem that the length of a rifle barrel was doubled, and the force on the bullet unchanged. By how much would the velocity of the emerging bullet differ?

7. One ounce of animal fat provides about 270 Calories when it is burned. Suppose you maintain a constant weight on a diet of 4000 Calories per day, and you cut your diet down to $\frac{3}{4}$ of your present consumption while maintaining all present physical activity. Estimate how many pounds of fat you might expect to lose in a month.

8. At what point in its motion is the kinetic energy of a pendulum bob a maximum? At what point is its potential energy a maximum? When its kinetic energy is half its maximum value, how much potential energy does it have?

9. The energy we require for existence comes from the chemically stored potential energy in food, which is transformed into other forms by the process of digestion. What happens to a person whose work output is less than the energy he consumes? When his work output is greater than the energy he consumes? Can an undernourished person perform extra work without extra food? Briefly discuss.

10. Food is a main determinant in setting the limits of population growth. Do you think that abundant energy from atomic power applied to agriculture will make a more comfortably fed world—or will the population simply increase to the edge of the new food supply? Briefly discuss.

7
Momentum

Did you ever wonder why a karate expert can sever a thick piece of lumber with the blow of his bare hand? Or just why a fall on a wooden floor is not nearly as damaging as a fall on a cement floor? Or why "follow through" is important in golf, baseball, and boxing? To understand these things we need to understand momentum and what produces momentum.

Momentum   We all know that a heavy truck is harder to stop than a small car moving at the same speed. We state this fact by saying that the truck has more momentum than the car. *By "momentum" we mean the product of the mass of an object and its velocity.* That is,

$$\text{Momentum} = \text{mass} \times \text{velocity}$$

or, in shorthand notation,

$$\text{Momentum} = mv$$

We can see from the definition that a moving body can have a large momentum if its mass is large, if its velocity is large, or if both its mass and velocity are large. The truck has more momentum than the car moving at the same speed because its mass is larger. We can see that a huge ship moving at a small velocity can have a large momentum while a small bullet moving at a high velocity can also have a large momentum—and, of course, a huge object moving at a high velocity, such as a 20-ton truck rolling down a steep hill with no brakes, has a huge momentum, while the same truck at rest has no momentum at all.

When a bullet or a truck crashes into a wall, a large force is exerted against the wall. Where does this force come from? It comes from a *change* in velocity. The force of impact is proportional to the change in velocity of the moving object. And the more massive the object, the greater the force—so the force of impact is also proportional to the mass of the moving object.

In the last chapter we considered the idea of a force acting through a distance. We found that when we pushed on an object, the product of the net force and the distance moved was equal to the gain in kinetic energy of the object. If instead we consider the idea of a force acting on an object through some interval of *time*, we find that the quantity "force × time" equals a gain in the momentum of the object.* We call the quantity "force × time" *impulse*. We can say

$$\text{Impulse} = \text{change in momentum}$$

or simply

$$Ft = \text{change in } mv$$

which reads, "force multiplied by the time-during-which-it-acts = change in momentum."

To change the momentum of a body we should consider the impulse, that is, the amount of force *and* the time of contact. A golf player hits a ball with great force to impart momentum to the ball; but to get maximum momentum, he "follows through" on his swing, extending the time of contact of the force upon the ball. A large force multiplied by a large time is a greater impulse which produces a greater change in the momentum of the ball. Any time we wish to impart the greatest momentum possible to an object, we simply apply the greatest force possible *and* extend as much as possible the time of contact.

A large change in momentum is often produced by a large force acting through a short time. This is particularly true of many violent blows and crashes where a large slowdown of momentum occurs in a short time. If $F \times$ (small t) = large change in mv, then F must be *very large*. When a car crashes against a massive concrete abutment, the time of contact is very small, resulting in a large force of contact. The idea of short time of contact explains why a karate expert can sever a thick board with the blow of his bare hand. He brings his hand swinging against the board with great speed which results in his hand having considerable momentum. This momentum is changed to zero when he delivers an impulse to the board. The impulse is the force of his hand against the board multiplied by the time his hand makes contact with the board. By making the time of contact as short as possible, he makes the force of impact huge.

Often we wish to change the momentum of an object with as small a force as possible. A boxer confronted with a high-

---

*Newton's second law states, $F = ma$, and since a = change in velocity/time, we can say $F = m[(\text{change in } v/t)]$. Simple algebraic rearrangement gives $Ft = $ change in mv.

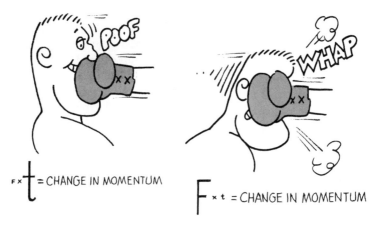

Fig. 7.1 In both cases the impulse by the boxer's jaw reduces the momentum of the punch. *Left:* the boxer is moving away when the glove hits, thereby extending the time of contact. Most of the impulse therefore involves time. *Right:* the boxer is moving into the glove, thereby lessening the time of contact. Most of the impulse therefore involves force.

$F \times t$ = CHANGE IN MOMENTUM

$F \times t$ = CHANGE IN MOMENTUM

momentum punch is interested in minimizing the force of impact. If he cannot avoid being hit, he at least has a choice between F and t in providing the impulse that will absorb and change the incoming momentum of his opponent's punch. The force of impact is lessened by extending the time of contact; hence, he "rides or rolls with the punch." If he is hit when approaching his opponent, the time of contact is reduced, resulting in an increased force. This force is further increased because of the additional impulse produced when his momentum of approach is stopped. This increased impulse and short time of impact results in forces that account for many knockouts.

A wrestler thrown to the floor tries to extend his time-of-arrival-on-the-floor by relaxing his muscles and spreading the crash into a series of impacts, as foot, knee, hip, ribs, and shoulder fold onto the floor in turn.

A person jumping from an elevated position to a floor below bends his knees upon making contact, thereby extending the time during which his momentum is being reduced by ten to twenty times that of a stiff-legged, abrupt landing. The forces absorbed by the bones are reduced by ten to twenty times by such knee bending.

A person is better off falling on a wooden floor than a concrete floor. This is because a wooden floor with "give" allows for a longer time of impact and therefore lesser force of impact than a concrete floor with little "give." A safety net used by acrobats provides an obvious example of small impact force over a long time to provide the required impulse to reduce the momentum of fall.

Conservation of Momentum

An external force is required to change the momentum of a body. The molecular forces within a baseball have no effect upon the momentum of the baseball, just as a person sitting inside an automobile pushing against the dashboard has no effect in changing the momentum of the automobile. This is because these forces are internal forces, that is, forces that act and react within the bodies themselves. An outside or external force acting on the baseball or automobile is required for a change in momentum. If no external force is present, then no change in momentum is possible.

When a bullet is fired from a rifle, the forces present are internal forces. The total momentum of the system comprising the bullet and rifle, therefore, undergoes no change. By Newton's third law of action and reaction, the force exerted on the bullet is equal and opposite to the force exerted on the rifle. The forces acting on the bullet and rifle act for the same time, resulting in equal but oppositely directed momenta that cancel one another, giving a total or net momentum of zero, Figure 7.2. So, the momentum before the firing and after the firing is unchanged. True, the bullet itself gains momentum, as does the rifle—but the bullet and rifle together as a system experiences no change in momentum. No momentum is gained and no momentum is lost. We say momentum is *conserved*.

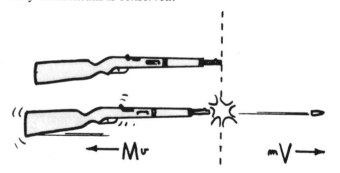

Fig. 7.2   The momentum before firing is zero. After firing the *total* or *net* momentum is still zero because the momentum of the rifle cancels the momentum of the bullet.

If we extend the idea of a rifle recoiling or "kicking" from the bullet it fires, we can understand rocket propulsion. Consider a machine gun recoiling each time a bullet is fired. The momentum of recoil increases by an amount equal to the momentum of each bullet fired. If the machine gun is free to move, mounted on a cart and track, for example, it will accelerate away from its

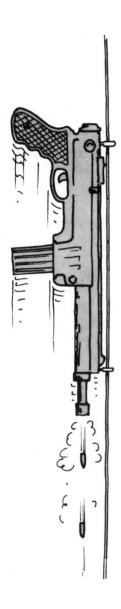

Fig. 7.3 The machine gun recoils from the bullets it fires and climbs upward.

target as the bullets are fired. A rocket accomplishes acceleration by the same means. It is continually "recoiling" from the ejected exhaust gases. Each molecule of exhaust gas can be thought of as a tiny bullet shot out of the rocket. An interesting point here is that if the external force of gravity is negligible, the total momentum of the rocket *and* gases does not change. That is, the momentum of the rocket at any moment is equal and opposite to the momentum of the gases. But we are not usually interested in the total momentum in such a case, and we concern ourselves with only the momentum of the rocket.

A common misconception is that a rocket is propelled by the exhaust gases pushing against the atmosphere. This is equivalent to saying that a gun kicks because the bullet pushes against the atmosphere. This is not the case for the recoiling gun or the recoiling rocket. In fact, a rocket works best above the atmosphere where there is no air resistance to restrict speed. A rocket simply recoils away from the gases it ejects. It will recoil best where air resistance is absent.

Collisions

The total momentum of a system of colliding bodies is unchanged before, during, and after the collision. This is because the forces that act during the collision are internal forces, forces acting and reacting within the system itself. There is only a redistribution or sharing of whatever momentum exists before the collision.

When a moving billiard ball makes a head-on collision with another billiard ball at rest, the moving ball comes to rest and the other ball moves with the speed of the colliding ball, Figure 7.5.

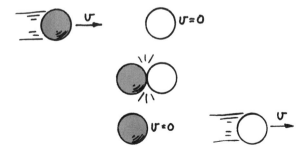

Fig. 7.4 The rocket recoils from the "molecular
bullets" it fires and climbs
upward.

Fig. 7.5 Momentum is transferred from one billiard ball to another.

In any collision we can say,

Total momentum before collision = Total momentum after collision

Suppose the colliding objects become entangled during the collision. Consider, for example, the case of a freight car moving along a track colliding with another freight car which is at rest, Figure 7.6. If the freight cars are of equal mass and are coupled by the collision, how does the velocity of the coupled cars compare with the initial velocity of the single moving freight car? Suppose the single car was moving at 10 miles per hour, and we

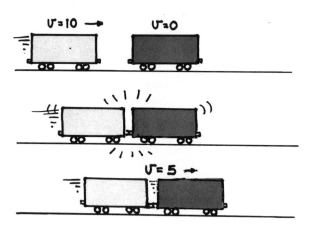

Fig. 7.6   The momentum of the freight car on the left is shared with the freight car on the right after collision.

consider the masses of each car to be M. Then from the conservation of momentum,

$$(\text{Total } mv)_{\text{before}} = (\text{Total } mv)_{\text{after}}$$

$$(M \times 10)_{\text{before}} = (2M \times \text{?})_{\text{after}}$$

Since twice as much mass is moving after the collision, the velocity must be half as much as the velocity before collision, or 5 miles per hour. Then both sides of the equation are equal.

For collisions that take place in directions other than head-on (in a straight line), we must treat momentum as a vector. When cars coming from different directions collide and interchange momentum, we find that the mv's obey vector addition. Figure 7.7 shows a bird's-eye view of a collision in which car A moving eastward crashes into car B moving northward on an icy, level road. If they become entangled they move in a slanting direction with momentum equal to the vector sum of the two original

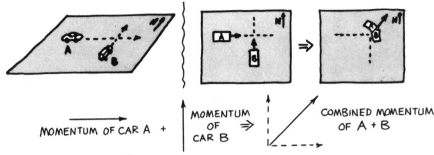

MOMENTUM OF CAR A + | MOMENTUM OF CAR B ⇒ | COMBINED MOMENTUM OF A + B

Fig. 7.7   Momentum is a vector quantity.

momenta. That is, the momentum after collision is the *resultant* of the momenta before collision.

Figure 7.8 shows a falling bomb exploding into two pieces. The momenta of the bomb fragments combine by vector addition to equal the original momentum of the falling bomb.

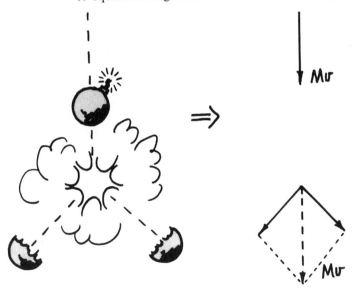

Fig. 7.8   When the bomb bursts, the momenta of its fragments add up (by vector addition) to the original momentum.

Whatever the nature of a collision or however complicated, the total momentum before, during, and after remains unchanged. This is an extremely useful concept, and enables us to learn much from collisions without regard to the form of the forces that interact in collisions. For example, by applying momentum and energy conservation to the collisions of atomic

Fig. 7.9 The internal forces that take place in the explosion of a shell do not change the motion of the center of mass of the shell. The center of mass of the shell fragments moves along the same trajectory before and after the explosion.

nuclei as observed in cloud and bubble chambers, Figure 7.10, we can compute the masses of elementary particles of matter. This information is obtained by measurements of momenta and energy before and after collisions. The forces of the collision processes, however complicated, need not be of concern.

The conservation of energy and the conservation of momentum are two of the most important concepts in physics.

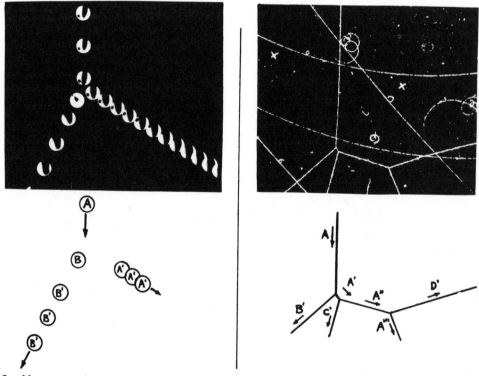

Fig. 7.10 Momentum is conserved for colliding billiard balls and for colliding nuclear particles in a liquid hydrogen bubble chamber. On the *left*, billiard ball A strikes billiard ball B which was initially at rest. On the *right*, proton A collides with protons B, C, and D. The moving protons leave tracks of tiny bubbles.

Questions   1. Suppose you throw a ball against a wall and catch it on the rebound. How many impulses were applied to the ball? Which impulse was greatest?

2. In terms of impulse and momentum, why are padded dashboards safer in automobiles?

3. In terms of impulse and momentum, why are nylon ropes, which stretch considerably under strain, favored by mountain climbers?

4. If only an external force can change the state of motion of the center of gravity of a body, how can the internal force of the brakes bring a car to rest?

5. A fully dressed gal is at rest in the middle of a pond on perfectly frictionless ice and must get to shore. How can she accomplish this?

6. Can a body have energy without having momentum? Explain. Can a body have momentum without having energy? Explain.

7. In the firing of a rifle, the force acting on the rifle is equal and opposite to the force acting on the bullet. Since these forces act for the same time, the momenta of the bullet and rifle have the same magnitude. The *distance* through which the bullet moves is considerably greater than the recoiling *distance* of the rifle while the equal and opposite forces are acting. How, then, does the kinetic energy of the bullet compare to the kinetic energy of the recoiling rifle?

8. Suppose there are three astronauts outside a space ship, and two of them decide to play catch with the third man. All the astronauts weigh the same on earth and are equally strong. The first astronaut throws the second one toward the third one and the game begins. Describe the motion of the astronauts as the game proceeds. How long will the game last?

9. Would you care to fire a gun that has a bullet ten times as massive as the gun? Explain.

10. The total momenta of the freight cars shown in Figure 7.6 is the same before and after the cars collide. Is the total kinetic energy of the cars before and after the collision the same? Explain.

Angular Momentum   Just as a mass moving in a straight line has momentum (usually called *linear* momentum), a mass moving in a circular path has *angular momentum*. Angular momentum is a measure of the *rotational* property of motion. The planets orbiting the sun, a rock whirling at the end of a string, and the tiny electrons whirling about their central nuclei in atoms, all have angular momentum. In addition to mass m and speed v, angular momentum depends on the distance r between the mass and the axis about which it rotates. If this radial distance is large compared to the size of the rotating body, angular momentum is simply equal to the product of mass, speed, and radial distance. In shorthand notation,

$$\text{Angular momentum} = mvr$$

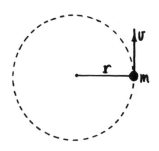

Fig. 7.11 A body of mass m whirling in a circular path of radius r with a speed v has angular momentum mvr.

Just as an external net force is required to change the linear momentum of a body, an external net *torque* is required to change the angular momentum of a body. (Recall that a torque is a force exerted at some lever-arm distance from the axis of rotation.) We can express Newton's first law of inertia for rotating systems as:

A body or system of bodies will maintain its state of angular momentum unless acted upon by an unbalanced external torque.

The greater the angular momentum, the greater is the torque required to change the angular momentum, either in magnitude or direction. Like linear momentum, angular momentum is also a vector quantity. We all know that it is difficult to balance on a bicycle which is at rest. The wheels have no angular momentum. If our center of gravity is not above a point of support, a slight torque is produced and we tumble over. When the bicycle is moving, however, the angular momentum of the wheels requires greater torque to produce any change in the magnitude or direction of spin. This makes it easier to balance on a moving bicycle.

A gyroscope, or gyrocompass, is typically a massive body set in rotation at a high angular speed to produce a large angular momentum. If the gyroscope is mounted so that no resultant torque acts on it, the direction of the angular momentum is unchanged relative to the fixed stars. Once pointed to the north star, for example, a gyrocompass remains pointed north, quite independent of the earth's rotation.

Conservation of Angular Momentum

Just as there is a law of conservation of momentum for bodies moving in a straight line, there is also a law of conservation of angular momentum for bodies in rotation. Providing no unbalanced external torque acts on a rotating system, the angular momentum of that system will not change. This is to say that the numerical quantity *mvr* at one time will equal the numerical quantity *mvr* at any other time.

An interesting example illustrating this principle is shown in Figure 7.12. A person stands on a turntable with weights in each hand. With arms fully extended horizontally, he is first set rotating slowly. When he draws the weights in toward his chest, thereby decreasing *r*, the angular speed *v* is increased. If he decreases *r* by half, for example, the speed doubles. If the arms are again extended the speed decreases to its original value. This experiment is best appreciated by the turning person who feels changes in speed by what seems to be a mysterious force. This principle is used by figure skaters who start to whirl with their arms and perhaps one leg extended, and then draw the arms and leg in to obtain a greater rotational speed.

Fig. 7.12 Conservation of angular momentum—when the radius of the whirling weights is decreased, the angular speed is correspondingly increased.

$$mvr = mUr$$

An astronaut taking a space walk from his orbiting capsule must take the conservation of angular momentum into account. He usually keeps physical contact with his space capsule by means of a tether line. If any rotational motion exists and he is drawn back to the ship by having the tether line pulled in, the decreasing *r* must be accompanied by an increasing *v* and he would find himself whirling around the capsule at a dangerous rate. To correct for this he uses a gas-spurting jet gun which he carries in his hand.

If a cat is held upside down and dropped, the cat has a constant angular momentum about its center of gravity. While falling, the cat rearranges its limbs and tail—thereby changing its rotational inertia. Repeated deformations result in the head and tail rotating one way and the feet the other so that its feet are downward when the cat strikes the ground. Similarly, a diver can change the angular speed of his body about his center of gravity by rearranging the position of his arms and legs.

Ocean tides moving around the earth experience friction at the ocean bottom. As a result, the earth slows in its daily rotation just as an automobile's wheels do when brakes are applied. According to the law of angular-momentum conservation, the slowing down of the earth and lessening of angular momentum is accompanied by an equal increase of angular momentum of the moon in its orbital motion around the earth. This increase in the moon's angular momentum results in an increasing distance from the earth and a decrease in its speed. This increase of distance amounts to one-third of an inch per rotation. Each time we see a new full moon, it is one-third of an inch farther away from us. Perhaps if all the earth's inhabitants together walked westward, the earth would speed up a bit in its rotation, the day would be a little shorter, and the moon would reverse its trend and come a little closer!

Summary of Terms

Impulse. The product of the force acting on a body and the time during which it acts.

Momentum. The product of the mass of a body and its velocity.

Relationship of impulse and momentum. Impulse is equal to the change in the momentum of that which the impulse acts upon. In symbol notation:

$$Ft = \text{change in } mv$$

Conservation of momentum. When no external net force acts on an object or system of objects, no change of momentum takes place. Hence the momentum before an event involving only internal forces is numerically equal to the momentum after the event.

$$mv_{\text{(before event)}} = mv_{\text{(after event)}}$$

Angular momentum. The product of mass, speed, and radial distance of rotation.

Law of inertia for rotating systems. A body or system of bodies will maintain its state of angular momentum unless acted upon by an unbalanced external torque.

Conservation of angular momentum. When no external torque acts on an object or system of objects, no change of angular momentum takes place. Hence the angular momentum before an event involving only internal torques is numerically equal to the angular momentum after the event.

$$mvr_{(\text{before event})} = mvr_{(\text{after event})}$$

Questions   1. Why does a typical small helicopter have a small propeller on its tail?

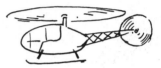

2. Why is it important that a hand-wound grinding wheel be massive?

3. A sizable quantity of earth is washed down the Mississippi River and deposited in the Gulf of Mexico. What effect does this tend to have on the length of day?

4. If the polar ice caps melted, how would this affect the length of the day?

5. Why are gun barrels bored with a spiral groove to make a bullet spin when fired?

6. If an astronaut on a "space walk" fires a rifle, what kinds of motion will he experience?

7. Suppose that a rotating ball of hot gas cools and contracts. What happens to its rate of rotation? What happens to its angular momentum?

Earthrise from the moon (NASA).

8
The Law of Gravitation

For thousands of years man has looked into the nighttime sky and wondered about the stars. With only his naked eye he never dreamed that the stars are greater in number than all the grains of sand on all the deserts and beaches of the world. Our ancient ancestors envisioned the earth at the center of the universe and considered the stars to be fixed on a great revolving crystal sphere. They distinguished the planets from the stars and placed them on inner spheres with more complicated motions. The ancients believed that the complicated motions and the positions of the planetary spheres influenced earthly events.* Copernicus in the fifteenth century discovered that the motions of the planets were much simpler if they were considered circling about the sun rather than the earth. The Copernican view was revolutionary and there were great debates as to whether the planets went around the sun or not.

The Danish astronomer Tycho Brahe had an idea that was different from anything proposed by his contemporaries: His idea was that these debates would best be resolved if the actual positions of the planets in the sky were accurately measured. If the measurements showed exactly how the planets moved, it would be possible to establish one viewpoint or another. This was a tremendous idea—that, in order to formulate a theory, it is better to perform some careful experiments and gather facts than to carry on with philosophical speculation. Pursuing this idea, Tycho Brahe built the first great observatory. Although telescopes had not yet been invented, he built huge brass protractorlike quadrants and cataloged the motions of the stars and planets so accurately that his measurements are still used today. He recorded the planets' positions for twenty years to $\frac{1}{60}$ of a degree. Just before his death he entrusted one of his students, Johannes Kepler, with editing and publishing his planetary tables. Kepler discovered from the data some very remarkably beautiful, but simple, laws regarding planetary motion.

---

*Terminology from ancient times has carried over to the present in many areas; for example, in political science we speak of "spheres of influence."

103

Kepler's Laws

Fig. 8.1 A simple method for constructing an ellipse.

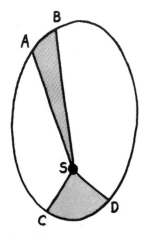

Fig. 8.2 Equal areas are swept out in equal intervals of time.

Kepler first found that each planet goes around the sun in a curve called an *ellipse*. An ellipse is not just an oval, but is a very specific curve. It is the path of a point that moves so that the sum of its distances from two fixed points (called *foci*) is constant. In the case of the planets, the sun is at one focus—the other focus is not occupied by anything in particular. An ellipse is easily constructed by using a pair of tacks, one at each focus, a loop of string, and a pencil, as shown in Figure 8.1. The closer the foci are to each other, the more the ellipse approximates a circle. A circle is actually a special case of an ellipse, in which both foci are at the same point, the center of the circle.

Next, Kepler found that the planets do not go around the sun at a uniform speed, but move faster when they are nearer the sun and more slowly when they are farther from the sun. They do this in such a way that a line joining the sun and a planet sweeps out equal areas of space in equal times. The triangular-shaped area swept out during a month when a planet is orbiting far from the sun ("triangle" *ABS* in Figure 8.2) is equal to the triangular area swept out during a month when the planet is orbiting closer to the sun ("triangle" *CDS* in Figure 8.2).

Ten years later Kepler discovered a third law. He had spent these years searching for a connection between the sizes of the planets' orbits and the times of their "years." From Brahe's measurements of the average radii and times of revolutions for the planets, Kepler found that the squares of the times of revolutions of the planets are proportional to the cubes of their average distances from the sun. He discovered this by noting that the fraction R^3/T^2 is the same for all the planets, where R is the planet's average orbit radius, and T is the planet's "year" measured in earth days. Thus Kepler's three laws of planetary motion are:

Law 1. *Each planet moves in an elliptical orbit with the sun at one focus.*

Law 2. *The line from the sun to any planet sweeps out equal areas of space in equal time intervals.*

Law 3. *The squares of the times of revolution (or years) of the planets are proportional to the cubes of their average distances from the sun.* ($R^3 \sim T^2$ for all planets.)

Except for Pluto, the elliptical orbits of the planets are very nearly circular. Only the precise measurements of Brahe showed the slight differences. Kepler had no idea *why* the planets traced elliptical paths about the sun, and no general reason for the mathematical relationships that he had discovered. He only knew he had discovered a beautifully simple pattern. If there was an explanation for this pattern, he was unaware of it. The explanation for planetary motion was left to Isaac Newton.

Development of the Law of Gravitation

From the time of Aristotle, circular motion was considered to be the "natural" motion of the heavens. It was simply the way stars and planets moved when left to themselves (and obviously man could do nothing but leave them to themselves). As far as the ancients were concerned, circular motion required no explanation.

Newton recognized that a force of some kind must be acting on the planets; otherwise, their paths would be straight lines. From an analysis of Kepler's second law, Newton saw that the origin of this force was the sun. From Kepler's third law he deducted that this force varied inversely as the square of the distance between the planet and the sun. But what sort of a force could act through a distance? Newton was aware of such a force—when an apple falls to the ground, it is accelerated from its position on the tree. He wondered if the same force extended to the moon, holding it in an elliptical path around the earth, a path similar to a planet's path around the sun.

To test this theory, Newton compared the fall of an apple with the "fall" of the moon. We might think that the moon doesn't fall, because it doesn't come any closer to the earth. But it does fall—it falls in the sense that *it falls away from the straight line it would follow if there were no forces acting on it.* Because of its tangential (sideways) speed, it "falls around" a round earth. The moon is sixty times farther from the center of the earth than an apple at the earth's surface (the earth's radius is 4000 miles; the distance to the moon is $60 \times 4000 = 240,000$ miles). The apple will fall 16 feet in its first second of fall. If the inverse-square theory is correct, the moon should fall $(\frac{1}{60})^2$ of 16 feet, which is roughly $\frac{1}{20}$ of an inch.

From the moon's rotational speed and distance from earth, Newton calculated the distance that the moon falls away from a straight-line tangent in one second and was disappointed to find disagreement with the predicted $\frac{1}{20}$ of an inch. Recognizing that brute fact must always win over beautiful hypothesis, he placed his papers in a drawer where they remained for twenty years. Finally a French expedition made a more accurate measurement of the earth and astronomers found they had been using an incorrect distance to the moon. When Newton heard of this he made the calculation again with the new figures and obtained excellent agreement. Only then did he publish what is one of the most far-reaching generalizations of the human mind: the Universal Law of Gravitation.

The Universal Law of Gravitation states that every object in the universe is attracted to every other object in the universe. Everything pulls on everything else, and in a beautifully simple way that involves only mass and distance. Newton stated that every body attracts every other body with a force which for any two bodies is proportional to the mass of each body and which varies as the square of the distance between them.

This statement can be expressed* symbolically as

$$F \sim \frac{mm'}{d^2}$$

where m is the mass of one body, m' is the mass of the other, and d is the distance separating them. The greater the masses, m and m', the greater the force of attraction between them. The greater the distance, d, between the bodies, the weaker the force of attraction; but weaker as the inverse square of the distance. For example, if the distance between the bodies is doubled, the attractive force is reduced to one-fourth; if the distance is tripled, the force is reduced to one-ninth, and so forth. The inverse-square law is treated more extensively in Figure 8.3.

Earth Satellites   Suppose we drop a stone from rest and observe its motion. It will fall to the ground in a straight-line path. If we move our hand horizontally and drop the stone, we would observe that it follows a curved path as it falls to the ground. Repeating this experiment for faster horizontal motions, we would conclude that the faster the initial horizontal motion as the stone is dropped (or thrown), the greater the "radius" of the curved path. What would happen if the horizontal motion was so great that the radius of the stone's curved path was equal to the radius of the earth? The answer is that the stone would fall *around* the earth rather than *into* it. If there were no air resistance or

---

*When the proportionality constant G is included, the relationship can be expressed as the equation, $F = G(mm'/d^2)$. G is called the Universal Gravitational Constant and is discussed in Appendix IV.

Fig. 8.3 The inverse-square law.

Hair spray travels radially away from the nozzle of the can in straight lines. Like gravity, the "strength" of the spray obeys the inverse-square law.

If the weight of an object is 1 pound at the earth's surface, it only weighs $\frac{1}{4}$ pound when it is twice as far from the center of the earth because the gravitational pull is only $\frac{1}{4}$ as strong. At three times the distance it weighs only $\frac{1}{9}$ pound. What would it weigh at four times the distance? Five times?

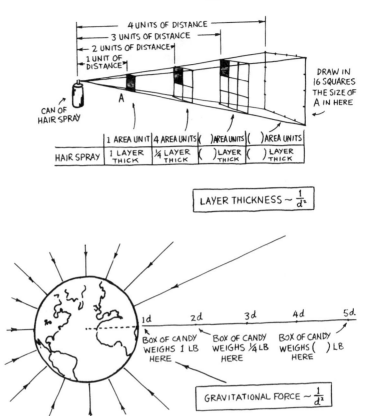

LAYER THICKNESS $\sim \frac{1}{d^2}$

GRAVITATIONAL FORCE $\sim \frac{1}{d^2}$

Fig. 8.4 The greater the stone's horizontal motion when released, the greater the "radius" of its curved path.

other obstructions, the stone would orbit the earth. It would be an earth satellite. How fast would the stone have to be thrown in order to orbit the earth? The answer to this depends on the rate at which the stone falls, and the rate at which the earth curves. The stone will accelerate 32 ft/sec² and fall a vertical distance of 16 feet during the first second of fall. The earth curves away from a line tangent to its surface a vertical distance of 16 feet for every 5 miles of surface, Figure 8.5. If the stone can be thrown fast enough to travel a horizontal distance of 5 miles during the time it falls a vertical distance of 16 feet, then it will follow the curvature of the earth. It will therefore have to travel at 5 miles per second. Convert this to miles per hour and you'll get about 18,000 miles per hour, the speed you see quoted in newspaper articles when satellites are launched (actually somewhat less for higher altitudes).

This idea is sufficiently important to merit another example. Suppose we borrow a laser from a physics lab, set it up at the

Fig. 8.5 Earth's curvature (not to scale!).

Fig. 8.6 A projectile moving horizontally at 5 miles per second falls 16 feet beneath successive 5-mile tangents every second.

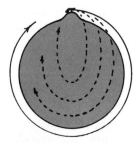

Fig. 8.7 When the muzzle velocity is 5 miles per second, the cannonball will fall around rather than into the earth.

seashore, and direct a beam of light out across the surface of the ocean. We would find that 5 miles from the seashore the beam would be 16 feet above the water (or really, the water would be 16 feet below the beam). This is because the earth is curved. Suppose further that we had a super-cannon with a fantastically high muzzle velocity. If we fired a projectile along the beam of light, 1 second later it would be 16 feet below the beam (remember, gravity does not take a holiday on moving objects—they are pulled toward the earth whether moving or not). If the projectile is to miss hitting the water, it must get 5 miles downrange during the time it falls 16 feet. It takes any object 1 second to fall 16 feet. So the muzzle velocity had better be at least 5 miles per second. This is, of course, neglecting the effects of air resistance.

For such circular motion the force of gravity is pulling in a direction perpendicular to the path of the projectile. So no change in speed occurs—only a change in direction. (Recall from Chapter 5 that, in the absence of a horizontally directed force, the horizontal component of motion for projectiles is constant. In circular orbit the projectile is always moving "horizontally.") Thus the projectile moves tangent to the surface of the earth at constant speed. After the first second it will be moving as fast as it was initially and the process of falling 16 feet beneath a 5-mile tangent repeats itself all the way around the earth, Figure 8.6. The time, or period, for a complete orbit near the earth's surface is 90 minutes. For higher orbits the speed is less and the period is longer (the moon, for example).

All this was deduced by Newton, who pointed out that any projectile is, in a sense, an earth satellite. He considered a cannon fired atop a high mountain, Figure 8.7. A cannonball fired horizontally with a small velocity falls to the ground along a parabolic path. The path is really a Kepler ellipse, with the lower focus at the earth's center. A parabolic orbit and an elliptical orbit are indistinguishable in the small part of the orbit between mountaintop and the ground below. A cannonball fired faster still follows an ellipse, but not so eccentric (flattened); fired still faster, the orbit is an even rounder ellipse. In the absence of air resistance, a cannonball fired fast enough would follow a circular path and orbit the earth again and again (provided the cannoneer and cannon got out of the way). Newton calculated the required speed to be 5 miles per second, and since such a cannon-muzzle velocity was clearly impossible, he did not foresee man launching artificial satellites (he was not hip to multistage rockets).

If a projectile is given a horizontal speed somewhat greater than 5 miles per second, will it spiral away from the earth? The answer would be "yes" if the projectile maintained a constant speed as it does when in circular orbit. But it doesn't—it slows down as it gets farther from the earth. Only for the special case of the circular orbit does the gravitational force pull perpendicular to the projectile's motion, changing only its direction and not its speed. But, for a projectile moving away from the earth this is not the case. Consider the projectile moving at position *A*, Figure 8.8. Gravitational force **F** is not pulling perpendicular to its path, but somewhat against the projectile's motion. There is a component force **f** which is along the orbit but against the motion of the projectile. This component reduces the speed of the projectile. The other component **f′**, changes the direction of the projectile's motion pulling the otherwise straight-line path into a curve. The projectile continues to lose speed until it gets to position *B*. At this farthest point from the earth (called the *apogee*), the gravitational force is perpendicular to the projectile's motion and component **f** is nonexistent. Speed has been reduced too much for circular orbit and the projectile begins to fall back toward the earth. It picks up speed as it falls because the component **f** is then in the direction of motion as shown at position *C*. It continues to pick up speed until it whips around to position *D* (called the *perigee*) where once again **F** is perpendicular to the projectile's motion and **f** is zero. The speed of the projectile is maximum at this point, and too fast for circular

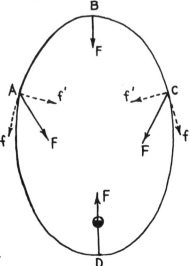

Fig. 8.8 Elliptical orbit.

orbit; thus the projectile again tends to spiral away from the earth and the cycle is repeated. The speed it loses as it travels from *D* to *A* to *B* is equal to the speed it gains as it travels from *B* to *C* to *D*. Newton proved that Kepler's second law of equal areas in equal times was a consequence of this motion.

If a projectile is given a speed exceeding 7 miles per second (25,000 miles per hour), the projectile will escape the earth altogether and never return. Although it will lose speed because it is moving against the earth's gravity, the gravitational pull decreases with increased distance. The high initial speed enables the projectile to "outrun" the deceleration due to the ever-present earth gravity.

So a satellite near the surface of the earth must have a tangential speed between 5 and 7 miles per second. Below 5 miles per second, it will fall into the earth; above 7 miles per second, it will escape the earth and orbit the sun or some other body. If a rocket is fired vertically from the earth it will return and crash into the earth (unless it exceeds 7 miles per second). In this case the adage, "What goes up must come down," is true. In order to orbit the earth, a rocket once above the drag of the atmosphere aims *horizontally* and gives the payload a final thrust to a speed of at least 5 miles per second. The payload then falls around the earth rather than into it and becomes an earth satellite.

Fig. 8.9 The initial thrust of the rocket pushes it up above the atmosphere. A second thrust to a horizontal speed of at least 5 miles per second is required if the rocket is to fall around rather than into the earth.

Weightlessness   When you stand on a spring balance such as a bathroom scale, you measure the gravitational attraction between the earth and yourself—your weight. Do the same thing on a moving elevator and you find your weight varies. When the elevator accelerates upward, your weight increases—the bathroom scale pushes harder against your feet. When the elevator accelerates downward, your weight decreases—the push from the scale declines. If the elevator cable breaks and the elevator falls freely, the reading on the scale goes to zero—according to the reading you are weightless. Are you really weightless? We can answer this question only if we first say what we mean by *weight*.

Loosely speaking, we can define the weight of a body as the force a body exerts against the floor—or the weighing scales. According to this definition, you are as heavy as you feel—so in the falling elevator you are weightless. But strictly speaking, we define the weight of a body as the gravitational force that acts on it. The weight of a body on earth is the gravitational attraction between the earth and the body. In the falling elevator your downward acceleration shows this attraction exists, so in the stricter sense you still have weight.

Consider an astronaut in orbit. In the looser sense the astronaut is in a state of weightlessness. He feels weightless because he is not pushing against anything. He would not compress the springs of a bathroom scale placed beneath his feet, because the bathroom scale is falling as fast as he is. Any objects that are released fall together with him and remain in his vicinity, unlike the situation on the ground. All the local effects of gravity are eliminated for him. The organs of his body respond as though the gravitational forces were absent and this gives the sensation of weightlessness. The astronaut experiences the same sensation in orbit that he would experience in a falling elevator —in both cases he is in a state of free fall.

In the strictest sense, however, the astronaut still has weight, for the earth's gravity still acts on him. If it didn't he would fly off into outer space. All objects under the influence of gravity have weight. In the looser sense of the word, however, weightlessness occurs in many cases, including orbiting astronauts and runaway elevators.

The Ocean Tides

Men have always thought there was a connection between the ocean tides and the moon, but no one could offer a satisfactory theory explaining the two high tides per day. Newton showed that the ocean tides are caused by the *differences* in the gravitational pulls by the moon on opposite sides of the earth. The moon pulls harder on the side of the earth nearest it, and not-so-hard on the side of the earth farthest from it. This is simply because the force of gravity gets weaker with increased distance. To understand why the difference in gravitational pulls by the moon on opposite sides of the earth produces tides, consider the example shown in Figure 8.10. Two masses, m_1 and m_2 are being pulled by a mass M. Since m_1 is closer to M, it is pulled harder and has a greater acceleration toward M than m_2. The more distant mass, m_2, accelerates toward M also, but not as rapidly as m_1, which is pulled harder. The unequal pulls by M cause the distance separating m_1 and m_2 to increase; m_1 pulls away from m_2. Suppose they were both enclosed in a large plastic bag and an observer were placed at the center of the bag, midway between m_1 and m_2. Then m_1 would fall faster than the observer, who would fall faster than m_2. As a result, the observer would see both masses getting farther apart. The

Fig. 8.10 m_1 is attracted to M with a greater force because it is nearer. As a result, the distance between m_1 and m_2 increases.

effect would be that he would see each pulling away from his midpoint position. He would see the bag being stretched, its elongation oriented toward the attractive mass M. If the bag were initially at rest, the gravitational attraction toward M would result in an eventual collision with M. If, however, the bag were given a sideways velocity, it would fall around, rather than into, M. While orbiting M, the bag would still be stretched because the nearer m_1 would be pulled harder and assume a tighter orbit than m_2. To the observer at the center of the bag it would appear that m_1 was being tugged away from his position and toward M, while he in turn was being pulled away from m_2; thus m_2 would seem to be pulled "outward," away from his and m_1's positions, Figure 8.11. What does this have to do with ocean tides? If we substitute the moon for M, the ocean on

Fig. 8.11   If m_1 and m_2 are enclosed in a plastic bag, the difference in gravitational pulls causes the bag to stretch.

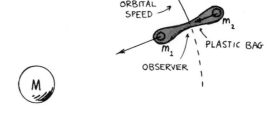

the side of the earth nearest the moon for m_1, the ocean on the side of the earth farthest from the moon for m_2, and the center of the earth for the position of the observer, we have a stretched earth and the resulting ocean tidal bulges, Figure 8.12. These bulges are held by the moon's gravity while the solid earth rotates daily beneath them, giving us two high tides for each 24-hour rotation.

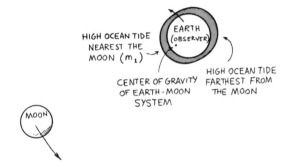

Fig. 8.12 This figure is similar to Fig. 8.11, where the plastic bag is replaced by the ocean, and the observer is replaced by the earth. The ocean is elongated like the plastic bag.

Does the earth orbit the moon or does the moon orbit the earth? *We* think of the moon orbiting the earth, but if we lived on the moon we would regard the earth as orbiting the moon. Actually both earth and moon circle a common point, the center of mass of the earth-moon combination. Where is this center of mass? If the earth and moon were of equal masses it would be midway between each. But the earth is about eighty times more massive than the moon, so the common center of mass between the two is one-eightieth of the distance from the center of the earth to the center of the moon. This is 3000 miles, which is less than the radius of the earth (4000 miles). So the center of mass of the earth-moon system is 1000 miles beneath the earth's surface. It is this point that follows the smooth elliptical (nearly circular) path around the sun. Both the earth and moon orbit this point each month. The earth and moon actually "wobble" about this point—like a lopsided dumbbell—and this wobbly motion also contributes to the ocean tides. This can be understood by considering the following example.

Suppose we push a knitting needle through a rubber ball—not through the center of the ball, but closer to the edge as shown in Figure 8.13. If we cover the ball with honey (or any viscous liquid that will stick to the ball) and spin the ball about the needle, what would we observe? Wouldn't the honey bunch up into a bulge at side *A*, as shown in the figure? It would, because side *A* is the farthest part of the ball from the axis of rotation and therefore the fastest part as the ball rotates about the needle. We can think of the liquid as being thrown out to this far side by "centrifugal" force. In the same way, water is "thrown" to the side of the earth farthest from the monthly

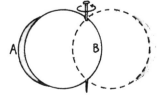

Fig. 8.13 The honey bunch.

rotational axis of the earth-moon system.* The tidal bulge on the side of the earth facing the moon is a consequence of the moon's pull rather than the wobbly motion of the earth.

So in addition to the differential pulling by the moon on the opposite sides of the earth, the rotational motion of the earth and moon about each other also contributes to the tides. But because of the slow rotational speed of the earth and moon about each other, the centrifugal tide effects are relatively small. The difference in gravitational pulls on opposite sides of the earth is the predominant cause of the tides.

Fig. 8.14 The earth has three axes of rotation: a daily axis through the north and south poles, a monthly axis through the center of mass of the earth-moon system, and a yearly axis through the sun (not shown).

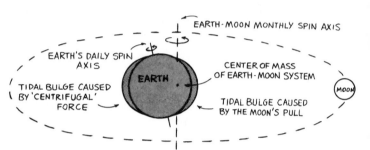

The sun also contributes to tides, although it is less than half as effective as the moon in raising tides. This often seems puzzling when it is realized that the sun pulls the earth with a force almost two hundred times stronger than the gravitational pull of the moon. Why, then, doesn't the sun cause tides two hundred times greater than, or at least as great as, the lunar tides? The reason has to do with the greater distance of the sun from the earth. The sun is so far away that its pull on the near side of the earth is not appreciably stronger than its pull on the far side of the earth. The extra 8000 miles to the far side of the earth is a tiny difference compared to the 93,000,000-mile distance to the sun. So although the sun pulls hard on the earth, its pull is very nearly equal on each side of the earth and only slightly elongates the earth's shape, thus producing only small tidal bulges. Although gravitational pull by the moon is much less, the *difference* between the pull on the near and far sides of the earth is more appreciable. The extra 8000-mile distance to the part of the earth farthest from the moon is $\frac{1}{30}$ of the 240,000-mile distance from the earth to the moon. This 8000 miles is,

---

*The earth has three axes of rotation: a daily axis through the north and south poles, a monthly axis through the center of gravity of the earth-moon system, and a yearly axis through the sun.

however, only $\frac{1}{11,625}$ of the 93,000,000-mile distance from the earth to the sun. For this reason the difference in gravitational force from the moon easily "out-tides" the sun—even though the sun pulls harder than the moon.

So the parts of the earth nearest and farthest from the moon are differentially pulled toward the moon, causing an elongation toward the moon. This elongation is evident in the freely moving waters of the oceans which bulge on the side of the earth nearest the moon and farthest from the moon. The bulges are held in place while the earth rotates beneath them. The daily rotation of the earth carries an observer at any given place alternately into regions of deeper and shallower water. As he is being carried toward the regions where the water is deepest, he says, "The tide is coming in"; and when carried away from those regions, he says, "The tide is going out." During one day he would be carried through two tidal bulges (one on each side of the earth) and would therefore experience two "high tides" and two "low tides."

The two high tides during the day need not be equally "high," however. Depending on the position of the moon and sun, the axis of the tidal bulges may be inclined to the equator, Figure 8.15. When the earth is as shown in the figure, we see that an observer in the northern hemisphere finds the high tide on the side of the earth under the moon much lower than the high tide half a day later. An observer in the southern hemisphere finds the opposite effect.

This simple theory of tides is complicated by the presence of

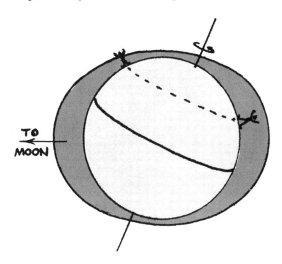

TO
MOON

Fig. 8.15 Inequality of the two high tides per day.

land masses stopping the flow of water, inertia of the water, forces of friction against the seabottom, the rotation of the earth, and the variable depth of the ocean. For instance, friction forces and the water's inertia produce lags in the motion of the bulges so that high tide does not coincide with the time when the moon is directly overhead. It often lags as much as one-quarter of a day. In midocean the variation in the water level—the range of the tide—is only a few feet between high and low tides. This range varies in different parts of the world, depending on latitude and the topography of the ocean floor. The Bay of Fundy, between New Brunswick and Nova Scotia in Southeast Canada, at times experiences tidal differences exceeding 50 feet. This is because the ocean floor funnels shoreward in a V-shape. The tide often comes in faster than a person can run. Don't dig clams near the water's edge at low tide in the Bay of Fundy!

When the sun's and moon's tides coincide, we have tides larger than usual. These are called "spring" tides. (Spring tides have nothing to do with the season Spring.) When the sun's and moon's tides are out of step, we have smaller tides than usual. These are called "neap" tides.

The earth is not absolutely rigid. Consequently, the moon-sun tidal forces produce earth tides as well as water tides. Every twelve hours the solid surface of the earth rises and falls as much as 9 inches! Earthquakes often occur when the earth is experiencing an earth "spring" tide.

Gravity, Light, and Einstein

Albert Einstein, in his general theory of relativity, presents a model for gravity quite unlike Newton's. We won't treat Einstein's model here, but will simply say that, like Newton's, it does not answer the question, "*Why* do bodies attract each other?" Physicists cannot answer the question "Why?" in this case. Both Newton's and Einstein's theories answer instead the question "*How* do bodies attract each other?" One important difference in the answer to this question has to do with time. Newton supposed that the gravitational interaction between two bodies was instantaneous. We have recent evidence to support Einstein's contention that gravity travels in the form of waves at the speed of light. So there is a slight time lag between the pulls of distant bodies.

According to Einstein, anything that has energy has mass—mass in the sense that it is attracted gravitationally. (We will discuss this in greater detail in Chapter 33.) Even light, which is pure energy, has a "mass." When light—from a star, for example—passes near the massive sun, it is deflected from its straight-line path. Although stars are not visible when the sun is in the sky, the deviation of starlight has been observed during the eclipse of the sun. The stars appear to be slightly displaced from their normal positions. The amount of displacement is exactly that predicted by Einstein. There is some speculation that stars exist which are so massive that the light they emit is pulled back by their enormous gravitation, making them invisible.

Shielding

Gravity cannot be shielded as electricity and magnetism can. We will see later that electricity and magnetism have repelling as well as attracting forces which enable shielding. Gravitation only attracts and therefore cannot be shielded. For example, in going around the earth, the moon is attracted by both the earth and the sun. If at the time of a lunar eclipse the attraction of the sun was shielded by the earth, the moon would follow a somewhat different orbit. Even if there were a slight shielding effect, it would accumulate in a period of years and would make future eclipses impossible to predict on the simple law of gravitation. The fact that future or past eclipses can be calculated with a high degree of accuracy is convincing evidence that there is no shielding effect in gravitation.

Universal Gravitation

We all know that the earth is round. But why is the earth round? It is round because of gravitation. Everything attracts everything else and so the earth has attracted itself together as far as it can! Any "corners" of the earth have been pulled in; as a result, every part of the surface is equidistant from the center of gravity—this makes it a sphere. We can thus deduce that the sun, the moon, and the earth should be spheres, just from the law of gravitation (rotational effects make them slightly elliptical).

If everything pulls on everything else, then the planets must pull on each other. The force that controls Jupiter, for example, is not just the force from the sun; there are also the pulls from the other planets. Their effect is small in comparison to the pull of the much more massive sun, but it still shows. When Saturn is near Jupiter, for example, its pull disturbs the otherwise smooth ellipse traced by Jupiter. Both planets "wobble" about their correct orbits. This wobbling is called a *perturbation*. Early in the nineteenth century, unexplained perturbations were observed for the planet Uranus. Even when the influences of the other planets were taken into account, Uranus was behaving strangely. Either the law of gravitation was failing at this great distance from the sun or some unknown influence such as another planet was perturbing Uranus. An Englishman and a Frenchman, Adams and Leverrier, assumed Newton's law to be valid and independently calculated where an eighth planet should be located to account for the perturbation. At about the same time both sent letters to their respective observatories with instructions to search a certain area of the sky. Adams' suggestion was politely ignored by astronomers at Greenwich, but Leverrier's letter to the director of the Berlin observatory was heeded right away—the planet Neptune was discovered that very night!

Perturbations of the planet Neptune led to the prediction and discovery of the ninth planet, Pluto. It was discovered in 1930 at the Lowell Observatory in Arizona. Pluto takes 248 years to make a single revolution about the sun so it won't be seen in its discovered position again until the year 2178.

Perturbations detected in Haley's Comet and two other reappearing comets indicate the presence of a tenth planet far beyond Pluto. A computer analysis of comet perturbations conducted by Joseph L. Brady at the Lawrence Livermore Laboratory of the University of California in 1972 predicted the tenth planet to be smaller than Jupiter and about three times as massive as Saturn, and to orbit nearly six billion miles from the sun with a period of revolution of about 465 years. At the time of Brady's study it was calculated to be among the numerous stars of the Milky Way in the constellation of Cassiopeia.

The perturbations of double stars and the shapes of distant galaxies are evidence that the law of gravitation is true at larger distances. Over still larger distances, gravitation underlies the oscillating theory of the universe. Simply stated, the theory holds that ten to fifteen billion years ago the matter making up the universe exploded from a central region and is still flying apart. Support for the theory comes from the observation that the galaxies are moving away at a decelerating rate, much as a ball thrown skyward leaves the earth at a decelerating rate, g. The theory predicts that like the ball, the outward motion will finally cease, because of gravitational attraction toward the center of gravity of the universe. Then it will, like the ball, begin its fall back to its initial position whereupon it implodes and reexplodes, repeating the cycle. The period of oscillation for the universe is calculated to be about eighty-two billion years. Who can say how many times this process has repeated itself? We know of no way a civilization can leave a trace of its ever having existed, for all the matter in the universe is reduced to bare protons, neutrons, and electrons during the big bang.* Formation of the elements, stars, galaxies, and life again takes place. All the laws of nature, such as the Law of Gravitation, are then rediscovered by the higher evolving life forms. And then students of these laws read about them, as you are doing now.

Few theories have affected science or civilization as much as Newton's theory of gravitation. All the moons and planets and stars and galaxies have such a beautifully simple rule to govern them; namely,

$$F \sim \frac{mm'}{d^2}$$

The deduction of this simple rule is one of the major reasons for the success of the sciences in following years, for it gave hope that other phenomena of the world might also obey equally simple laws.

Summary of Terms   *Kepler's laws of planetary motion.*

Law 1. Each planet moves in an elliptical orbit with the sun at one focus.

Law 2. The line from the sun to any planet sweeps out equal areas of space in equal time intervals.

Law 3. The squares of the times of revolution (or years) of the planets are proportional to the cubes of their average distances from the sun. ($R^3 \sim T^2$ for all planets.)

The Universal Law of Gravitation. Every body in the universe attracts every other body with a force which for two bodies is proportional to the masses of the bodies and inversely proportional to the square of the distance separating them.

$$F \sim \frac{mm'}{d^2}$$

Suggested Reading   Gamow, George, *Gravity* (Science Study Series), Garden City, N. Y., Doubleday (Anchor), 1962.

Rogers, Eric, *Physics for the Inquiring Mind*, Princeton, N. J., Princeton University Press, 1960. Part II of this book contains an interesting account of the history of astronomical theory.

Thorne, Kip S., "Gravitational Collapse," *Scientific American*, November, 1967.

---

*It may be that the galaxies, being so sparse, pass through each other or miss each other completely upon falling in toward the center, and then travel "out on the other side," expanding into a new cycle. There are also other theories on the origin of the universe which include the single big-bang, the steady-state, and the continuous-creation theories.

Questions

1. The force of gravity acts on all bodies in proportion to their masses. Why, then, doesn't a heavy body fall faster than a light body?

2. What is the magnitude and direction of the gravitational force that acts on a 150-pound man at the surface of the earth?

3. Both you and the earth have mass. We know the earth attracts you, but do you attract the earth? If so, with how much force?

4. The earth is closer to the sun in winter than in summer (in the northern hemisphere). How does the orbital speed of the earth about the sun vary with the seasons?

5. If an object is set sliding on an enormous frictionless plane in contact with the earth's surface, it will not continue indefinitely at constant velocity. Why not?

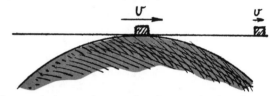

6. The earth is acted upon by the gravitational attraction to the sun. Why, therefore, doesn't the earth fall into the sun? Explain.

7. Explain why the following reasoning is wrong. "The sun attracts all bodies on the earth. At midnight, when the sun is directly below, it pulls on an object in the same direction as the pull of the earth on that object; at noon, when the sun is directly overhead, it pulls on an object in a direction opposite to the pull of the earth. Therefore, all objects should be heavier at midnight than they are at noon."

8. Would the speed of a satellite in circular orbit close to and around the moon be greater than, equal to, or less than 5 mi/sec? Why?

9. Most people today know that the ocean tides are caused by the gravitational influence of the moon. And most people therefore would think that the gravitational pull of the moon upon the earth is greater than the gravitational pull of the sun upon the earth. What do you think?

10. The earth and the moon are attracted to each other by gravitational force. Does the larger earth attract the smaller moon with a greater force than the force with which the moon attracts the earth?

11. A man standing on the surface of the earth has a mass of 70 kilograms and a weight of 154 pounds. If he is instead floating freely inside a space ship far away from the earth, what is his mass? His weight?

12. Is the center of mass of the solar system located at the geometric center of the sun? Does it vary? Why or why not?

13. Why is the wobbly motion of a single star evidence that the star has a planet or system of planets?

14. Is there a place between the moon and the earth where a body would have no weight and would not fall in any direction? Explain.

15. We believe our galaxy was formed from a huge cloud of gas and particles. The original cloud was far larger than the present size of the galaxy, more or less spherical, and was rotating very much slower than the galaxy is now. Below is a rough sketch of the original cloud, and the galaxy as it is now (seen "edgewise"). In terms of the law of gravitation and the con-

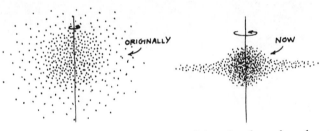

servation of angular momentum, explain why the galaxy has its present shape, and why it rotates faster now than when it was a larger spherical cloud.

Photo by Ron Fitzgerald.

PART 2

Properties of Matter

9
The Atomic Nature of Matter

Take a trip into fantasy sometime when you have a few quiet moments. The only ticket required is a fertile imagination. Imagine that you fall off your chair in slow motion, and while falling to the floor you also slowly shrink in size. What would such a trip be like? What would you see? As you topple off the chair and approach the floor you brace yourself for impact against the smooth solid surface. And as you get nearer and nearer to it, becoming smaller and smaller all the while, you note that the floor is not as smooth as you supposed it to be, for great cracks appear. These are the microscopic irregularities found in all ordinarily smooth surfaces. In falling into one of these cracks, which appear as canyons as you continue to shrink in size, you again brace yourself for impact against the canyon floor only to find that the bottom of the canyon is itself a myriad of cracks and crevices. Falling into one of these crevices and becoming still smaller, you note that the solid walls have given way to nebulous surfaces that throb and pucker. If greater detail were seen you would notice that the throbbing surfaces consist of hazy blobs, mostly spherical, some egg-shaped, some larger than others, and all oozing into each other, making up long chains of complicated structures. And falling still farther you again brace yourself for impact as you approach one of these cloudy spheroids—closer and closer, smaller and smaller, and, wow!—you find you have penetrated into a new universe. You fall into a sea of emptiness, occupied by an occasional few specks that whirl past at unbelievably high speeds. You are in an *atom*, as empty of matter as the solar system. You have found that the solid floor you have fallen to is, except for specks of matter here and there, empty space. If you continue falling, you might fall for hours before making a direct hit with a subatomic speck.

All matter, however solid it appears, is made up of tiny building blocks which themselves are mostly empty space. These are atoms—the atoms which combine to form molecules, which in turn combine to form the compounds and substances of which matter is composed. In this chapter we will study the atomic nature of matter. We will follow this up in succeeding chapters by investigating the properties of matter in the solid, liquid, and gaseous states.

The Beginning of the Atomic Theory of Matter

The idea that matter consists of atoms goes back to the fifth century B.C. The ancient Greeks were concerned with whether the ultimate nature of matter was continuous or discontinuous. Matter appears at first to be continuous in structure. A rock, for example, appears to be continuous throughout. But we can break a rock into small rocks, and break these into pebbles, and them into sand. The sand can be pulverized into powder, and further subdivision would yield still smaller grains or particles. Water presents a different situation. We can keep subdividing water into smaller drops, and there seems to be no reason, on the face of things, why this process should not be continued forever. It is not readily apparent that water is composed of grains.

The "atomic" school, founded by Democritus, Leucippus, and Lucretius, believed that matter was discontinuous; they taught that any substance, after it had been subdivided a sufficient number of times, would be found to consist of hard discrete particles that could not be further subdivided. They called these particles *atoms*.

Empedocles, on the other hand, taught that all matter was composed of combinations of earth, air, fire, and water. Aristotle rejected the atomic theory of Democritus and accepted earth, air, fire, and water as the four basic elements. This view seemed reasonable, for in the world around us matter is seen in only four forms; solid (earth), gases (air), liquids (water), and the state of flames (fire). To the Greeks fire was the element of change, since fire was observed to work some change on the burning substance. Because of Aristotle's compelling authority and the backing of his ideas by the early and later medieval Christian Church, the ideas of Democritus and those of the atomic school were not revived until the rise of experimental science in the sixteenth and seventeenth centuries. The story of this revival by John Dalton and others may be found in the books listed as recommended reading at the end of the chapter.

Molecules and Atoms

It is not difficult to think of solids, such as grains of sand, as consisting of hard discrete particles. The subdivision of drops of water into granular particles, however, is harder to conceptu-

Fig. 9.1   On an idealized scale the weight of a vessel of water decreases in jumps as evaporation takes place. (In practice, no such scales are sensitive enough to detect these jumps.)

alize. This is easier if we consider the process of evaporation. Evaporation is the breaking up of water at the surface into its separate, ultimate, granular particles. These are called *molecules*. Suppose we place an ordinary tumbler of water on a very sensitive spring balance, and gently apply heat to prompt the evaporation, Figure 9.1. If our balance were fantastically sensitive, we would see that the process of evaporation does not proceed continuously, but jerkily, molecule by molecule. We would find the weight of water in the tumbler changing by jumps, each jump corresponding to the weight of a single molecule (or multiples of single molecular weights when more than a single molecule escapes the liquid at the same time).

A molecule is the smallest subdivision of matter that still retains the chemical properties of the substance from which it originates. For example, each separate water vapor molecule will moisten salt or sugar, and combine with the same substances that water does.

Can a molecule be further subdivided? A simple experiment will show that it can. Slide two wires connected to the terminals of an ordinary battery into a tumbler of water, Figure 9.2. Position the wires on opposite sides and note that bubbles of gas will form on the wires. Chemical examination shows that the gases on the two wires have entirely different properties. They cannot, then, both be water vapor, and neither of them is; one is hydrogen and the other is oxygen. If the hydrogen gas and oxygen gas are mixed and ignited with a match, a quick fire, or explosion, results. In the explosion the gases combine again

Fig. 9.2   When electric current passes through tap water, bubbles of oxygen form at the left wire and bubbles of hydrogen form at the right wire.

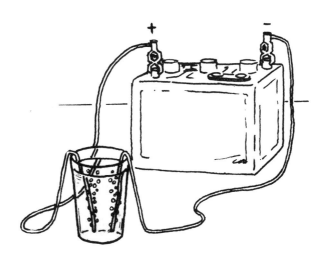

to form water. The smaller units into which a molecule is broken are the atoms. Each molecule of water consists of two atoms of hydrogen (H) and one atom of oxygen (O); this is expressed in its chemical formula H_2O.

Fig. 9.3 Models of simple molecules. The atoms in a molecule are not just mixed together, but are joined in a well-defined way.

All the innumerable substances that occur—shoes, ships, mice, men, stars, everything we can think of—can be analyzed into their constituent atoms. Everything is made of atoms. It might be thought that an incredible number of different kinds of atoms exist to account for the rich variety of substances we find. Actually the number is surprisingly small. The great variety of substances we find results, not from any great variety of atoms, but from the great variety of ways in which a few types of atoms can be combined—just as in a color print three colors can be combined so as to form almost every conceivable color. To date (1971) we know of 105 distinct atoms. These are called the chemical *elements*. Of these only 92 kinds occur in nature—the others are made in the laboratory with high-energy atomic accelerators and nuclear reactors and are too unstable (radioactive) to occur naturally.

The elements are the building blocks of all matter. And all matter, however complex, living or nonliving, is some combination of these elements. From a pantry having 92 bins, each containing a different element, we have all the materials needed to make up any substance occurring in the universe. Most of the things we are daily familiar with are composed of about a dozen or so elements,* for the majority of elements are exceedingly rare. Living things, for example, are composed primarily of four elements: carbon (C), hydrogen (H), oxygen (O), and nitrogen (N). The letters in the parentheses represent the chemical symbols for these elements.

Atoms are small. There are more atoms in a thimble full of water than there are drops of water in the Atlantic Ocean. Still

*Most common substances are formed out of combinations of two or more of these most common elements: hydrogen (H), carbon (C), nitrogen (N), oxygen (O), sodium (Na), magnesium (Mg), aluminum (Al), silicon (Si), phosphorus (P), sulfur (S), chlorine (Cl), potassium (K), calcium (Ca), and iron (Fe).

it is hard to imagine how small atoms are. Atoms are so small, in fact, that the question "What do they look like?" has no meaning. Atoms do not look like anything—they have no visible appearance. We could stack microscope on top of microscope and never "see" an atom. This is because light travels in waves, and atoms are smaller than the wavelengths of visible light. The size of a particle visible under the highest magnification must be larger than the wavelength of light. We can better understand this by considering an analogy of water waves. The wavelength of the water waves is simply the distance between the crests of successive waves. Consider the ship in Figure 9.4. The ship is much larger than the crest-to-crest distance, or wavelength of the waves incident upon it. Information about the ship is easily revealed by its influence on the

Fig. 9.4 Information about the ship is revealed by passing waves because the distance between wave crests is small compared to the size of the ship.

passing waves. Consider Figure 9.5. Waves are incident upon the blades of grass. The grass shoots are much smaller than the incident waves which pass by as if they weren't there. Only if the blades of grass were thicker—that is, wider than the distance

Fig. 9.5 Information about the grass shoots is not revealed by passing waves because the distance between wave crests is large compared to the size of the blades of grass.

between wave crests—would the waves carry information regarding details of the grass. In the same way, waves of visible light are too coarse compared to the size of an atom to reveal details of the size and shape of atoms. Atoms are incredibly small.

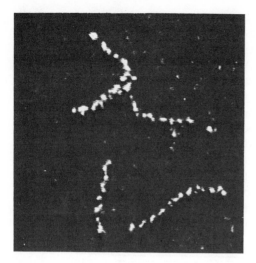

Fig. 9.6 The strings of dots are chains of thorium atoms as revealed by a scanning electron microscope at the University of Chicago.

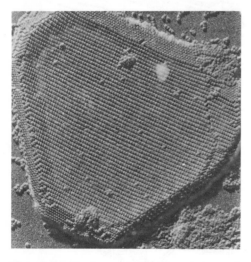

Fig. 9.7 Electron-microscope picture of virus molecules. (Courtesy of Dr. R. W. G. Wyckoff, University of Arizona.)

A photograph of individual atoms is shown in Figure 9.6. The photograph was not made with visible light, but with an electron beam. An electron beam, such as that which sprays a picture on your television screen, is a stream of particles. But particles have wave properties,* and a high-energy electron beam has a wavelength more than a thousand times smaller than the wavelength of visible light. In an electron microscope the beam is focused not by mirrors and lenses, but by magnetic fields. The photograph in Figure 9.6 was taken with a very powerful yet extremely thin (twenty billionths of an inch) electron beam in an electron microscope developed by Albert Crewe at the University of Chicago's Enrico Fermi Institute in 1970. It is the first photograph of individual atoms.

The electron-microscope photograph in Figure 9.7 is of virus molecules composed of thousands of atoms. These giant molecules are still too small to be seen with visible light. So we see that an atom or molecule that is invisible to light may be visible to a shorter-wavelength electron beam.

We often say that seeing is believing. But we don't always have to see something to believe in its existence. We don't have to look inside a closed cardboard box that is too heavy to lift to know that something is in it. And we could measure its mass, for example, without benefit of light. Atoms and molecules are too small to be seen with light, but this doesn't prevent us from measuring their masses with great precision.

---

*More about the wave properties of particles in Chapter 32.

**Molecular and
Atomic Masses**

The earliest determination of molecular and atomic masses was made with the measurements of gases at the beginning of the nineteenth century. As an example of how this is done, consider the gases of hydrogen and oxygen collected when water is decomposed by electricity. It is found that the mass of water decomposed is exactly equal to the sum of the masses of the two gases collected. Figure 9.8 shows that twice as much hydrogen gas is collected as oxygen gas. Water is composed of two parts of hydrogen to one part of oxygen; hence the chemical formula H_2O. The water molecule is simply two hydrogen atoms combined with a single oxygen atom. When the masses of these two gases are compared to each other, we find that for every two grams of hydrogen formed, sixteen grams of oxygen are formed. Since there are twice as many hydrogen molecules as oxygen, it follows that the oxygen molecule is sixteen times heavier than the hydrogen molecule. The key assumption in this analysis is that twice the number of hydrogen molecules were formed as were oxygen molecules. Our observation was that twice the *volume* of hydrogen gas was formed. Our assumption, then, is that equal volumes of gas (at the same temperature and pressure) contain the same number of molecules.

This was first proposed in 1811 by the Italian physicist Amadeo Avogadro de Quarenga. He stated that equal volumes of gas at the same temperature and pressure contain equal numbers of molecules—regardless of the size of the molecules. This statement makes sense only when it is realized that in a gas the molecules are very far apart when compared with the sizes of the molecules themselves. Water vapor (steam), for example, occupies about 1700 times the volume of the same mass of liquid. If the molecules are just touching each other in the liquid, they must be quite far apart in the gas.

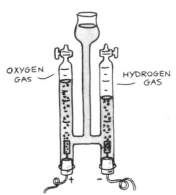

Fig. 9.8   In the electrolysis of water (slightly salted to conduct electricity), twice the volume of hydrogen gas as oxygen gas is collected.

The relative masses of molecules follows from Avogadro's hypothesis. One simply weighs equal volumes of gases and compares the mass of one sample with another. The ratio of these masses of gas is identical to the ratio of the masses of the individual molecules making up the gases. For example, if gas *A* is twice as heavy as an equal volume of gas *B*, then molecule *A* has twice the mass of molecule *B*. If the chemical formula for the molecule is known, the relative masses of individual atoms can be determined.

To compare the masses of the elements, one element is chosen as a standard and the masses of the other elements are expressed relative to that standard. The original standard chosen was oxygen, which combines chemically with more elements than any other. It was assigned an arbitrary mass of 16.0000, which made the mass of hydrogen come out to 1.0.

Our present atomic-mass scale takes the common carbon atom as standard and assigns it a value of 12.0000. One-twelfth of the mass of carbon is called the atomic-mass unit, abbreviated amu. The mass of a carbon atom therefore is 12 amu. Hydrogen, the lightest atom, has a mass of 1 amu; uranium, the heaviest, is 238 amu.

The Periodic Table of the Elements

By the latter part of the nineteenth century knowledge of relative atomic masses was rapidly accumulating and a search for regularity and system was well under way. It was known that some of the chemical elements behaved in similar ways. The similarities allowed for the grouping of families of elements. The elements lithium, sodium, potassium, rubidium, and cesium were all found to be silvery metals that combined violently with water to form basic solutions. This family of elements was called the *alkali metals*. The gases chlorine, fluorine, and iodine were known to have common properties and were in the family of *halogens*. Attempts to relate physical and chemical properties of the elements to their atomic masses were numerous, but a simple comprehensive scheme eluded the searchers until 1871.

Then two men working independently of each other made an important discovery. Dmitri Mendeleev, a Russian chemist, and Lothar Meyer, a German scientist, each made a list of the members of the halogen group, arranging the elements in a column from lightest to heaviest. After this they formed a second column by listing beside each halogen the name of the element with the next heaviest atomic mass. This second column contained a second known family of elements! A third column formed on the same scheme yielded a third family. Nor did it stop there—all the known elements fitted the scheme. This arrangement of elements by atomic mass and family is called the *periodic table*.

The table made by Mendeleev is shown in Figure 9.9. The elements are represented by their chemical symbols. The atomic mass is in parentheses beside each symbol. When Mendeleev arranged each element in vertical columns according to chemical similarities and in order of their masses, a number of blank spaces occurred. He predicted that elements unknown at that time would be found—elements whose atomic masses and chemical properties would place them in the blank spaces. With his periodic table, Mendeleev was able to predict the properties of several elements, then undiscovered, with considerable accuracy.

	GROUP							
SERIES	I	II	III	IV	V	VI	VII	VIII
1	H(1)							
2	Li(7)	Be(9.4)	B(11)	C(12)	N(14)	O(16)	F(19)	
3	Na(23)	Mg(24)	Al(27.3)	Si(28)	P(31)	S(32)	Cl(35.5)	
4	K(39)	Ca(40)	__(44)	Ti(48)	V(51)	Cr(52)	Mn(55)	Fe(56),Co(59), Ni(59),Cu(63)
5	[Cu(63)]	Zn(65)	__(68)	__(72)	As(75)	Se(78)	Br(80)	
6	Rb(85)	Sr(87)	?Yt(88)	Zr(90)	Nb(94)	Mo(96)	__(100)	Ru(104),Rh(104), Pd(106),Ag(108
7	[Ag(108)]	Cd(112)	In(113)	Sn(118)	Sb(122)	Te(125)	I(127)	
8	Cs(133)	Ba(137)	?Di(138)	?Ce(140)	_____	_____	_____	
9	_____	_____	_____	_____	_____	_____	_____	
10	_____	_____	?Er(178)	?La(180)	Ta(182)	W(184)	_____	Os(195),Ir(197), Pt(198),Au(199)
11	[Au(199)]	Hg(200)	Tl(204)	Pb(207)	Bi(208)	_____	_____	
12	_____	_____	_____	Th(231)	_____	U(240)		

Fig. 9.9   Periodic classification of the elements by Mendeleev in 1872.

Figure 9.10 shows the present periodic table of the elements. Until the 1940s the last element in the table was uranium. Since then a number of heavier elements have been made artificially in nuclear reactors and accelerators, and the present table contains 105 elements. Undoubtedly, more will be made. Like Mendeleev's table, the chemically similar elements are listed in vertical columns. The elements are represented by their chemical symbols with the atomic mass below each symbol. A second number above each symbol is the *atomic number* of the element. We will return later in the chapter to this number and its meaning.

Fig. 9.10 Periodic table of the elements. The number above the chemical symbol is the atomic number; the number below is the atomic mass. *Note:* The names for the newest elements (104 and 105) are at this printing not official.

Ia	IIa	IIIb	IVb	Vb	VIb	VIIb	VIIIb			IB	IIB	IIIa	IVa	Va	VIa	VIIa	O
1 H 1.008																	2 He 4.00
3 Li 6.94	4 Be 9.01											5 B 10.81	6 C 12.01	7 N 14.00	8 O 15.99	9 F 18.99	10 Ne 20.18
11 Na 22.99	12 Mg 24.31											13 Al 26.98	14 Si 28.09	15 P 30.97	16 S 32.06	17 Cl 35.45	18 Ar 39.95
19 K 39.10	20 Ca 40.08	21 Sc 44.96	22 Ti 47.90	23 V 50.94	24 Cr 51.99	25 Mn 54.94	26 Fe 55.85	27 Co 58.93	28 Ni 58.71	29 Cu 63.54	30 Zn 65.37	31 Ga 69.72	32 Ge 72.59	33 As 74.92	34 Se 78.96	35 Br 79.91	36 Kr 83.80
37 Rb 85.47	38 Sr 87.62	39 Y 88.91	40 Zr 91.22	41 Nb 92.91	42 Mo 95.94	43 Tc (99)	44 Ru 101.07	45 Rh 102.91	46 Pd 106.4	47 Ag 107.87	48 Cd 112.40	49 In 114.82	50 Sn 118.69	51 Sb 121.75	52 Te 127.60	53 I 126.90	54 Xe 131.30
55 Cs 132.91	56 Ba 137.34	see below 57-71	72 Hf 178.49	73 Ta 180.95	74 W 183.85	75 Re 186.2	76 Os 190.2	77 Ir 192.2	78 Pt 195.09	79 Au 196.97	80 Hg 200.59	81 Tl 204.37	82 Pb 207.19	83 Bi 208.98	84 Po (210)	85 At (210)	86 Rn (222)
87 Fr (223)	88 Ra (226)	see below 89-103	104 Rf (261)	105 Ha (262)													

57 La 138.91	58 Ce 140.12	59 Pr 140.91	60 Nd 144.24	61 Pm (147)	62 Sm 150.35	63 Eu 151.96	64 Gd 157.25	65 Tb 158.92	66 Dy 162.50	67 Ho 164.93	68 Er 167.26	69 Tm 168.93	70 Yb 173.04	71 Lu 174.97
89 Ac (227)	90 Th 232.04	91 Pa (231)	92 U 238.03	93 Np (237)	94 Pu (242)	95 Am (243)	96 Cm (247)	97 Bk (247)	98 Cf (251)	99 Es (254)	100 Fm (253)	101 Md (256)	102 No (254)	103 Lw (257)

The following sections are from Volume I of the *Feynman Lectures on Physics*. They are an edited transcription of a lecture given to freshmen and sophomore physics students at the California Institute of Technology in 1961. Richard P. Feynman, in addition to being a bongo-drum expert, is a physics Nobel Prize laureate and professor of physics at Caltech.

Matter Is Made of Atoms. If, in some cataclysm, all of scientific knowledge were to be destroyed, and only one sentence passed on to the next generations of creatures, what statement would contain the most information in the fewest words? I believe it is the *atomic hypothesis* (or the atomic *fact*, or whatever you wish to call it) that *all things are made of atoms—little particles that move around in perpetual motion, attracting each other when they are a little distance apart, but repelling upon being squeezed into one another.* In that one sentence, you will see, there is an *enormous* amount of information about the world, if just a little imagination and thinking are applied.

To illustrate the power of the atomic idea, suppose that we have a drop of water a quarter of an inch on the side. If we look at it very closely we see nothing but water—smooth, continuous water. Even if we magnify it with the best optical microscope available—roughly two thousand times— then the water drop will be roughly forty feet across, about as big as a large room, and if we looked rather closely, we would *still* see relatively smooth water—but here and there small football-shaped things swimming back and forth. Very interesting. These are paramecia. You may stop at this point and get so curious about the paramecia with their wiggling cilia and twisting bodies that you go no further, except perhaps to magnify the paramecia still more and see inside. This, of course, is a subject for biology, but for the present we pass on and look still more closely at the water material itself, magnifying it two thousand times again. Now the drop of water extends about fifteen miles across, and if we look very closely at it we see a kind of teeming, something which no longer has a smooth appearance—it looks something like a crowd at a football game as seen from a very great distance. In order to see what this teeming is about, we will magnify it another two hundred and fifty times and we will see something similar to what is shown in Fig. 1-1. This is a picture of water magnified a billion times, but idealized in several ways. In the first place, the

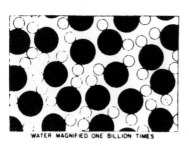

WATER MAGNIFIED ONE BILLION TIMES

Figure 1-1

particles are drawn in a simple manner with sharp edges, which is inaccurate. Secondly, for simplicity, they are sketched almost schematically in a two-dimensional arrangement, but of course they are moving around in three dimensions. Notice that there are two kinds of "blobs" or circles to represent the atoms of oxygen (black) and hydrogen (white), and that each oxygen has two hydrogens tied to it. (Each little group of an oxygen with its two hydrogens is called a molecule.) The picture is idealized further in that the real particles in nature are continually jiggling and bouncing, turning and twisting around one another. You will have to imagine this as a dynamic rather than a static picture. Another thing that cannot be illustrated in a drawing is the fact that the particles are "stuck together"—that they attract each other, this one pulled by that one, etc. The whole group is "glued together," so to speak. On the other hand, the particles do not squeeze through each other. If you try to squeeze two of them too close together, they repel.

The atoms are 1 or 2×10^{-8} cm in radius. Now 10^{-8} cm is called an *angstrom* (just as another name), so we say they are 1 or 2 angstroms (A) in radius. Another way to remember their size is this: if an apple is magnified to the size of the earth, then the atoms in the apple are approximately the size of the original apple.

Now imagine this great drop of water with all of these jiggling particles stuck together and tagging along with each other. The water keeps its volume; it does not fall apart, because of the attraction of the molecules for each other. If the drop is on a slope, where it can move from one place to another, the water will flow, but it does not just disappear—things do not just fly apart—because of the molecular attraction. Now the jiggling motion is what we represent as *heat*: when we increase the temperature, we increase the motion. If we heat the water, the jiggling increases and the volume between the atoms increases, and if the heating continues there comes a time when the pull between the molecules is not enough to hold them together and they do fly apart and become separated from one another. Of course, this is how we manufacture steam out of water—by increasing the temperature; the particles fly apart because of the increased motion.

In Figure 1-2 we have a picture of steam. This picture of steam fails in one respect: at ordinary atmospheric pressure there might be only a few molecules in a whole room, and

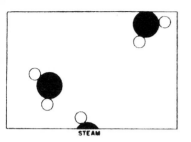

Figure 1–2

there certainly would not be as many as three in this figure. Most squares this size would contain none—but we accidently have two and a half or three in the picture (just so it would not be completely blank). Now in the case of steam we see the characteristic molecules more clearly than in the case of water. For simplicity, the molecules are drawn so that there is a 120° angle between. In actual fact the angle is 105°3′, and the distance between the center of a hydrogen and the center of the oxygen is 0.957 A, so we know this molecule very well.

Let us see what some of the properties of steam vapor or any other gas are. The molecules, being separated from one another, will bounce against the walls. Imagine a room with a number of tennis balls (a hundred or so) bouncing around in perpetual motion. When they bombard the wall, this pushes the wall away. (Of course we would have to push the wall back.) This means that the gas exerts a jittery force which our coarse senses (not being ourselves magnified a billion times) feels only as an *average push.* In order to confine a gas we must apply a pressure. Figure 1-3 shows a standard vessel for holding gases (used in all textbooks), a cylinder with a piston in it. Now, it makes no difference what the shapes of water molecules are, so for simplicity we shall draw them as tennis balls or little dots. These things are in perpetual motion in all directions. So many of them are hitting the top piston all the time that to keep it from being patiently knocked out of the tank by this continuous banging, we shall have to hold the piston down by a certain force, which we call the *pressure* (really, the pressure times the area is the force). Clearly, the force is proportional to the area, for if we increase the area but keep the number of molecules per cubic centimeter the same, we increase the number of collisions with the piston in the same proportion as the area was increased.

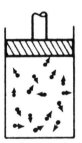

Figure 1–3

Now let us put twice as many molecules in this tank, so as to double the density, and let them have the same speed, i.e., the same temperature. Then, to a close approximation, the number of collisions will be doubled, and since each will be just as "energetic" as before, the pressure is proportional to the density. If we consider the true nature of the forces between the atoms, we would expect a slight decrease in pressure because of the attraction between the atoms, and a slight increase because of the finite volume they occupy. Nevertheless, to an excellent approximation, if the density is low enough that there are not many atoms, *the pressure is proportional to the density.*

We can also see something else: If we increase the temperature without changing the density of the gas, i.e., if we increase the speed of the atoms, what is going to happen to the pressure? Well, the atoms hit harder because they are moving faster, and in addition they hit more often, so the pressure increases. You see how simple the ideas of atomic theory are.

Let us consider another situation. Suppose that the piston moves inward, so that the atoms are slowly compressed into a smaller space. What happens when an atom hits the moving piston? Evidently it picks up speed from the collision. You can try it by bouncing a ping-pong ball from a forward-moving paddle, for example, and you will find that it comes off with more speed than that with which it struck. (Special example: if an atom happens to be standing still and the piston hits it, it will certainly move.) So the atoms are "hotter" when they come away from the piston than they were before they struck it. Therefore all the atoms which are in the vessel will have picked up speed. This means that *when we compress a gas slowly, the temperature of the gas increases.* So, under slow *compression,* a gas will increase in temperature, and under slow *expansion* it will *decrease* in temperature.

We now return to our drop of water and look in another direction. Suppose that we decrease the temperature of our drop of water. Suppose that the jiggling of the molecules of the atoms in the water is steadily decreasing. We know that there are forces of attraction between the atoms, so that after a while they will not be able to jiggle so well. What will happen at very low temperatures is indicated in Figure 1-4: the molecules lock into a new pattern which is *ice.* This particular schematic diagram of ice is wrong because it is in two dimensions, but it is right qualitatively. The interesting point is that the material has a *definite place for every atom,* and you can easily appreciate that if somehow or other we were to hold all the atoms at one end of the drop in a certain arrangement, each atom in a certain place, then because of the structure of inter-connections, which is rigid, the other end miles away (at our magnified scale) will have a definite location. So if we hold a needle of ice at one end, the other end resists our pushing it aside, unlike the case of water, in which the structure is broken down because of the increased jiggling so that the atoms all move around in different ways. The difference between solids and liquids is, then, that in a solid the atoms are arranged in some kind of an array, called a *crystalline array,* and they do not have a random position at long distances; the position of the atoms on one side of the crystal is determined by that of other atoms millions of atoms away on the other side of the crystal. Figure 1-4 is an invented arrangement for ice, and although it contains many of the correct features of ice, it is not the true arrangement. One of the correct features is that there is a part of the symmetry that is hexagonal. You can see that if we turn the picture around an axis by 120°, the picture returns to itself. So there is a *symmetry* in the ice which accounts for the six-sided appearance of snowflakes. Another thing we can see from Figure 1-4 is why ice shrinks when it melts. The particular crystal pattern of ice shown here has many "holes" in it, as does the true ice structure. When the organization breaks down, these holes can be occupied

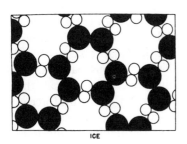

ICE

Figure 1-4

by molecules. Most simple substances, with the exception of water and type metal, *expand* upon melting, because the atoms are closely packed in the solid crystal and upon melting need more room to jiggle around, but an open structure collapses, as in the case of water.

Now although ice has a "rigid" crystalline form, its temperature can change—ice has heat. If we wish, we can change the amount of heat. What is the heat in the case of ice? The atoms are not standing still. They are jiggling and vibrating. So even though there is a definite order to the crystal—a definite structure—all of the atoms are vibrating "in place." As we increase the temperature, they vibrate with greater and greater amplitude, until they shake themselves out of place. We call this *melting*. As we decrease the temperature, the vibration decreases and decreases until, at absolute zero, there is a minimum amount of vibration that the atoms can have, but *not zero*. This minimum amount of motion that atoms can have is not enough to melt a substance, with one exception: helium. Helium merely decreases the atomic motions as much as it can, but even at absolute zero there is still enough motion to keep it from freezing. Helium, even at absolute zero, does not freeze, unless the pressure is made so great as to make the atoms squash together. If we increase the pressure, we *can* make it solidify.

Atomic Processes. So much for the description of solids, liquids, and gases from the atomic point of view. However, the atomic hypothesis also describes *processes*, and so we shall now look at a number of processes from an atomic standpoint. The first process that we shall look at is associated with the surface of the water. What happens at the surface of the water? We shall now make the picture more complicated—and more realistic—by imagining that the surface is in air. Figure 1-5 shows the surface of water in air. We see the water molecules as before, forming a body of liquid water, but now we also see the surface of the water. Above the surface we find a number of things: First of all there are water molecules, as in steam. This is *water vapor*, which is always found above liquid water. (There is an equilibrium between the steam vapor and the water which will be described later.) In addition we find some other molecules—here two oxygen atoms stuck together by themselves, forming an *oxygen molecule*, there two nitrogen atoms also stuck together to make a nitrogen molecule. Air consists almost entirely of nitrogen, oxygen, some water vapor, and lesser amounts of carbon dioxide, argon, and other things. So above the water surface is the air, a gas, containing some water vapor. Now what is happening in this picture? The molecules in the water are always jiggling around. From time to time, one on the surface happens to be hit

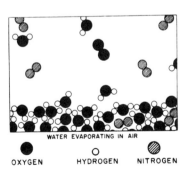

WATER EVAPORATING IN AIR

● OXYGEN   ○ HYDROGEN   ◍ NITROGEN

Figure 1-5

a little harder than usual, and gets knocked away. It is hard to see that happening in the picture because it is a *still* picture. But we can imagine that one molecule near the surface has just been hit and is flying out, or perhaps another one has been hit and is flying out. Thus, molecule by molecule, the water disappears—it evaporates. But if we *close* the vessel above, after a while we shall find a large number of molecules of water amongst the air molecules. From time to time, one of these vapor molecules comes flying down to the water and gets stuck again. So we see that what looks like a dead, uninteresting thing—a glass of water with a cover, that has been sitting there for perhaps twenty years—really contains a dynamic and interesting phenomenon which is going on all the time. To our eyes, our crude eyes, nothing is changing, but if we could see it a billion times magnified, we would see that from its own point of view it is always changing: molecules are leaving the surface, molecules are coming back.

Why do *we* see *no change*? Because just as many molecules are leaving as are coming back! In the long run "nothing happens." If we then take the top of the vessel off and blow the moist air away, replacing it with dry air, then the number of molecules leaving is just the same as it was before, because this depends on the jiggling of the water, but the number coming back is greatly reduced because there are so many fewer water molecules above the water. Therefore there are more going out than coming in, and the water evaporates. Hence, if you wish to evaporate water turn on the fan!

Here is something else: which molecules leave? When a molecule leaves it is due to an accidental, extra accumulation of a little bit more than ordinary energy, which it needs if it is to break away from the attractions of its neighbors. Therefore, since those that leave have more energy than the average, the ones that are left have *less* average motion than they had before. So the liquid gradually *cools* if it evaporates. Of course, when a molecule of vapor comes from the air to the water below there is a sudden great attraction as the molecule approaches the surface. This speeds up the incoming molecule and results in generation of heat. So when they leave they take away heat; when they come back they generate heat. Of course when there is no net evaporation the result is nothing—the water is not changing temperature. If we blow on the water so as to maintain a continuous preponderance in the number evaporating, then the water is cooled. Hence, blow on soup to cool it!

Of course you should realize that the processes just described are more complicated than we have indicated. Not only does the water go into the air, but also, from time to time, one of the oxygen or nitrogen molecules will come in and "get lost" in the mass of water molecules, and work its way into the water. Thus the air dissolves in the water; oxygen and nitrogen molecules will work their way into the water and the water will contain air. If we suddenly take the air away from the vessel, then the air molecules will leave more rapidly than they come in, and in doing so will make bubbles. This is very bad for divers, as you may know.

Now we go on to another process. In Figure 1-6 we see, from an atomic point of view, a solid dissolving in water. If we put a crystal of salt in the water, what will happen? Salt is a solid, a crystal, an organized arrangement of "salt atoms." Figure 1-7 is an illustration of

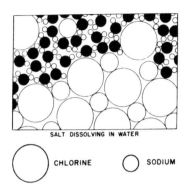

SALT DISSOLVING IN WATER

○ CHLORINE   ◯ SODIUM

Figure 1-6

Crystal	●	○	a(Å)
Rocksalt	Na	Cl	5.64
Sylvine	K	Cl	6.28
	Ag	Cl	5.54
	Mg	O	4.20
Galena	Pb	S	5.97
	Pb	Se	6.14
	Pb	Te	6.34

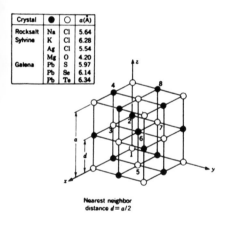

Nearest neighbor
distance $d = a/2$

Figure 1-7

the three-dimensional structure of common salt, sodium chloride. Strictly speaking, the crystal is not made of atoms, but of what we call *ions*. An ion is an atom which either has a few extra electrons or has lost a few electrons. In a salt crystal we find chlorine ions (chlorine atoms with an extra electron) and sodium ions (sodium atoms with one electron missing). The ions all stick together by electrical attraction in the solid salt, but when we put them in the water we find, because of the attractions of the negative oxygen and positive hydrogen for the ions, that some of the ions jiggle loose. In Figure 1-6 we see a chlorine ion getting loose, and other atoms floating in the water in the form of ions. This picture was made with some care. Notice, for example, that the hydrogen ends of the water molecules are more likely to be near the chlorine ion, while near the sodium ion we are more likely to find the oxygen end, because the sodium is positive and the oxygen end of the water is negative, and they attract electrically. Can we tell from this picture whether the salt is *dissolving in* water or *crystallizing out* of water? Of course we *cannot* tell, because while some of the atoms are leaving the crystal other atoms are rejoining it. The process is a *dynamic* one, just as in the case of evaporation, and it depends on whether there is more or less salt in the water than the amount needed for equilibrium. By equilibrium we mean that situation in which the rate at which atoms are leaving just matches the rate at which they are coming back. If there is almost no salt in the water, more atoms leave than return, and the salt dissolves. If, on the other hand, there are too many "salt atoms," more return than leave, and the salt is crystallizing.

In passing, we mention that the concept of a *molecule* of a substance is only approximate and exists only for a certain class of substances. It is clear in the case of water that the three atoms are actually stuck together. It is not so clear in the case of sodium chloride in the solid. There is just an arrangement of sodium and chlorine ions in a cubic pattern. There is no natural way to group them as "molecules of salt."

Returning to our discussion of solution and precipitation, if we increase the temperature of the salt solution, then the rate at which atoms are taken away is increased, and so is the rate at which atoms are brought back. It turns out to be very difficult, in general, to predict which way it is going to go, whether more or less of the solid will dissolve. Most substances dissolve more, but some substances dissolve less, as the temperature increases.

Chemical Reactions. In all of the processes which have been described so far, the atoms and the ions have not changed partners, but of course there are circumstances in which the atoms do change combinations, forming new molecules. This is illustrated in Figure 1-8. A process in which the rearrangement of the atomic partners occurs is what we call a *chemical reaction*. The other processes so far described are called physical processes, but there is no sharp distinction between the two. (Nature does not care what we call it, she just keeps on doing it.) This figure is supposed to represent carbon burning in oxygen. In the case of oxygen, *two* oxygen atoms stick together very strongly. (Why do not *three* or even *four* stick together? That is one of the very peculiar characteristics of such atomic processes. Atoms are very special: they like certain particular partners, certain particular directions, and so on. It is the job of physics to analyze why each one wants what it wants. At any rate, two oxygen atoms form, saturated and happy, a molecule.)

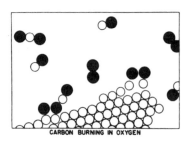

CARBON BURNING IN OXYGEN

Figure 1-8

The carbon atoms are supposed to be in a solid crystal (which could be graphite or diamond*). Now, for example, one of the oxygen molecules can come over to the carbon, and each atom can pick up a carbon atom and go flying off in a new combination—"carbon-oxygen"—which is a molecule of the gas called carbon monoxide. It is given the chemical name CO. It is very simple: the letters "CO" are practically a picture of that molecule. But carbon attracts oxygen much more than oxygen attracts oxygen or carbon attracts carbon. Therefore in this process the oxygen may arrive with only a little energy, but the oxygen and carbon will snap together with a tremendous vengeance and commotion, and everything near them will pick up the energy. A large amount of motion energy, kinetic energy, is thus generated. This of course is *burning*; we are getting *heat* from the combination of oxygen and carbon. The heat is ordinarily in the form of the molecular motion of the hot gas, but in certain circumstances it can be so enormous that it generates *light*. That is how one gets *flames*.

In addition, the carbon monoxide is not quite satisfied. It is possible for it to attach another oxygen, so that we might have a much more complicated reaction in which the oxygen is combining with the carbon, while at the same time there happens to be a collision with a carbon monoxide molecule. One oxygen atom could attach itself to the CO and ultimately form a molecule, composed of one carbon and two oxygens, which is designated CO_2 and

---

*One can burn a diamond in air.

called carbon dioxide. If we burn the carbon with very little oxygen in a very rapid reaction (for example, in an automobile engine, where the explosion is so fast that there is not time for it to make carbon dioxide) a considerable amount of carbon monoxide is formed. In many such rearrangements, a very large amount of energy is released, forming explosions, flames, etc., depending on the reactions. Chemists have studied these arrangements of the atoms, and found that every substance is some type of *arrangement of atoms*.

To illustrate this idea, let us consider another example. If we go into a field of small violets, we know what "that smell" is. It is some kind of *molecule*, or arrangement of atoms, that has worked its way into our noses. First of all, *how* did it work its way in? That is rather easy. If the smell is some kind of molecule in the air, jiggling around and being knocked every which way, it might have *accidentally* worked its way into the nose. Certainly it has no particular desire to get into our nose. It is merely one helpless part of a jostling crowd of molecules, and in its aimless wanderings this particular chunk of matter happens to find itself in the nose.

Now chemists can take special molecules like the odor of violets, and analyze them and tell us the *exact arrangement* of the atoms in space. We know that the carbon dioxide molecule is straight and symmetrical: O—C—O. (That can be determined easily, too, by physical methods.) However, even for the vastly more complicated arrangements of atoms that there are in chemistry, one can, by a long, remarkable process of detective work, find the arrangements of the atoms. Figure 1-9 is a picture of the air in the neighborhood of a violet; again we

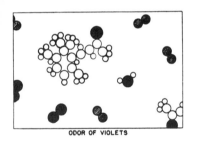

ODOR OF VIOLETS

Figure 1–9

find nitrogen and oxygen in the air, and water vapor. (Why is there water vapor? Because the violet is *wet*. All plants transpire.) However, we also see a "monster" composed of carbon atoms, hydrogen atoms, and oxygen atoms, which have picked a certain particular pattern in which to be arranged. It is a much more complicated arrangement than that of carbon dioxide; in fact, it is an enormously complicated arrangement. Unfortunately, we cannot picture all that is really known about it chemically, because the precise arrangement of all the atoms is actually known in three dimensions, while our picture is in only two dimensions. The six carbons which form a ring do not form a flat ring, but a kind of "puckered" ring. All of the angles and distances are known. So a chemical *formula* is merely a picture of such a molecule. When the chemist writes such a thing on the blackboard, he is trying to "draw," roughly speaking, in two dimensions. For example, we see a "ring" of six carbons, and a "chain" of carbons hanging on the end, with an oxygen second from the end, three hydrogens tied to that carbon, two carbons and three hydrogens sticking up here, etc.

How does the chemist find what the arrangement is? He mixes bottles full of stuff together, and if it turns red, it tells him that it consists of one hydrogen and two carbons tied on here; if it turns blue, on the other hand, that is not the way it is at all. This is one of the most fantastic pieces of detective work that has ever been done—organic chemistry. To discover the arrangement of the atoms in these enormously complicated arrays the chemist looks at what happens when he mixes two different substances together. The physicist could never quite believe that the chemist knew what he was talking about when he described the arrangement of the atoms. For about twenty years it has been possible, in some cases, to look at such molecules (not quite as complicated as this one, but some which contain parts of it) by a physical method, and it has been possible to locate every atom, not by looking at colors, but by *measuring where they are.* And lo and behold! the chemists are almost always correct.

It turns out, in fact, that in the odor of violets there are three slightly different molecules, which differ only in the arrangement of the hydrogen atoms.

One problem of chemistry is to name a substance, so that we will know what it is. Find a name for this shape. Not only must the name tell the shape, but it must also tell that here is an oxygen atom, there is a hydrogen—exactly what and where each atom is. So we can appreciate that the chemical names must be complex in order to be complete. You see that the name of this thing in the more complete form that will tell you the structure of it is 4-(2, 2, 3, 6 tetramethyl-5-cyclohexanyl)-3-buten-2-one, and that tells you that this is the arrangement. We can appreciate the difficulties that the chemists have, and also appreciate the reason for such long names. It is not that they wish to be obscure, but they have an extremely difficult problem in trying to describe the molecules in words!

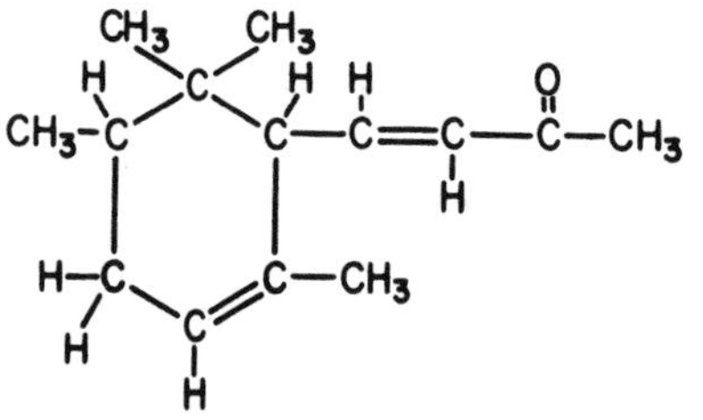

Fig. 1–10.   The substance pictured is α-irone.

How do we *know* that there are atoms? By one of the tricks mentioned earlier: we make the *hypothesis* that there are atoms, and one after the other results come out the way we predict, as they ought to if things *are* made of atoms. There is also somewhat more direct evidence, a good example of which is the following: The atoms are so small that you cannot see them with a light microscope. [Only the latest scanning *electron* microscopes, first built in 1970, are able to "see" individual atoms, as shown in Figure 9.6.] Now if the atoms are always in motion, say in water, and we put a big ball of something in the water, a ball much bigger than the atoms, the ball will jiggle around—much as in a push ball game, where a great big ball is pushed around by a lot of people. The people are pushing in various directions, and the ball moves around the field in an irregular fashion. So, in the same way, the "large ball" will move because of the inequalities of the collisions on one side to the other, from one moment to the next. Therefore, if we look at very tiny particles (colloids) in water through an excellent microscope, we see a perpetual jiggling of the particles, which is the result of the bombardment of the atoms. This is called the *Brownian motion.*

We can see further evidence for atoms in the structure of crystals. In many cases the structures deduced by x-ray analysis agree in their spatial "shapes" with the forms actually exhibited by crystals as they occur in nature. The angles between the various "faces" of a crystal agree, within seconds of arc, with angles deduced on the assumption that a crystal is made of many "layers" of atoms.

Everything is made of atoms. That is the key hypothesis. The most important hypothesis in all of biology, for example, is that *everything that animals do, atoms do.* In other words, *there is nothing that living things do that cannot be understood from the point of view that they are made of atoms acting according to the laws of physics.* This was not known from the beginning: it took some experimenting and theorizing to suggest this hypothesis, but now it is accepted, and it is the most useful theory for producing new ideas in the field of biology.

If a piece of steel or a piece of salt, consisting of atoms one next to the other, can have such interesting properties; if water—which is nothing but these little blobs, mile upon mile of the same thing over the earth—can form waves and foam, and make rushing noises and strange patterns as it runs over cement; if all of this, all the life of a stream of water, can be nothing but a pile of atoms, *how much more is possible*? If instead of arranging the atoms in some definite pattern, again and again repeated, on and on, or even forming little lumps of complexity like the odor of violets, we make an arrangement which is *always different* from place to place, with different kinds of atoms arranged in many ways, continually changing, not repeating, how much more marvelously is it possible that this thing might behave? Is it possible that that "thing" walking back and forth in front of you, talking to you, is a great glob of these atoms in a very complex arrangement, such that the sheer complexity of it staggers the imagination as to what it can do? When we say we are a pile of atoms, we do not mean we are *merely* a pile of atoms, because a pile of atoms which is not repeated from one to the other might well have the possibilities which you see before you in the mirror.

Atomic Structure   If we could magnify an atom a billion times, we would find that it has structure in some sense similar to a cherry. At the center is the dense core, and filling the rest of the space are tiny whirling electrons. It differs from a cherry, however, in several ways. The core, called the *nucleus*, is very small compared to the rest of the atom. The diameter of the nucleus is only about $\frac{1}{10,000}$ the diameter of the atom. It is incredibly tiny, yet the nucleus contains nearly all the mass of the atom. The nucleus therefore is extremely dense. If bare atomic nuclei could be packed against each other into a lump one centimeter in diameter (about the size of a large pea), it would weigh 133,000,000 tons! Huge electrical forces of repulsion prevent such close packing of atomic nuclei. Each nucleus is electrically charged, and repels other nuclei. Only under special circumstances do the nuclei of two or more atoms come into contact, and when they do, a violent reaction takes place. This is what occurs in a hydrogen bomb, and will be discussed in Chapter 35.

The nucleus is composed of two basic building blocks—

protons and neutrons. The protons are electrically charged and constitute the electrical charge of the nucleus. The neutrons are slightly more massive than the protons and have no electrical charge.

Surrounding the nucleus are electrons, the particles that make up the flow of electricity in electrical circuits. They are exceedingly light, almost two thousand times lighter than protons and neutrons, and contribute very little mass to the atom. Electrons are electrically charged, and repel other electrons. But electrons are attracted to the nucleus. We say the electrons are negatively charged and the nucleus is positively charged. Like kinds of electrical charge repel one another and unlike charges attract one another. We can think of the electrons as attracted to the nucleus and whirling about it like the planets around the sun. The situation is far from this simple, but it affords a picture useful in thinking and talking about atoms. We can refine this model of the atom as we gain more information.

Like the solar system of planets, the atom is mostly empty space. The nucleus and surrounding electrons occupy only a tiny fraction of the atomic volume. If it weren't for the electrical forces of repulsion between the electrons of neighboring atoms, solid matter would be much more dense than it is. These same electrical repulsions prevent us from falling through the solid floor. We and the solid floor are mostly empty space, because the atoms making up these and all materials are themselves mostly empty space. Electrical forces keep atoms from caving in on each other under pressure.

Depending upon the configuration of electrons, atoms may attract each other when close together and form molecules. If atoms are too close they will repel, and when atoms are several atomic diameters apart the electrical forces on each other are negligible.

The main characteristic that distinguishes the atoms from one another is the number of electrons about the nucleus. Hydrogen, which is the simplest and lightest atom, and first in the periodic table with atomic number 1, has one electron. Helium, atomic number 2, has two electrons. Lithium, the next element in the periodic table, atomic number 3, has three electrons orbiting the nucleus. This regularity continues through the entire list of the elements. The number of electrons in each atom is given by the atomic number of the atom.*

---

*Sometimes atoms have an excess or deficiency of electrons. Such atoms, called *ions*, have a net electric charge. More about this in Chapter 21.

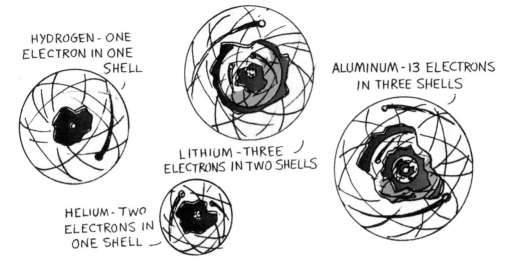

HYDROGEN - ONE ELECTRON IN ONE SHELL

ALUMINUM - 13 ELECTRONS IN THREE SHELLS

LITHIUM - THREE ELECTRONS IN TWO SHELLS

HELIUM - TWO ELECTRONS IN ONE SHELL

Fig. 9.11 The classic model of the atom consists of a tiny nucleus surrounded by electrons that orbit within spherical shells. As the size and charge of the nuclei increase, electrons are pulled closer, and the shells become smaller.

We find that electrons revolve about the nucleus in orbits or perhaps in "waves," sweeping out concentric shells at various distances from the nucleus.* In the innermost shell there are at most 2 electrons; in the second shell, 8 electrons; in the third shell, 18. In atoms having more than 86 electrons, there are 7 shells altogether. It is the configuration of electrons in the outer shell of the atom that, quite literally, give life and color to the world. Some of the properties of matter that can be attributed to the outer electrons of the atom are these: the bonding of atoms to form molecules; the temperatures of freezing and boiling; electrical and magnetic properties of materials; the taste, feel, appearance, and color of substances.

The States of Matter

Matter exists in four states: the solid state, the liquid state, the gaseous state, and the plasma state. In all states the molecules are perpetually moving. In the solid state the atoms and molecules vibrate about fixed positions. If the rate of molecular vibration is increased sufficiently, molecules will shake apart and wander throughout the material, vibrating in nonfixed positions. The shape of the material is no longer fixed but takes the shape of its container. This is the liquid state. If more energy is put into the material and the molecules vibrate at even greater rates,

*The wave nature of electrons is discussed in Chapter 32.

they may break away from one another and assume the gaseous state. H_2O is a common example of this changing of states. When solid, it is ice. If we heat the ice the increased molecular motion jiggles the molecules out of their fixed positions and we have water. If we heat the water, we can reach a stage where continued molecular vibration results in a dissociation between water molecules and we have steam. Continued heating causes the molecules to separate into atoms—if we heat the steam to temperatures exceeding 3500°F, the atoms themselves will be shaken apart, making a gas of free electrons and bare nuclei called plasma.

Although the plasma state is less common to our everyday experience, it may be considered the normal state of matter in the universe—the sun and other stars as well as much of the intergalactic matter are in the plasma state. All substances can be transformed from any state to another.

Summary of Terms

Atom. The smallest particle of an element that has all of its chemical properties.

Molecule. The smallest particle of a substance that has all its chemical and physical properties; atoms combine to form molecules.

Avogadro's Principle. Equal volumes of all gases at the same temperature and pressure contain the same number of molecules.

Angstrom. A unit of length equal to 10^{-8} (0.00000001) centimeter.* Atoms have a radius of about one to two angstroms.

Chemical reaction. A process in which rearrangement of atoms from one molecule to another occurs.

Brownian motion. The haphazard movement of tiny particles suspended in a gas or liquid resulting from bombardment by the fast-moving molecules of the gas or liquid.

Atomic nucleus. The core of an atom, consisting of two basic building blocks—protons and neutrons. The protons have a positive electric charge, giving the nucleus a positive electric charge; the neutrons have no electrical charge.

Electron. The negatively charged part of the atom that orbits the nucleus.

Atomic-mass unit (amu). The standard unit of atomic mass which is equal to one-twelfth the mass of an atom of carbon, arbitrarily given the value of exactly 12.

*See Appendix I at the end of the book for a discussion of *scientific notation.*

Atomic number. The number of protons in the atomic nucleus; also the number of electrons surrounding the nucleus. The atomic number of an atom signifies its numerical position in the periodic table of the elements.

Suggested Reading

Asimov, Isaac, *A Short History of Chemistry*, Chaps. 5 and 8 (Science Studies Series), Garden City, N. Y., Doubleday (Anchor).

Williams, George A., *Elementary Physics—Atoms, Waves, Particles,* Part III, New York, McGraw-Hill, 1969.

Questions

1. Why would an atom still be invisible when viewed with an *ideal* optical microscope?

2. A cat strolls across your back yard. An hour later a dog with his nose to the ground follows the footsteps of the cat. Explain this occurrence from an atomic point of view.

3. Atoms are mostly empty space; hence solid objects are mostly empty space. Why, then, cannot solid objects pass through one another?

4. What is the principal variable that distinguishes one element from another?

5. What is the principal variable that determines whether atoms or molecules will form a solid or liquid or gaseous or plasma state?

10
Solids

The classification of solids began when the earliest cave man distinguished between rocks for shelter and rocks for tools. Since then the list of solids has grown without pause. Yet only within the last sixty years has the actual structure of solids been confirmed beyond doubt.

Prior to this, it was thought that the content of a solid was what determined its characteristics—what made diamonds hard, lead soft, iron magnetic, and copper electrically conducting. It was believed that to change a substance one merely varied the contents. Today we know that many of the properties of a solid are determined by its *structure*—by the way the atoms in the material are ordered, and by the way they join together.

The shift in interest from the content to the structure of a solid has enabled man to greatly alter his physical environment. From being a mere finder and assembler of materials, he has become a maker of them, a genuine architect of matter. In his laboratories he daily extends the long list of synthetic materials.

A striking example of the structure of solid matter is shown on the opposite page and on the cover of this book. The picture is a micrograph produced by Dr. Erwin Mueller. Dr. Mueller took an extremely fine platinum needle, ending in a hemisphere sixteen millionths of an inch in diameter. He enclosed it in a tube of rarefied helium and applied to it a very high positive voltage (25,000 volts). Under such electrical pressure the helium atoms "settling" on the atoms of the needle tip were ionized and torn off as positive ions streaming away from the tip in a direction almost perpendicular to the surface at every point. They then struck a fluorescent screen, producing the picture of the needle tip, which is enlarged approximately 750,000 times. Clearly, the platinum is crystalline, the atoms arranged like oranges in a grocer's display. Although the cover is not a photograph of the atoms in the needletip themselves, it shows the positions of the atoms, revealing the microarchitecture of the solids that make up our world.

How Atoms Are Ordered in a Solid

It was realized, near the turn of the nineteenth century, that many solids are composed of crystals. As the atomic theory of matter was being established, crystals themselves were thought to be made up of a particular arrangement of atoms. This was confirmed in 1912 with the use of X-rays. Atoms in a crystal are very close together, most between 3 and 10 angstrom units apart, which is about the same as the wavelength of X-rays. The German physicist Max von Laue discovered that a beam of X-rays directed upon a crystal is dispersed into a pattern characteristic of the crystal, called a *diffraction pattern*, Figure 10.1. The diffraction patterns made by X-rays on photographic film reveal the crystal as a neat mosaic of atoms sited on a regular lattice, like a three-dimensional chess board, or a child's jungle gym. Metals such as iron, copper, and gold are relatively simple crystal structures. Tin and cobalt are only a little more complex. And all are made up of interlocking crystals, each almost perfect, each with the same regular lattice, but at a different inclination to the crystal nearby. These metal crystals can be seen when a clean metal surface is cleaned (etched) with acid. You can see them on the surface of galvanized iron that has been exposed to the weather, or on brass door knobs that have been etched by the perspiration of hands.

Von Laue's photographs of the X-ray diffraction patterns fascinated a father-and-son team of English scientists, William Henry Bragg and his 22-year-old son William Lawrence Bragg.

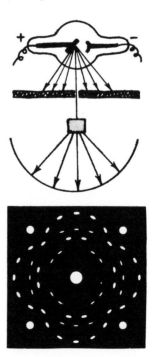

Fig. 10.1   X-ray determination of crystal structure. The photograph of salt is a product of X-ray diffraction. Rays from the X-ray tube are blocked by a lead screen except for a narrow beam which hits the crystal of sodium chloride (common table salt). The radiation that penetrates the crystal to the photographic film makes the pattern shown. The white spot in the center is the main unscattered beam of X-rays. The size and arrangement of the other spots result from the bouncing around of the rays in the latticework structure of sodium and chlorine atoms in the crystal. Every crystalline structure has its own unique X-ray diffraction picture. A crystal of sodium chloride will always produce this same design.

Experimenting on their own, the Braggs developed a mathematical formula for calculating how the regularly spaced crystalline structures should reflect X-rays from the various layers of atoms. By the proper measurement of the spots of light and dark formed by the diffraction patterns, it was possible to determine the thickness of each of the layers inside the crystal and therefore the distances between atoms.

How Atoms Are Held Together in a Solid

A solid is a crystalline latticework of atoms. Each atom vibrates about its own fixed position and is unable to move through the lattice. What ties one atom to a neighboring atom is a bonding force of electrical attraction between the total positive charge of one atom and the negatively charged electrons of the other. There are four varieties of such bonding, and it is the subtle differences between them that account for the particular properties of solid substances—their solubility, their conductivity, the ease with which they melt or freeze, and so on.

In *ionic bonding*, an electron of one element is lost to another element, creating charged atoms—ions—of such strong attraction for each other that the resulting bond is extremely strong. The atoms of sodium and chloride in the crystals of common table salt are held together by ionic bonding. An atom of sodium

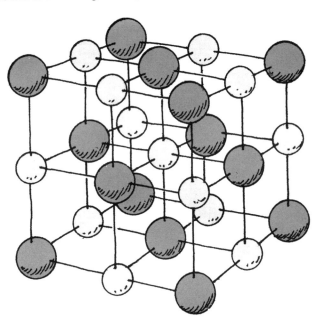

Fig. 10.2 Sodium chloride crystal — the large spheres represent chlorine atoms.

loses one of its electrons to an atom of chlorine, resulting in a strong attraction between the oppositely charged ions. High temperatures are required to shake this bond apart and melt crystals of table salt.

Covalent bonding consists of the sharing of one or more electrons of one atom with another atom. Instead of circling one atom, the outer electrons circle both atoms, thus binding them into one package. It is a link that produces the tremendous hardness in a diamond. Both diamond and graphite—two forms of pure carbon that are chemically identical yet physically far different—are examples of covalent bonding. While the diamond is the hardest substance known to man, graphite is "soft" enough to be used as a lubricant. Carbon atoms in a diamond are bonded to neighboring carbon atoms in all directions, while in graphite the bonding takes place in layers. The crystal-line layers in graphite are relatively far apart, so only a very weak bond exists between the atoms of different layers. This allows the layers to slip freely over one another, and accounts for the excellent lubrication property of graphite.

Metallic bonding is similar to covalent bonding, except the specific electrons are not shared between specific atoms. Instead, the electrons exist in a kind of roaming cloud, free to travel and hook up between any two atoms in the lattice. This bonding is directly responsible for the conductivity of heat and electricity in metals. When an electric voltage is applied, this "cloud" of electrons comprises an electric current drifting through the atomic lattice. When heat is applied to a spot, the free electrons gain speed in random directions and collide with other particles in the crystal. The heat therefore is transferred throughout the material.

The weakest bond in solid crystals is provided by what are called *Van der Waals forces*. They result from electrons orbiting the atomic nucleus occasionally bunching up on one side, creating a temporary preponderance on that side of a negative electric charge. This charge is matched by an equal positive charge on the other side. A molecule with this distortion is then "polarized"—that is, it has positive and negative charges at opposite ends. Oppositely charged sides of neighboring molecules are attracted to each other. These forces, which link molecules rather than atoms, are relatively weak. Occasion-ally certain molecules break away from their neighbors and fly off helter-skelter into space. This explains, for instance, why dry ice sublimes so readily; that is, why it passes directly from the solid to the gaseous state without going through the liquid state.

More than one kind of bonding may occur within a single crystal. The bonds are elastic enough to permit vibrations of the atoms about their positions in the lattice. As temperature rises, motion increases, finally straining bonds to the breaking point; the crystal then melts, and the solid becomes a liquid.

Density   The masses of atoms and the spacing between atoms determine the *density* of a material. We think of density as the "lightness" or "heaviness" of materials. It is a measure of the compactness of matter. More precisely, it is the amount of matter per unit volume,*

$$\text{Density} = \frac{\text{mass}}{\text{volume}}$$

The densities of a few materials are given in the table in Figure 10.3. Mass is measured in grams and volume in cubic centimeters (cc). A gram of material is defined as equal to the mass

DENSITIES OF A FEW SUBSTANCES	
MATERIAL	GRAMS/CC
ICE	0.92
WATER	1.0
QUARTZ	2.65
ALUMINUM	2.7
TIN	7.3
IRON	7.8
BRASS	8.5
COPPER	8.9
SILVER	10.5
LEAD	11.3
MERCURY	13.6
GOLD	19.3
PLATINUM	21.4
OSMIUM	22.48

Fig. 10.3   Densities of a few substances.

*Density can also be expressed as weight per unit volume.

of 1 cc of water at a temperature of 4° Centigrade. Therefore water has density of 1 gram per cubic centimeter. Gold, which has a density of 19.3 grams per cubic centimeter is therefore 19.3 times heavier than an equal volume of water. Osmium, a hard bluish-white metallic element, is the densest substance known. Although the individual osmium atom is less massive than individual atoms of gold, mercury, lead, and uranium, the close spacing of osmium atoms in crystalline form gives it the highest density. More atoms fit into a cubic centimeter than the heavier, more widely spaced atoms.

Elasticity

When an object is subjected to external forces, it usually undergoes changes in size or shape or both. These changes depend on the arrangement and bonding of the atoms making up the material.

A weight hanging on a spring causes the spring to stretch. Additional weight stretches the spring still more. The stretch is directly proportional to the applied force.* When we remove the weights the spring returns to its original length. When a batter hits a baseball he temporarily changes its shape, Figure 10.5. When an archer shoots an arrow, he first bends the bow, which springs back to its original form when the arrow is released. The spring, the baseball, and the bow are examples of *elastic* objects. Elasticity is that property of a body by which it experiences a change in shape when a deforming force acts upon it and by which it returns to its original shape when the deforming force is removed.

Materials that do not resume their original shape after being distorted are said to be *inelastic*. Clay, putty, and dough are inelastic materials. Lead is relatively inelastic, since it is easy to distort it permanently.

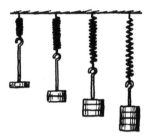

Fig. 10.4 The stretch of the spring is directly proportional to the applied force. If the weight is doubled, the spring stretches twice as much.

On the Size of Solids

Did you ever notice how strong an ant is for his size? An ant can easily lift much more than his own weight. What if an ant could somehow increase, in his natural proportion, to the size of a man? Would this "super ant" be many times stronger than a man? Could he lift loads heavier than those that an

---

*This relationship, which applies only within the limits of permanent distortion of the material being stretched, was noted by Robert Hooke in the mid-seventeenth century and is called Hooke's Law, $F \sim d$.

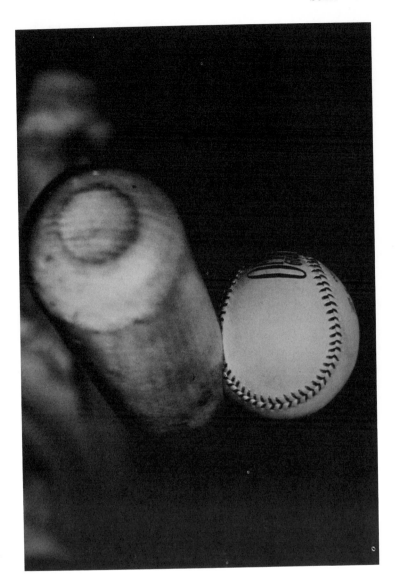

Fig. 10.5 A baseball is elastic. (Courtesy of Harold E. Edgerson, Massachusetts Institute of Technology.)

elephant can deal with? The answer is no. Such an ant would not be able to lift his own weight off the ground. His legs would probably break under his own weight. Let's consider a simpler example. How would a six-foot, 200-pound man fare if he were somehow doubled in size? That is, if he were a giant twelve feet tall, twice as wide, his bones twice as thick, and every linear dimension increased by a factor of 2.* Could he press a barbell equal to his new weight over his head? And what would this weight be? In doubling his height, is his weight doubled? The answer is no—his weight is increased by a factor of 8—he would weigh 1600 pounds! He would have trouble doing push-ups, let alone trying to lift his own weight. To see why this is so, consider the simplest case of a solid cube of matter, 1 inch on a side. To make the numbers easy we'll assume the cube has weight density of 1 pound per cubic inch.

A 1-cubic-inch cube would have a cross section of 1 square inch. That is, if we sliced through the cube parallel to one of its faces, the sliced area would be 1 square inch. Compare this cube to a cube which has double the linear dimensions. Then it will be 2 inches on each side. Its cross-sectional area will be 2×2 or 4 square inches and its volume $2 \times 2 \times 2$ or 8 cubic inches. At the same density of 1 pound per cubic inch, it would weigh 8 pounds. Investigation of Figure 10.6 shows that the area increases as the square of the linear increases, and the volume and weight increase as the cube of the linear increases. The weight goes up much more than the corresponding increase of cross-sectional area. Although we use the simple example of a cube in the figure, the principle applies to an object of any shape. Double the size of any object and you multiply its area four times—but its volume (and hence weight) eight times. For our six-foot man, the cross section of his bones is increased fourfold when his height and other linear dimensions are doubled, but his weight is increased eight times. The fibers in his bones are then subjected to twice the stress. Unless his legs were increased out of proportion in thickness or constructed with a material stronger than bone, he would have to walk very carefully and avoid jumping. Otherwise his legs would be in splints much of the time. In the case of the ant, if his height, width, and length were increased by 100, the cross section of his legs would go up as the square of this increase, $(100)^2$ or 10,000 times, but his volume and weight would increase by $(100)^3$ or 1,000,000. His legs would be too thin to support his weight.

Thus we find in nature that large animals have disproportionally thick legs compared to small animals. The smaller

---

*It is interesting to note that man is already a giant—one of the largest of all the animals. The names of all animals larger than man could be written on a single sheet of paper, while the names of those that are smaller would fill volumes.

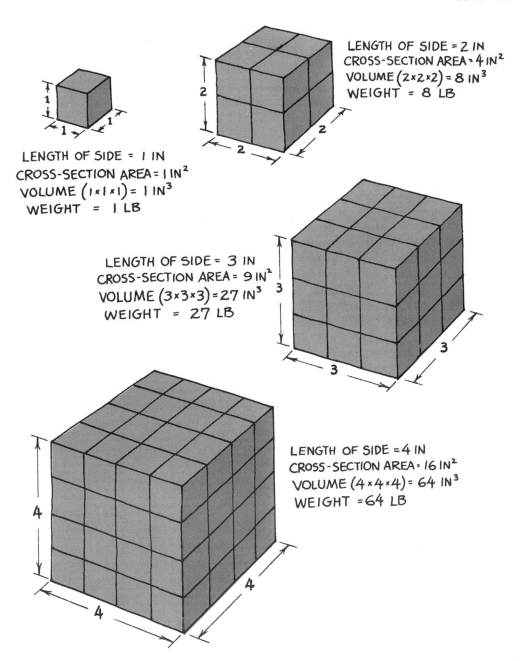

LENGTH OF SIDE = 2 IN
CROSS-SECTION AREA = 4 IN²
VOLUME (2×2×2) = 8 IN³
WEIGHT = 8 LB

LENGTH OF SIDE = 1 IN
CROSS-SECTION AREA = 1 IN²
VOLUME (1×1×1) = 1 IN³
WEIGHT = 1 LB

LENGTH OF SIDE = 3 IN
CROSS-SECTION AREA = 9 IN²
VOLUME (3×3×3) = 27 IN³
WEIGHT = 27 LB

LENGTH OF SIDE = 4 IN
CROSS-SECTION AREA = 16 IN²
VOLUME (4×4×4) = 64 IN³
WEIGHT = 64 LB

Fig. 10.6   As the linear dimensions of an object are increased, the area increases as the square of the increase, and the volume (and hence the weight) increases as the cube of the increase.

the size of a creature, the thinner its legs are proportionally. Consider the different legs of an elephant and a daddy longlegs.

It is interesting to compare the overall surface area of an object with its volume. A study of Figure 10.7 shows that as the size of an object is increased, the volume increases disproportionally to the surface area. The increase in volume is greater than the corresponding increase in surface area. Conversely, as an object becomes smaller, its surface area increases when compared to its volume or weight. This principle applies to objects of any shape. A good cook knows that more skin results when peeling 10 pounds of small potatoes as compared to peeling 10 pounds of large potatoes. Smaller objects have more surface area per pound.

For phenomena involving surface area, this effect is very important. The surface of ice cools the beverage in which it is immersed. Therefore an ice cube will cool the beverage much faster if it is crushed. When crushed, the surface area is multiplied many times. The rusting of iron is a surface phenomenon. Iron rusts when exposed to moist air, but it rusts much faster, and is soon eaten away, if it is first reduced to a heap of small filings.

The fact that smaller things have proportionally more surface area is especially important to living organisms. The cells of living organisms obtain nourishment by diffusion and osmosis through the cell membranes. Small cells have a sufficiently large surface area in comparison to their size, which is crucial to their existence. As cells increase in size, area increases, but not in proportion to volume. The surface area per volume decreases. As a result, the cell cannot adequately nourish itself because the diffusion rate increases only in proportion to the increase in surface area, and not in proportion to the more important and greater increase in volume.

Consider falling bodies. Air resistance to movement in the air is proportional to the surface of the moving object. Small bodies therefore fall slower than large bodies because of their greater surface area per weight. A mouse can fall down a thousand-yard mine shaft and walk away from the impact with little more than a slight shock. A rat would probably be killed, a man would certainly be killed, and a horse would splash on impact. Divide an animal's length, breadth, and height each by ten; its weight is reduced to a thousandth, but its surface only to a hundredth. So, the resistance to falling in the case of the small animal is relatively ten times greater when compared to the driving force.

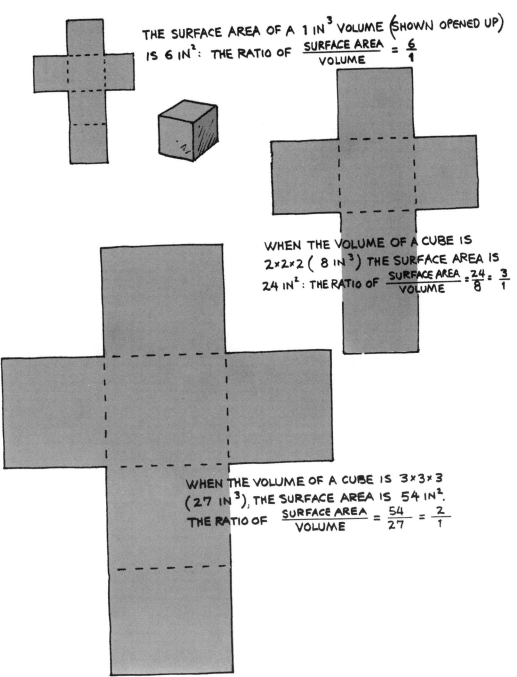

THE SURFACE AREA OF A 1 IN^3 VOLUME (SHOWN OPENED UP) IS 6 IN^2: THE RATIO OF $\frac{\text{SURFACE AREA}}{\text{VOLUME}} = \frac{6}{1}$

WHEN THE VOLUME OF A CUBE IS 2×2×2 (8 IN^3) THE SURFACE AREA IS 24 IN^2: THE RATIO OF $\frac{\text{SURFACE AREA}}{\text{VOLUME}} = \frac{24}{8} = \frac{3}{1}$

WHEN THE VOLUME OF A CUBE IS 3×3×3 (27 IN^3), THE SURFACE AREA IS 54 IN^2. THE RATIO OF $\frac{\text{SURFACE AREA}}{\text{VOLUME}} = \frac{54}{27} = \frac{2}{1}$

Fig. 10.7 As the size of an object increases, the volume increases at a greater rate than the surface area—as a result the surface area becomes proportionally less when compared to the volume.

For this reason an insect is not in danger of gravity. But there is a force which is as formidable to an insect as gravitation is to a mammal. This is surface tension. A man coming out of a bath carries with him a film of water of about one-fiftieth of an inch thickness. This weighs roughly a pound. A wet mouse has to carry about its own weight of water. A wet fly has to lift many times its own weight and once wetted by water or any other liquid is in a serious position. An insect going for a drink is in as great danger as a man leaning out over a precipice in search of food. If it once falls into the grip of the surface tension of the water—that is, if it gets wet—it is likely to remain so until it drowns. A few insects, such as water beetles, contrive to be unwettable, and keep away from their drink by means of a long proboscis.

The heat that a mammal radiates is proportional to the mammal's surface area. The ultimate source of this heat is the food the mammal eats. Five thousand mice weigh as much as one man, but that many mice could not survive on the amount of food consumed by a single man. Their combined surfaces and food consumption is about seventeen times a man's. A mouse eats about a quarter of its own weight in food every day to keep warm. A mouse has a relatively large surface area and loses more heat per body weight than, say, an elephant who consumes only a tiny fraction of his body weight in food each day. For this reason small animals cannot live in cold countries. In the arctic regions there are no small mammals.

Summary of Terms

Atomic bonding. The linking together of atoms to form solids. The different kinds of bonding are ionic bonding, covalent bonding, metallic bonding, and Van der Waals forces.

Density. The mass of a substance per unit volume,

$$\text{Density} = \frac{\text{mass}}{\text{volume}}$$

Elasticity. The property of a material by which it experiences a change in shape when a deforming force acts upon it and by which it returns to its original shape when the deforming force is removed.

Suggested Reading

Feinberg, Gerald, "Ordinary Matter," *Scientific American*, May, 1967.

For more about the relationships between the size, area, and volume of objects, read these essays: "On Being the Right Size," by J. B. S. Haldane, and "On Magnitude," by D'arcy Wentworth Thompson, both in James R. Newman (ed.), *The World of Mathematics*, Vol. II, New York, Simon and Schuster, 1956.

Questions   1. What happens to the density of a loaf of bread when you squeeze it?

2. Which has a greater density, a pound of lead or ten pounds of aluminum?

3. A candy maker making taffy apples decides to use 100 pounds of large apples rather than 100 pounds of small apples. Will the candy maker need to make more or less taffy?

4. Will a person twice as heavy as another use more or less than twice as much suntan lotion at the beach?

5. Nourishment is obtained from food through the inner surface area of the intestines. Why is it that a small organism, such as a worm, has a simple and relatively straight intestinal tract while a large organism, such as a human being, has a complex and many-folded intestinal tract?

II

Liquids

Unlike the molecules in a solid, molecules in the liquid state are not confined to fixed positions in a lattice structure. They easily move from position to position sliding over one another, the body of liquid assuming the shape of its container. Molecules of a liquid are close together and offer large resistance to compressive forces. Liquids are practically incompressible.

A liquid contained in a vessel exerts forces against the walls of the vessel. In order to discuss the interaction between the liquid and the walls, it is convenient to introduce the concept of *pressure*. Pressure is defined as force per area on which it acts,

$$\text{Pressure} = \frac{\text{force}}{\text{area}}$$

As an illustration of the distinction between pressure and force, consider the two blocks in Figure 11.1. The blocks are identical but one stands on its end and the other on its side. Both blocks are of equal weight and therefore exert the same force on the surface, but the upright block is exerting a greater pressure against the surface. This is because the force is distributed over a smaller area, which increases the pressure. If the block were tipped up so that it made contact with a single corner, the pressure would be greater still.

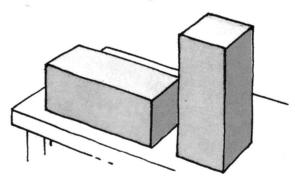

Fig. 11.1 Although the weight of both blocks is the same, the upright block exerts greater pressure against the table.

Pressure in a Liquid

When you swim under water you can feel the water pressure acting against your eardrums. The deeper you swim, the greater the pressure. What causes this pressure? It is simply the weight of the water above you pushing against the area of your eardrums (or the area of anything below the surface). If you swim twice as deep there is twice the weight of water above and you therefore feel twice the water pressure. Liquid pressure depends on depth. If you were submerged in a liquid more dense than water, the pressure would be proportionally greater. Liquid pressure depends also on the density of the liquid. The pressure in a liquid is equal to the product of density and depth.*

Liquid pressure = density × depth

The density of water is 62.4 lb/ft³ (read, "62.4 pounds per cubic foot"). The water pressure beneath the surface of a lake is simply equal to this density multiplied by the depth in feet. For example, water pressure is 624 lb/ft² at a 10-foot depth.†

It is important to note that the pressure does not depend on the volume of liquid, but on its depth. For example, you feel the same pressure whether you dunk your head a couple of feet under a small pool of water or you dunk your head a couple of feet under water in the middle of a large lake. The same is true for a fish. Refer to the connecting vases in Figure 11.2. If we hold a goldfish by its tail and dunk its head a couple of inches under the surface, the water pressure against the fish's head will be the same in any of the vases. If we release the

Fig. 11.2 Liquid pressure is the same for any given depth below the surface, regardless of the shape of the containing vessel.

---

*This is derived from the definitions of pressure and density. Consider an area at the bottom of a vessel of liquid. Pressure is produced by the weight of the column of liquid directly above this area. From the definition, density = weight/volume, we can express this weight of liquid as weight = density × volume, where the volume of the column is simply the area multiplied by the depth. Then we get

$$\text{Pressure} = \frac{\text{force}}{\text{area}} = \frac{\text{weight}}{\text{area}} = \frac{\text{density} \times \text{volume}}{\text{area}}$$

$$= \frac{\text{density} \times \text{area} \times \text{depth}}{\text{area}} = \text{density} \times \text{depth}$$

†We could express this in lb/in² (psi) by dividing by 144, the number of square inches in a square foot. In psi the water pressure at any depth is 62.4/144 × depth, or 0.434 × depth in feet.

fish and it swims a few inches deeper, the pressure on the fish will increase with depth, but be the same no matter what vase it is in. If the fish swims to the bottom, the pressure will be greater—but it makes no difference what vase it is under. All vases are filled to equal depths, so the water pressure is the same at the bottom of each vase, regardless of its shape or volume. If the water pressure at the bottom of a vase were greater than the water pressure at the bottom of a neighboring narrower vase of smaller volume, the greater pressure would force water sideways and then up the narrower vase to a higher level until the pressures at the bottom were equalized. But this doesn't happen. Pressure is depth dependent, and not volume dependent, so we see there is a reason why water seeks its own level.

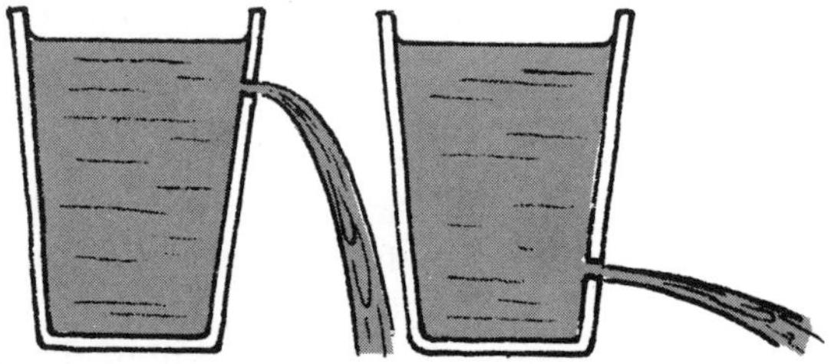

Fig. 11.3 Water pressure pushes perpendicular to the sides of its container, and increases with increasing depth.

Another interesting fact about liquid pressure is that at any given depth, no matter which way we tilt our heads, we feel the same amount of water pressure on our ears. Because a liquid can flow, the pressure isn't only downward. We know that pressure acts sideways because if a leak occurs in a dam, water spurts out. We know pressure acts upward because if we try to push a beach ball beneath the surface of the water, we can feel the pressure of the water opposing our downward push. The bottom of a boat is certainly pushed upward by water pressure. Pressure in a liquid at any point is exerted in equal amounts in all directions.

Fig. 11.4 The water pressure acting against the dams depends on the depth of the water and not on the volume of water held back. The large shallow lake exerts only one-half the pressure that the small deep pond exerts.

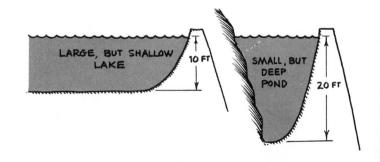

Buoyancy

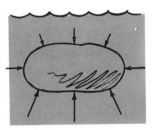

Fig. 11.5 The greater pressure against the bottom of the object produces an upward buoyant force.

Fig. 11.6 When a stone is submerged it displaces a volume of water equal to the volume of the stone.

Fig. 11.7 The raised level equals that which would occur if water equal to the stone's volume were poured in.

Anyone who has ever lifted a submerged object out of water is familiar with buoyancy, the apparent loss of weight of objects submerged in a liquid. For example, lifting a large boulder off the bottom of a river bed is a relatively easy task as long as the boulder is below the surface. When it is lifted above the surface, however, the force required to lift it is considerably more. It would seem that at least one of two things is happening; either gravity is partially shielded by the water, or the water is exerting an upward force on the boulder. But since gravity can't be shielded, it is easy to see that the latter is correct. The water does exert an upward force on the boulder. It is called the *buoyant force*, and it is a consequence of pressure increasing with depth. Figure 11.5 shows why the buoyant force acts upward. Pressure is exerted everywhere against the object in a direction perpendicular to its surface. The arrows represent the magnitude and directions of points of pressure. Pressures against the sides are equal at equal depths and cancel one another. Pressure is greatest against the bottom of the boulder because the bottom of the boulder is at a greater depth. Since this upward pressure is greater than the downward pressure acting against the top, they do not cancel and there is a net pressure upward. This net pressure distributed over the area of the bottom of the boulder produces a net upward force, which is the buoyant force.

If the weight of the submerged object is greater than the buoyant force, the object will sink. If the weight is equal to the buoyant force on the submerged object, it will remain at any level like a fish. If the buoyant force is greater than the weight of the submerged object, it will float to the surface.

To understand the magnitude of buoyant force, it is necessary to understand the meaning of a technical and yet common expression, "volume of water displaced." If a container is filled full of water and a stone dropped into it, some water will overflow, Figure 11.6. Water is said to have been *displaced* by the stone. A little thought will tell us that the *volume*—that is, the amount of space taken up or the number of cubic inches—*of water displaced* is equal to the *volume of the stone*. When any object is dropped into a container partly filled with water, the level of the surface is raised, Figure 11.7. The change in level is exactly the same as if a volume of water equal to the volume of the submerged object had been poured in. This is a good method for determining the volume of irregularly shaped objects. *A completely submerged object always displaces a volume of liquid equal to its own volume.*

The relationship between buoyancy and displaced liquid was first discovered by the ancient Greek philosopher Archimedes, and is stated as follows:

An immersed body is buoyed up by a force equal to the weight of the volume of fluid it displaces.

This is called *Archimedes' Principle*. It is true of liquids and gases, which are both fluids. If an immersed body displaces 10 pounds of fluid, the buoyant force acting on it is 10 pounds. *By immersed we mean either completely or partially submerged.* For example, if we immerse a 1 ft³ (1 cubic foot) solid block of material halfway into the water it will displace $\frac{1}{2}$ ft³ of water, and be buoyed up by the weight of $\frac{1}{2}$ ft³ of water, 31.2 pounds. If we immerse it all the way (submerge it), it will be buoyed up by the weight of 1 ft³ of water, 62.4 pounds. The buoyant force will be 62.4 pounds at *any* depth, so long as the block is completely submerged. This is because at any depth it can displace no greater volume of water than its own volume. And the weight of this volume of water (not the weight of the submerged object!) is equal to the buoyant force.

Questions

1. A cubic foot of lead that weighs 700 pounds is submerged in water. What is the buoyant force acting on it?*

2. A boulder is thrown into a deep lake. As it sinks deeper and deeper into the water, does the buoyant force increase? Decrease?†

If a 25-pound body displaces 20 pounds of fluid upon immersion, its apparent weight will be 5 pounds. Note that in Figure 11.8 the 3-pound block has an apparent weight of 1 pound when submerged. The apparent weight of a submerged object is its weight in air minus the buoyant force.

A numerical example will show that the buoyant force is equal to the weight of displaced fluid. Consider a 1 × 1 × 1 foot

---

Answer: The buoyant force is 62.4 pounds, because the *volume* of water displaced is 1 ft³, which *weighs* 62.4 pounds. The 700-pound weight of the lead is irrelevant; 1 ft³ of anything submerged will displace 1 ft³ of water and be buoyed upward with a force of 62.4 pounds.

†*Answer*: Buoyant force does not change as the boulder sinks because it displaces the same volume of water at any depth. Since water is incompressible its density is the same at all depths; hence the weight of water displaced, or the buoyant force, is the same at all depths.

Fig. 11.8 The object weighs 3 pounds in air and only 1 pound when submerged in the liquid. This is because it is buoyed up with a force of 2 pounds, exactly the weight of liquid it displaces.

cube submerged in water so that its top surface is 1 foot deep, Figure 11.9. The pressure acting down against the top then is density × depth, or 62.4 × 1 = 62.4 lb/ft². The sideways pressures cancel one another. The pressure acting against the bottom of the cubical shape is 62.4 × 2 = 124.8 lb/ft² because it is 2 feet deep. Since the area of the top or bottom surface of the cube is 1 ft², the *force* acting against the bottom is 124.8 pounds and the *force* acting against the top is 62.4 pounds. (This is because force is equal to pressure × area.) The buoyant force is simply the *difference* between the force acting up and the force acting down, or (124.8 − 62.4) which equals 62.4 pounds. And this is numerically equal to the weight of water displaced by the submerged cube. We would obtain the same answer no matter how deep we placed the cube, for although the pressure is greater with increasing depth, we are concerned only with the *difference* in upward and downward pressure. This difference is the same at any depth. We have used the simple case of a cubical shape to make the computation easy, but the same would apply for any shape. The buoyant force is equal to the weight of fluid displaced.

Note again that the buoyant force has to do with the volume of water displaced and not the weight of the object displacing the water. The buoyant force that acts on a submerged cubic foot of lead is identical to the buoyant force acting on a cubic foot of aluminum, or a cubic foot of any submerged material. The buoyant force depends only on the volume of water displaced, and is numerically equal to the weight of this displaced volume of water.

We can see from the previous example that if the object itself weighs 62.4 pounds, that the net force on it when submerged in water is zero. It will neither sink nor float, as there

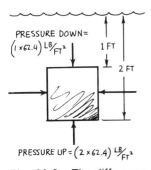

PRESSURE DOWN=
$\left(1 \times 62.4\right) \text{LB}/\text{FT}^2$ 1 FT

2 FT

PRESSURE UP = $\left(2 \times 62.4\right) \text{LB}/\text{FT}^2$

Fig. 11.9 The difference in the upward and downward force acting on the submerged block is equal to 62.4 pounds, which is the buoyant force.

is no net force to move it from its submerged position. Since it has a volume of 1 ft³, its density is 62.4 lb/ft³, exactly that of water. From this we can deduce a simple rule relating the density and behavior of objects immersed in a fluid.

1. If an object is denser than the fluid in which it is immersed, it will sink.

2. If an object is less dense than the fluid in which it is immersed, it will float.

3. If an object has a density equal to the density of the fluid in which it is immersed, it will neither sink nor float.

Hence an object with a density exceeding 62.4 lb/ft³ will sink in water and an object with a density less than 62.4 lb/ft³ will float in water. We can see that the overall density of a fish must be 62.4 lb/ft³. Most people can float, so the density of an average human being must be slightly less than 62.4 lb/ft³. Some people, try as they may, cannot float. They're simply too dense.

The purpose of a life jacket is to decrease one's overall density by increasing volume while correspondingly adding very little to an increase in weight. The density of a submarine is controlled by taking water into and out of its ballast tanks. In this way the weight of the submarine can be varied to achieve the desired density. A fish regulates its density by expanding and contracting an air sac which changes its volume. The fish can move upward by increasing its volume (which displaces more water and increases buoyant force) and downward by contracting its volume (which decreases the buoyant force to a value slightly less than its weight). The overall density of a crocodile is increased when he swallows stones. From 8 to 10 pounds of stones have been found lodged in the front part of the stomach in large crocodiles. Because of this increased density the crocodile swims lower in the water, thus exposing less of himself to his prey.

Iron is much denser than water and therefore sinks; but an iron ship floats. Why is this so? Consider a solid-cubic-foot block of iron. It weighs 450 pounds. If we submerge it in water it will displace its own volume of water and be buoyed up with a force of 62.4 pounds, which is hardly enough to prevent it from sinking. Suppose we reshape the same iron

Fig. 11.10   A crocodile coming toward you in the water.

A stoned crocodile coming toward you in the water.

block into a bowl-shape as shown in Figure 11.11. It still weighs 450 pounds. When we place it in water it settles into the water, displacing a greater volume of water than before. The deeper it is immersed, the more water is displaced and the greater the buoyant force acting upon it. When the buoyant force equals 450 pounds it will sink no further. When the iron boat displaces a weight of water equal to its own weight it

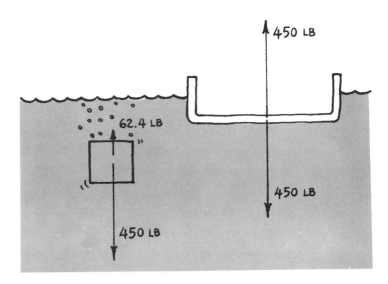

Fig. 11.11   A 450-pound iron block sinks while a 450-pound iron bowl floats.

floats. This is sometimes called the principle of flotation, which states:

A floating object displaces a weight of fluid equal to its own weight.

Fig. 11.12 The weight of a floating object equals the weight of the water displaced by the submerged part.

Fig. 11.13 A floating object displaces a weight of fluid equal to its own weight.

Pascal's Principle

Every ship, every submarine, and every dirigible must be designed to displace a weight of fluid equal to its own weight. Thus a 10,000-ton ship must be built wide enough to displace 10,000 tons of water before it sinks too deep in the water. The same holds true in air. A dirigible or balloon that weighs 100 tons displaces at least 100 tons of air. If it displaces more, it rises; if it displaces less, it falls. If it displaces exactly its weight it hovers at constant altitude.

Since the buoyant force upon a body is equal to the weight of the fluid it displaces, denser fluids will exert a greater buoyant force upon a body than less dense fluids. A ship therefore floats higher in salt water than in fresh water because salt water is denser (64 lb/ft³) than fresh water. In the same way, a solid chunk of iron will sink in water but float in mercury.

One of the most important facts about fluid pressure is that an increase in pressure at one part of the fluid will be transmitted to other parts. For example, if the pressure of the city water is increased at the pumping station, say by an amount equal to 10 pounds per square inch, the pressure everywhere in·the pipes of the connected system will be increased by the same amount (provided the water is at rest). The pressure will be increased 10 psi in the lower parts of the city as well as in the higher parts. The *increase* is the same everywhere. This rule is called Pascal's Principle:*

---

*Named after the seventeenth-century theologian and scientist, Blaise Pascal.

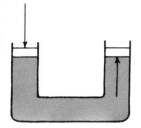

Fig. 11.14 The force exerted on the left piston increases the pressure in the liquid and is transmitted to the right piston.

The pressure applied to a fluid confined in a container is transmitted undiminished throughout the fluid and acts in all directions.

For example, if we fill a U-tube with water and place pistons at each end, as shown in Figure 11.14, pressure exerted against the left piston will be transmitted throughout the liquid, and against the bottom of the right piston. The pressure acting down on the left piston will be exactly equal to the pressure acting upward on the right piston. Well, this is really nothing to get excited about. But suppose we make the tube on the right wider and use a piston of larger area, Figure 11.15. Suppose that the small piston has a cross-sectional area of 1 square inch, and that the right piston has ten times the area of the small piston. Now let's exert a force of 5 pounds to the smaller piston. When we do this a pressure of 5 psi is applied to the fluid and transmitted to the larger piston. A pressure of 5 psi is exerted up against the bottom of the larger piston. This means that a *force* of 5 pounds is distributed over *every* square inch of its surface. Since there are 10 square inches, the force acting on the piston is 10 × 5 or 50 pounds. This is a remarkable consequence, for we can lift 50 pounds with only 5 pounds of effort; or 500 pounds with 50 pounds of effort, and so on. By further increasing the area of the large piston (or reducing the area of the smaller piston), we can multiply forces to any amount. This is the principle of the hydraulic press, which enables us to multiply forces very effectively. This is in keeping with energy conservation, for the multiplication in force is compensated for in distance. When the small piston in the foregoing example is moved downward 10 inches, the large piston will be raised only 1 inch. The input force multiplied by the distance it moves is equal to the output force multiplied by the distance it moves.

Fig. 11.15 A 5-pound load on the left piston increases the pressure in the liquid by 5 psi; 5 psi on each square inch of the right piston produces a lifting force of 50 pounds.

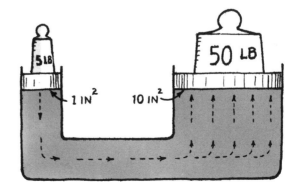

Pascal's Principle applies to all fluids, gases as well as liquids. A typical application of Pascal's Principle to gases and liquids is the automobile lift pump seen in gasoline stations, Figure 11.16. Compressed air exerts pressure on the oil in a reservoir. The oil in turn transmits the pressure to a cylinder which lifts the automobile. A pressure of 30 psi will exert a force of 3000 pounds against a piston of area 100 square inches.

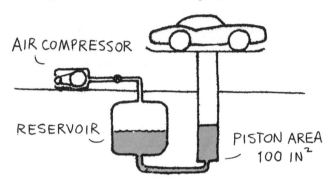

AIR COMPRESSOR

RESERVOIR

PISTON AREA
100 IN²

Fig. 11.16 Pascal's Principle in a gas station.

Surface Tension

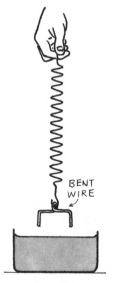

BENT WIRE

Fig. 11.17 When the bent wire is lowered into the water and then raised, the spring will stretch because of surface tension.

Suppose we bend a piece of clean wire as shown in Figure 11.17 and hang it by a sensitive spiral spring of fine wire. If we lower the bent wire into water and raise it, we find that the surface of the water pulls on the wire with a force large enough to produce a considerable stretching of the spring. The *surface* of water exerts an appreciable force. The water surface has a greater resistance to being stretched than the spring. The surface of water tends to contract. We note this tendency when a fine-haired brush has been wet. When the brush is under water, the hairs look pretty much as they do when the brush is dry, but when the brush is lifted out it is covered with a film of water, which contracts and pulls the hairs together, Figure 11.18. We call this contractive force of the surface of liquids *surface tension*.

Surface tension accounts for the spherical shape of liquid drops. Raindrops, drops of oil, and falling drops of molten metal are all spherical because their surfaces tend to contract and force each drop into the shape having the *least* surface. This is a sphere, for a sphere is the geometrical figure that has the least surface for a given volume. For this reason the mist and dewdrops on spider webs or on the downy leaves of plants are minute spheres.

An interesting result of this tendency for a liquid's surface to contract is seen when we add more water to a glass tumbler

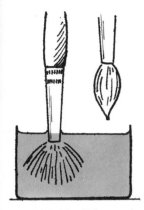

Fig. 11.18 When the brush is taken out of the water, the hairs are held together by surface tension.

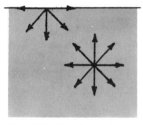

Fig. 11.19 A molecule at the surface is pulled only sideways and downward by neighboring molecules. A molecule beneath the surface is pulled equally in all directions.

already full of water. If we add the water carefully the surface of the water in the tumbler can be raised higher than the edge of the tumbler. The tendency of the surface to contract prevents spilling. If the water is to flow over the edge its surface would have to increase—surface tension resists this increase and prevents the water from spilling over.

Surface tension, or the tendency of surfaces to contract, is caused by molecular attractions. The surface of a liquid is made up of molecules that attract each other. Beneath the surface each molecule is attracted in every direction by neighboring molecules, with the result that there is no tendency to be pulled in any preferred direction. A molecule on the surface of a liquid, however, is attracted by its neighbors to the side and downward, but not upward, Figure 11.19. The resultant of the molecular attractions thus tends to pull the molecule from the surface into the liquid. This tendency to pull surface molecules into the liquid causes the surface to become as small as possible. The surface behaves as if it were tightened into an elastic film. This is evident when floating dry steel needles or razor blades are supported by the surface tension of water. The surface tension of water is larger than that of other common liquids.

Clean water has a stronger surface tension than soapy water. For this reason a little soap film on the surface of water will be pulled out over the entire surface. Maybe you have observed that a little oil or grease floating on water is drawn out into a film covering the entire surface. Hot water provides an interesting exception. When water is hot its surface tension is much less because the faster-moving molecules are not held as cohesively. This allows the grease or oil in hot soups to float in little bubbles on the surface of the soup. But when the soup gets cool and the surface tension of water increases, the grease or oil is dragged out over the entire surface of the soup and the soup becomes "greasy." Hot soup has a different taste than cold soup, primarily because of the change in the surface tension of water with temperature.

Capillarity

If the end of a clean glass tube having a small inside diameter is dipped into water, water will stand higher in the tube than the level of the water outside. In a tube with a bore of about a hundredth of an inch in diameter, the water will rise about $1\frac{1}{2}$ inches. With a still smaller bore, water will rise much higher.

Water molecules are attracted to glass more than to each

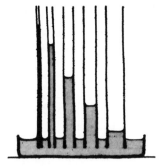

Fig. 11.20 Capillary tubes.

other. The attraction between unlike substances is called *adhesion*. The attractive forces between like substances is called *cohesion*. When a glass tube is dipped into water the adhesion between the glass and the water causes a thin film of water to be drawn up over the surfaces of the tube, Figure 11.21*a*. Surface tension causes this film to contract, Figure 11.21*b*. The film on the inner surface continues to contract, raising water with it until the adhesive force is balanced by the weight of the water lifted, Figure 11.21*c*. In a small tube, the weight of the water in the tube is small, and is lifted higher than if the tube were larger.

If one end of a paintbrush is dipped into water, the water will rise up into the bristles by capillary action; it is not filling hollow bristles but flowing up into narrow spaces between the bristles. Hang your hair in the bathtub and water will seep up to your scalp in the same way. This is how oil is pulled up in a lamp wick and water into a bath towel. If one end of a lump of sugar is dipped into coffee, the entire lump is quickly wet. The capillary action in soils is important in bringing water to the roots of plants. Capillary action plays an important part in many phenomena of nature.

Fig. 11.21 "Stages" of capillary action.

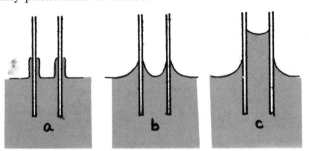

Summary of Terms

Pressure. The ratio of the amount of force per area over which that force is distributed.

$$\text{Pressure} = \frac{\text{force}}{\text{area}}$$

$$\text{Liquid pressure} = \text{density} \times \text{depth}$$

Buoyant force. The net force that a fluid exerts on an immersed object.

Archimedes' Principle. An immersed body is buoyed up by a force equal to the weight of the volume of fluid it displaces.

Principle of flotation. A floating object displaces a weight of fluid equal to its own weight.

Pascal's Principle. The pressure applied to a fluid confined in a container is transmitted undiminished throughout the fluid and acts in all directions.

Surface tension. The tendency of the surface of a liquid to contract in area and thus behave like a stretched rubber membrane.

Capillarity. The rise or fall of a liquid in a fine hollow tube or in narrow spaces.

Suggested Reading

Boys, C. V., *Soap Bubbles and the Forces Which Mould Them* (Science Study Series), Garden City, N. Y., Doubleday (Anchor), 1959.

McDonald, James E., "The Shape of Raindrops," *Scientific American*, February, 1954.

Zimmermann, Martin H., "How Sap Moves in Trees," *Scientific American*, March, 1963.

Questions

1. Distinguish between the quantities 62.4 lb, 62.4 lb/ft^2, and 62.4 lb/ft^3.

2. A child often finds it less painful than an adult to walk barefoot. Aside from the fact that he may have toughened his skin by spending a lot of his time walking barefoot, is there any reason why the child should not feel as much pain?

3. When you are bathing on a stony beach, why do the stones hurt your feet less when you get into deep water?

4. If a submarine starts to sink, will it continue to sink to the bottom if no changes are made? Explain.

5. A barge filled with scrap iron is in a canal lock. If the iron is thrown overboard, does the water level at the side of the lock rise, fall, or remain unchanged? Explain.

6. A leaky tramp steamer that is barely able to float in the Gulf of Mexico steams up the Mississippi River and sinks. Why?

7. A balloon is weighted so that it is barely able to float in water. If it is pushed beneath the surface, will it come back to the surface, stay at the depth to which it is pushed, or sink? Explain. (*Hint*: What change in density, if any, does the balloon undergo?)

8. Alcohol is less dense than water. Do ice cubes float higher or lower in a mixed drink? What can you say about a cocktail in which the ice cubes lie submerged at the bottom of the glass?

9. When an ice cube in a glass of water melts, does the water level in the glass rise, fall, or remain unchanged?

10. Suppose the ice cube in the preceding question has many air bubbles. When it melts, what happens to the water level in the glass? What if the ice cube contains many grains of heavy sand?

11. In the hydraulic arrangement shown, the larger piston has an area which is fifty times that of the smaller piston. The strong man hopes to exert enough force on the large piston to raise the 10-pound weight that rests on the small piston. Do you think he will be successful?

12. Why is it that wet sand is firm under your feet while dry sand is not?

13. Why is cold soup greasy?

14. Why will hot water leak more readily through small leaks in a car radiator than cold water?

15. Would it be correct to say that the *reason* water rises in small hollow tubes is because of capillarity? Explain.

12
Gases

Gases differ from liquids in that the distance between molecules is such that no cohesive forces exist. As the molecules in a gas collide with one another and with the walls of a container, they rebound without loss of kinetic energy. A gas expands indefinitely, filling all space available to it and taking the shape of its container. Only when the quantity of gas is very large, such as the earth's atmosphere or a star, do the gravitational forces limit the size or determine the shape of the mass of gas.

The Atmosphere

Because gas molecules are energized by energy from the sun and are continually in motion, and because of gravity, the earth has an atmosphere. If gas molecules were not in constant motion our "atmosphere" would be just so much more matter on the ground. It would lie on the surface of the earth like dormant popcorn lies at the bottom of a popcorn machine. But add heat to the popcorn and the atmospheric gases and both will bumble their way up to higher altitudes. Pieces of popcorn in a popper attain speeds of a few miles per hour and are able to occupy altitudes up to several feet; molecules in the air move at speeds of about 1000 miles per hour and bumble up to many miles in altitude. If there were no gravity both the popcorn and the atmospheric gases would fly off into outer space. Fortunately there is an energizing sun, and there is gravity, and so we have an atmosphere.

The exact height of the atmosphere has no real meaning, for the air gets thinner and thinner the higher one goes and eventually thins out into interplanetary space. Even in interstellar space, which is often referred to as the most perfect vacuum, there is a gas density of about one molecule per cubic centimeter. This is primarily hydrogen, the most plentiful element in the universe. Fifty percent of the atmosphere is below 3.5 miles, 90 percent is below 11 miles, and 99 percent of the atmosphere is below an altitude of about 19 miles, Figure 12.1.

A description of the atmosphere can be found in any encyclopedia.

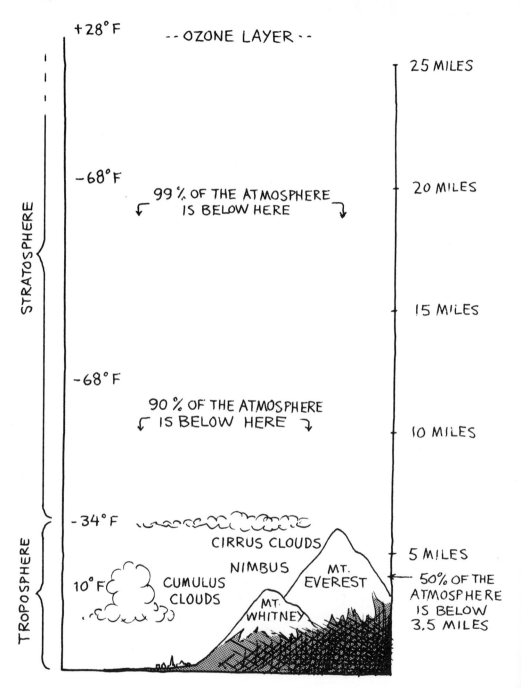

Fig. 12.1   The atmosphere.

Atmospheric Pressure

Fig. 12.2 The Magdeburg hemispheres.

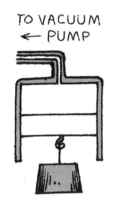

Fig. 12.3 Is the weight pulled up or pushed up?

We live at the bottom of an ocean of air. The atmosphere, much like the water in a lake, exerts a pressure. One of the most celebrated experiments demonstrating the pressure of the atmosphere was conducted in 1654 by Otto von Guericke.* Two copper hemispheres, about 22 inches in diameter, were placed together to form a sphere as shown in Figure 12.2. A ring of leather soaked in oil and wax was set as a gasket between them to make an airtight joint. When the sphere was evacuated with an air pump, two teams of eight horses each were unable to pull the hemispheres apart.

When the air pressure inside a cylinder like that shown in Figure 12.3 is reduced, there is an upward force on the piston. This force is large enough to lift a heavy weight. If the inside diameter of the cylinder is 4 inches or greater, a man may be lifted by this force.

What do the experiments of Figures 12.2 and 12.3 demonstrate? Do they show that air exerts pressure or that there is a "force of suction?" To say that there is a force of suction assumes that a vacuum can exert a force. But what is a vacuum? It is an absence of matter; it is a condition of nothingness. How can nothing exert a force? The hemispheres are not sucked together nor is the piston holding the weight sucked upward. The hemispheres and the piston are being pushed against by the pressure of the atmosphere.

Just as water pressure is caused by the weight of water, atmospheric pressure is caused by the weight of air. We have adapted so completely to the invisible air that we sometimes forget that it has weight. Perhaps a fish "forgets" about the weight of water in the same way. At sea level 1 cubic foot of air weighs about 1.2 ounces. A cubic yard weighs about 2 pounds. A column of air 1 square inch in cross section extending up through the atmosphere weighs 14.7 pounds. Atmospheric pressure, at sea level, is therefore 14.7 psi.

The pressure of the atmosphere is far from uniform. Aside from varying with altitude, there are variations in atmospheric pressure at any one locality that are due to moving air currents and storms. This sometimes causes a change in pressure of about 1 psi. Measurement of changing air pressure is important to meteorologists in predicting weather.

---

*Von Guericke was burgomaster of Magdeburg; the experiment is called the "Magdeburg hemispheres."

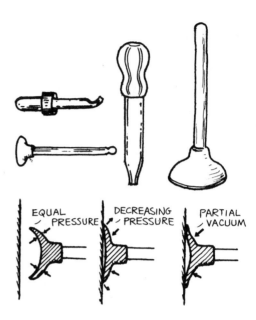

Fig. 12.4   Some suction cups.

The Barometer

Instruments used for measuring the pressure of the atmosphere are called *barometers*. Figure 12.5 illustrates a simple form of mercury barometer. A glass tube, longer than 30 inches, is filled with mercury and inverted into a dish of mercury. The mercury in the tube will run out the submerged open bottom until the level falls to about 30 inches above the level in the dish. Since no air was allowed to enter the tube, the empty space above is a vacuum. The vacuum, of course, does not pull the mercury up; the mercury is supported in the tube because the atmosphere outside is pushing on the surface of the mercury in the open dish. This pressure is transmitted through the mercury (Pascal's Principle) and up into the mouth of the inverted tube. The transmitted atmospheric pressure pushes upward in the tube as hard as the column of mercury is pushing down. At a level in the tube, equal to the level of the free surface outside, atmospheric pressure is exactly counterbalanced by a downward pressure due to the weight of the column of mercury. Since the downward and upward pressures are equal (since there is no motion), the mercury must extend high enough in the tube to produce a pressure equal to that of the air outside. If the column of mercury is 1 square inch in cross section, it

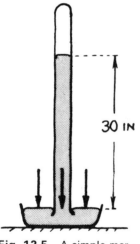

Fig. 12.5   A simple mercury barometer.

would weigh 14.7 pounds, exactly as much as the weight of a 1-square-inch, 20-mile-or-so counterbalancing column of air. When air pressure is exactly 14.7 psi, the mercury will stand 29.9 inches high. This is equivalent to 76 centimeters or 760 millimeters. As the atmospheric pressure decreases, the level of mercury in the barometer falls. Increased pressure pushes the mercury to a higher level in the tube.

If water were used in a barometer instead of mercury, would the column be higher or lower than a mercury column? Since water is so much less dense than mercury, we can see that a much higher column would be needed to push down as hard as denser mercury. In fact, it's easy to find just how high it would be. Since water is only 1/13.6 as dense as mercury, the column would have to be 13.6 times taller than a 30-inch mercury column. This would be about 34 feet. A water barometer would have to be too tall to be feasible!

A small portable instrument that measures atmospheric pressure is the *aneroid barometer*, Figure 12.6. It utilizes a small metal box partially exhausted of air with a slightly flexible lid that bends in or out with atmospheric-pressure changes. Motion of the lid is indicated on a scale by a mechanical spring-and-lever system. Since the atmospheric pressure decreases with increasing altitude, a barometer can be used to determine elevation. An aneroid barometer calibrated for altitude is called an *altimeter* (altitude meter). Some of these instruments are sensitive enough to indicate a change in elevation of 1 foot.

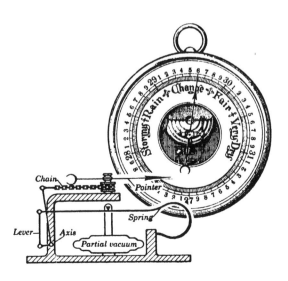

Fig. 12.6 The aneroid barometer.

Buoyancy of Air

Fig. 12.7 An object in air is buoyed up by a force equal to the weight of air displaced.

A crab lives at the bottom of his ocean of water and looks upward at jellyfish and other lighter-than-water objects floating above him. Similarly, we live at the bottom of our ocean of air and look upward to balloons and other lighter-than-air objects floating above us. A balloon floats in air like a jellyfish "floats" in water for the same reason; both are buoyed upward by a displaced weight of fluid equal to their own weights. In one case the displaced fluid is air, and in the other case it is water. In the case of water, immersed objects are buoyed upward because the pressure acting up against the bottom of the object exceeds the pressure acting down against the top. Likewise, air pressure acting up against an object immersed in air is greater than the pressure above pushing down. The buoyancy in both cases is numerically equal to the weight of fluid displaced. We can state Archimedes' Principle for the case of air as:

An object surrounded by air is buoyed up by a force equal to the weight of the air displaced.

A cubic foot of air, at ordinary atmospheric pressure and ordinary temperatures, weighs about 1.2 ounces. Therefore any 1-cubic-foot object in air is buoyed up with a force of 1.2 ounces. If the object weighs more than 1.2 ounces, it falls when dropped. If the object weighs less than 1.2 ounces, it rises in the air. Any object whose weight is less than the weight of an equal volume of air will rise in air. Lighter-than-air, gas-filled balloons rise for this reason.

Gas is used in balloons simply because its presence prevents the atmosphere from collapsing the balloon. Helium is usually used because its weight is small enough so that the combined weight of helium, balloon, and whatever the cargo happens to be, is less than the weight of air it displaces.* Helium is used in a balloon for the same reason cork is used in a swimmer's life preserver. The cork possesses no strange tendency to be drawn toward the surface of water and helium possesses no strange tendency to rise. Both are buoyed upward like anything else. They are simply light enough for the buoyancy to be significant.

Unlike water, there is no sharp surface at the "top" of the atmosphere. Furthermore, unlike water, the atmosphere be-

---

*Hydrogen is the least dense gas but is highly flammable so is not used.

comes less dense with altitude. Whereas cork will float to the surface of water, a released helium-filled balloon does not rise to any atmospheric surface. Will a lighter-than-air balloon rise indefinitely? How high will a balloon rise? We could state the answer in several ways. A balloon will rise only so long as it displaces a weight of air greater than its own weight. As air becomes less dense with altitude, a lesser weight of air is displaced per given volume as the balloon rises. When the weight of displaced air equals the weight of the balloon, upward acceleration of the balloon will cease. Or we could say that when the buoyant force on the balloon equals its weight, the balloon will cease rising. Or equivalently, when the density of the balloon equals the density of the surrounding air, the balloon will cease rising. Helium-filled toy balloons usually break when released in the air because as the balloon rises to regions of less pressure, the helium in the balloon expands, increasing the volume and stretching the rubber until it ruptures.

Large dirigible airships are so designed that when loaded they will slowly rise in air; that is, their total weight is a little less than the weight of air displaced. When in motion, the ship may be raised or lowered by means of horizontal rudders or "elevators."

Summary of Terms

Atmospheric pressure. The pressure exerted against bodies immersed in the atmosphere which results from the weight and motion of molecules of atmospheric gases. At sea level, atmospheric pressure is about 14.7 pounds per square inch.

Barometer. Any device that measures atmospheric pressure.

Archimedes' Principle for air. An object surrounded by air is buoyed up with a force equal to the weight of displaced air.

Suggested Reading

Fenn, Wallace O., "The Mechanism of Breathing," *Scientific American,* January, 1960.

Questions

1. Why is there no atmosphere on the moon?

2. How would the density of air in a deep mine compare to the air density at the earth's surface?

3. Approximately how much buoyant force does the atmosphere exert on you?

4. Why do your ears "pop" when you ascend to higher altitudes?

5. In drinking through a straw, is the liquid sucked up or pushed up? Explain.

6. From how deep a well can water be pumped with a perfect vacuum pump?

7. From how deep a vessel could mercury be drawn with a siphon?

8. How high will a helium-filled balloon rise in the atmosphere?

9. A little gal sits in a car at a traffic light holding a helium-filled balloon, as shown to the left. The windows are up and the car is relatively airtight. When the light turns green and the car accelerates forward, her head pitches backward but the balloon pitches forward. Explain why.

10. Two balloons that have the same weight and volume are filled with helium at atmospheric pressure. One is rigid and the other is free to expand as the pressure outside decreases. When released, which will rise higher? Explain.

11. Estimate the *force* that the atmosphere exerts on you. To do this, estimate the number of square inches of surface area you have and multiply by 14.7 (you can estimate your area from your clothes).

12. Nitrogen and oxygen in their liquid states have densities only 0.8 and 0.9 that of water. Atmospheric pressure is due primarily to the weight of nitrogen and oxygen gas in the air. If the atmosphere liquefied, would its depth be greater or less than 34 feet?

13
Fluids in Motion

Bernoulli's Principle
Mark this statement true or false: Tornadoes sometimes blow the roofs off houses. If you answered true, sorry; the statement is false. The air *inside* the house blows the roof off. It isn't the tremendous speed of the onrushing tornado that makes the roof pop off. It's the fact that the pressure of the swiftly moving air inside the tornado is lower than that of the stagnant air in the house.

At first thought, this may seem silly, for you couldn't go out into a 100-mile-per-hour gale without having your hat blown off. But the speed of a fluid and the pressure within that fluid are entirely different things. The air pressure inside a gale is less than the pressure of still air of the same density. When the speed of the fluid goes up, the internal pressure goes down proportionally. This is true whether the fluid be a gas or liquid.

Consider liquid initially at rest in a container. The pressure that the liquid exerts against the walls of the container depends on both the density and depth of the liquid. Because of this pressure the liquid tends to force itself out by way of the sides or the bottom of the container. But this pressure on the sides or bottom is reduced if there is an opening for the liquid to get moving. The molecules in the liquid no longer push against the side of the container, but move toward the opening. The

Fig. 13.1 The pressure in the spout is reduced when the plug is removed.

pressure at the opening is lessened. As a result, the pressure in the moving liquid is lessened. In fact, the faster the liquid moves, the lesser is the pressure in that liquid. Daniel Bernoulli, a Swiss scientist of the eighteenth century, studied the relationship of fluid velocity and pressure. This relationship is called Bernoulli's Principle. It states:

The pressure in a fluid decreases with increased velocity of the fluid.

When a fluid flows through a narrow constriction its velocity increases, Figure 13.2. This is easily noticed by the increased flow of water in a brook through the narrow parts. The fluid must speed up in the constricted region if the flow of fluid is to be continuous. How does the fluid pick up this extra speed? Bernoulli reasoned that it acquired it at the expense of a lowered internal pressure.

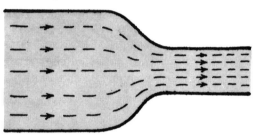

Fig. 13.2 Water speeds up when it flows into the narrower pipe. The constricted streamlines indicate increased speed and decreased internal pressure.

When a fluid is moving there is energy present in the fluid in different forms. Some of the energy is stored in the pressure of the fluid, and some is stored in the motion of the fluid, as kinetic energy. If the speed of the fluid does not change, each of these forms has its fixed share of the energy. But if the speed of the fluid changes, one of the forms of energy gets a larger share at the expense of the other. If the speed suddenly increases, there is more kinetic energy than there was before. To make up for this increase in kinetic energy, the pressure within the fluid suddenly drops.

This is illustrated in Figure 13.3. Water flows from a wide pipe into a narrow pipe. Vertical tubes indicate the pressure of the water flowing through the pipe. These vertical tubes act as pressure gauges. A high level of water (big *h*) indicates high pressure, and a lower level of water (little *h*) indicates a lower pressure. Anything that is lifted has increased gravitational potential energy. The higher level in the vertical tube corresponds to a higher potential energy, which is the energy stored in the pressure of the water. The total energy of the water in region *A* is the sum of the kinetic and potential energies. Because energy cannot be destroyed, the total energy in region

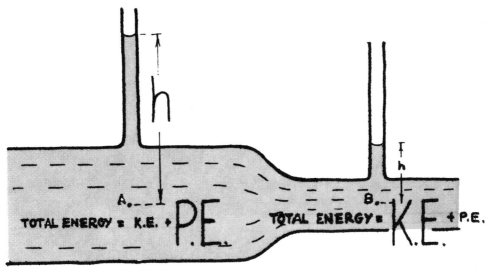

Fig. 13.3 Total energy (kinetic + potential) is the same at points *A* and *B*. The greater kinetic energy at *B* is at the expense of potential energy, which is evidenced by the lower level of fluid in the vertical tube.

B is the same, even though the velocity of the water has increased. The increase in the kinetic energy is accomplished at the expense of potential energy, as evidenced by the decreased water level in the vertical tube. Bernoulli's Principle, then, is a consequence of the conservation of energy.

Another way to understand Bernoulli's Principle is as follows: Consider a small blob of fluid flowing along a pipe at *A* in Figure 13.4. When it reaches *C* it is flowing faster and therefore has more momentum. Somehow between *A* and *C* it must have accelerated. This acceleration requires a forward force; and, for the sample of moving fluid, such a force must be provided by the pressure of the neighboring fluid. Acceleration occurs in region B, where the blob of fluid experiences a net force. This net force can occur only if fluid pressure in region *A* is greater

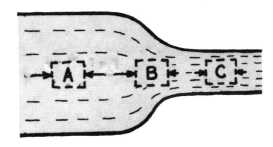

Fig. 13.4 The water accelerates in region *B* because pressure in region *A* is greater than in *C*.

than at *C*. If the pressure were the same all along, *A*, *B*, and *C*, there could be no accelerating force. The pressure difference must exist to produce the acceleration.

The velocity of fluid is best represented with *streamlines*. These are the smooth paths of steady flow shaped by the boundaries of flow. Streamlines are indicated in the figures by broken lines. The lines are crowded in the narrower regions, indicating a greater flow velocity. Where streamlines are closer together, the pressure within the fluid is less. If the velocity of flow is too great, the streamlines may become turbulent and curl into *eddies* or *vortices*. The proportional relationship between fluid flow and pressure then breaks down. Bernoulli's Principle applies only to steady flow and does not apply to turbulent flow.

Applications of Bernoulli's Principle

Hold a sheet of paper in front of your mouth as shown in Figure 13.5. When you blow across the top surface the paper rises. This is because the moving air pushes against the top surface of the paper with less pressure than the air at rest, which pushes against the lower surface. The greater pressure beneath pushes the paper upward into the region of reduced pressure. An airplane wing behaves the same way.

Fig. 13.5 Blow hard across the top surface of the paper and it rises.

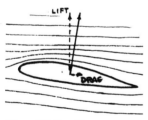

Fig. 13.6 Air pressure against the top surface of the wing is less than air pressure against the bottom surface, which results in a force shown by the solid vector. The vertical and horizontal components of this force are lift and drag.

A wing is designed so that air passing over the top surface has a higher velocity than air passing across the bottom surface. The streamlines are more concentrated above the top surface due to the greater curvature of the surface. A wing therefore has more pressure acting against the bottom surface than against the top surface. The difference between the pressure up and pressure down gives a net pressure acting upward. This net pressure multiplied by the surface area of the wing produces a net force that is upward in a direction perpendicular to the wing. The vertical component of this force is called *lift* and the horizontal component is called *drag*. The lift is greater when there is a large wing area and when the plane is traveling fast. Gliders have a very large wing area so that they do not have to be going very fast for sufficient lift. At the other extreme, fighter planes designed for high speed have very small wing areas. Consequently, they must take off and land at relatively high speeds. The larger the wing area, the larger the drag. Drag increases with higher speeds and must be counteracted with the

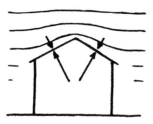

Fig. 13.7 Air pressure above the roof is less than air pressure beneath the roof.

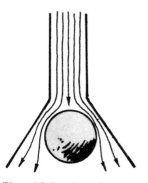

Fig. 13.8 An airstream directed downward through this funnel results in a lessened air pressure above the ball. The greater atmospheric pressure below the ball prevents it from falling.

Fig. 13.9 A baseball curves toward the region of crowded streamlines.

thrust of the engines. When thrust equals drag, and lift equals weight, the aircraft travels horizontally at constant speed.

We began this chapter by stating the roofs of houses in a tornado or gale were pushed off by the air in the house rather than blown off by the wind. When the wind is directed over a peaked roof as shown in Figure 13.7, the effect is even more pronounced. This is seen by the crowding of the streamlines. The difference in outside and inside pressures need not really be very much. Suppose, for example, the difference in pressures is 1 psi. Then your roof experiences a lifting *force* of 144 pounds for every square foot of surface. How many square feet do you have over your head? Next time you're in a hurricane, better open the windows and let the wind blow inside the house too, so that the pressures inside and outside are more equal.

A light ball such as a ping-pong ball will be held in position rather than blown away in the air jet shown in Figure 13.8. This is because the air pressure is less than atmospheric in the region between the ball and the sides of the funnel wall. The ball is actually pushed into this region of reduced pressure by the greater pressure beneath where the streamlines are not as crowded. Unless the ball is too heavy, it will remain supported in midair.

We all know that a baseball pitcher can throw a ball in such a way that it will curve off to one side in its trajectory. Any ball will follow a curved path if it is hit or thrown in such a way that it has both a high speed and a large spin. A thin layer of air is

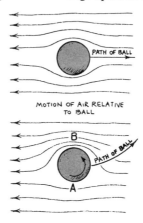

dragged by friction around the spinning ball, producing a crowding of streamlines on one side, Figure 13.9. Note that the streamlines are more crowded in *B* than in *A* for the direction of spin

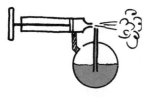

Fig. 13.10 Why does the liquid in the reservoir go up the tube?

shown. Air pressure is greater at *A* and the ball curves in the direction shown.

A sprayer, such as a common perfume atomizer, involves Bernoulli's Principle. Air is forced past the upper end of a tube, the lower end of which is immersed in the liquid to be sprayed, Figure 13.10. The motion of air across the open end of the tube results in a lessened pressure in the tube. The greater atmospheric pressure outside the tube forces the liquid up into the tube where it is carried away by the stream of air. The mixture of air and liquid results in a spray.

Bernoulli's Principle accounts for the fact that passing ships run the risk of a sideways collision. Water flowing between the

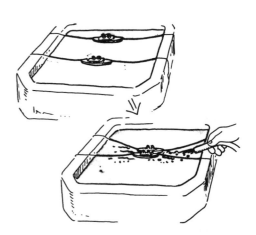

Fig. 13.11 Try this in your sink. Loosely moor a pair of toy boats side by side, top. Then direct a stream of water between them, bottom. The boats will draw together and collide. Why?

ships travels faster than water flowing past the outer sides. The streamlines are more compressed between the ships than outside. Water pressure acting against the hulls therefore is reduced between the ships. Unless the ships are steered to compensate for this, the greater pressure against the outer sides of the ships then forces them together. Figure 13.11 shows how this can be demonstrated in your kitchen sink or bathtub.

The curved shape of a sail is very important to sailcraft. Sailmakers cut the canvas so that the sail has an "airfoil" when the wind puffs it out, Figure 13.12. Like an airplane wing, wind passes faster along the outer curved surface of the sail, producing a reduction in pressure. A sailboat could tack into the wind even if the sail were perfectly flat (as discussed in Chapter 5),

Fig. 13.12 Top view of a sailboat tacking into the wind.

but in practice the Bernoulli effect is the predominant factor. The curved shape of the sail and the resulting pressure differences upon the two sides of the sail greatly increase the speeds that can be attained. To increase the Bernoulli effect a smaller sail, called a *jib*, is rigged in front of the main sail. When the jib is properly rigged it channels and increases the speed of air flow over the main sail, Figure 13.13.

Fig. 13.13 The smaller front sail (jib) acts as a channel that speeds up the air passing over the main sail, which results in a greater driving force.

Superfluidity

Although the topic of this section does not lend itself to everyday observations or to kitchen-sink demonstrations, it illustrates the strange properties that a fluid can have in unusual environments. In this case the environment we are considering is a very cold one.

We know that as liquids are cooled they become more *viscous*, that is, they exhibit more internal friction. Cold oil in an engine block flows more slowly than hot oil. Pancake syrup is thicker and harder to pour when cold. Liquid helium, however, flows without friction when cooled to about $-270°C$. This low temperature is near the absolute zero of temperature, which we shall discuss in detail in the next chapter. At these low temperatures liquid helium has zero viscosity.

A most amazing demonstration of the nonviscous properties of supercooled liquid helium occurs when an open vessel is partially filled with this strange liquid. The vessel will quickly empty itself of the liquid helium, which crawls up the inside surface (no matter how tall the vessel is), over the rim, and down the outside, Figure 13.14a. The reverse phenomenon also occurs, Figure 13.14b. If an empty glass is partially immersed in a bath of supercooled liquid helium, the liquid will quickly crawl up the glass, over the rim, and down the inside surface until the levels inside and outside the glass are equal. The glass surface acts as a siphon. This strange behavior of supercooled liquid helium is called *superfluidity*.

The strangest property of this amazing liquid is that it cannot exert forces on anything. A high-pressure firehose shooting a stream of supercooled liquid helium could not even knock over a coin balanced on its edge. The liquid would freely flow around the coin without exerting any net force on the coin. This liquid will freely flow through spaces only 0.00002 inch wide, which ordinary liquids could never do. The explanation for this behavior is as yet incomplete, and has to do with the wave properties (quantum mechanics) of matter.

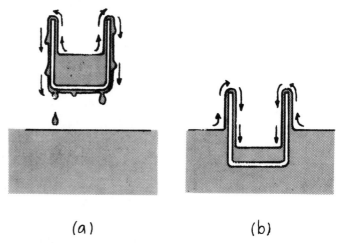

Fig. 13.14 The strange behavior of supercooled liquid helium.

(a)   (b)

Questions

1. Why is it that when passing an oncoming truck on the highway your car tends to lurch toward the truck?

2. Why is it that the shower curtain draws toward you when you are taking a shower with the water on full blast?

3. Why is it that the canvas roof of a convertible automobile, when erect, bulges upward when the car is traveling at high speeds?

4. Why is it that the windows of older trains have been known to break when a high-speed train passes by on the next track?

5. A steady wind blows over the waves of an ocean. Why does the wind increase the humps and troughs of the waves?

6. Wharfs are made with pilings that permit the free passage of water. Why would a solid-walled wharf be disadvantageous to ships attempting to pull alongside?

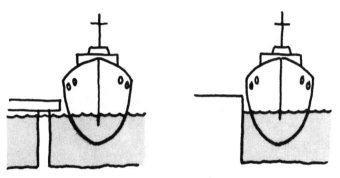

7. Could a fish swim in supercooled liquid helium if it were somehow able to resist freezing?

PART 3

Heat

14

Temperature, Heat, and Expansion

We have discussed the fact that all matter is composed of continually jiggling atoms and molecules. Whether the atoms and molecules combine to form solids, liquids, gases, or plasmas depends on the rate of molecular vibrations. In this and the following two chapters we are going to investigate more closely the effects of molecular motion. That which a body has by virtue of its energetic jostling of atoms and molecules, we call *thermal energy*.

Thermal energy is involved in all aspects of our everyday lives from cooking our food to warming our feet. The molecules of every substance are constantly jiggling in some sort of back-and-forth vibratory motion. The greater this molecular kinetic energy in a substance, the hotter the substance is. When we strike a piece of metal with a hammer, for example, it becomes warm. This is because the hammer's blow causes the molecules in the metal to jostle faster. Later, as the molecules in the substance slow down by giving some of their energy to the air or surrounding medium, the metal becomes cool again.

As recently as the eighteenth century, there was no way of accurately measuring the hotness or coldness of a body. No one could ever be sure how much hotter or colder one day was than another except by the use of his senses. A physician, for example, had to gauge the extent of his patient's fever by feeling his forehead—just as good cooks used their experiences with fires to judge the degrees of heat in their ovens.

Temperature　　　When we touch a hot stove, thermal energy enters the hand because the stove is warmer than our hands. When we touch a piece of ice, however, thermal energy passes out of the hand and into the colder ice. The direction of energy transfer is always from a warmer body to a neighboring cooler body. The quantity that tells how warm or cold a body is with respect to some standard body is called *temperature*. The thermal energy that is transferred from one body to another because of a temperature difference is called *heat*. Heat will always pass from a substance at a higher

HOT STOVE

Fig. 14.1 Although the same quantity of heat is supplied to both containers, the container with the smaller amount of water has the higher temperature.

temperature into a substance at a lower temperature, but not necessarily from a substance with more thermal energy into a substance with less thermal energy. For example, there is far more thermal energy in the ocean than there is in a hot cup of coffee; if the cup is partially immersed in the ocean, heat will not flow from the ocean to the cup. Instead, heat will flow from the hot cup to the cooler surrounding water. Heat never flows of itself from a cooler body into a hotter body. From this we can see that heat and temperature are different things.

To illustrate this distinction, suppose that a small quantity and a large quantity of water, in two identical containers, are placed on the same hot stove for the same length of time. At the end of this time the temperature of the small amount of water will have risen higher than that of the large amount. In this instance, equal quantities of heat have been supplied to each container of water, but the increases in temperature are not equal.

Heat is the thermal energy that transfers from one body to another by virtue of a temperature difference; thermal energy is a measure of the total molecular energies in a body; and temperature is a measure of the *average kinetic energy* of each molecule in the body. If a body has a high temperature, each of its molecules has, on the average, a large amount of kinetic energy; if a body has a low temperature, each molecule on the average has a small kinetic energy. Molecules have internal potential energy states in addition to their kinetic energies. Scientists call the total energy content of a body its *internal energy*. A piece of coal has more internal energy than a piece of granite of the same size; a great deal of energy is locked into the molecular structure of the coal. Internal energy consists of both the potential energy within molecules, and the kinetic (thermal) energy of the molecules themselves. Temperature is a measure only of the average *kinetic* energy of each molecule.

Measuring Temperature

Generally, when the temperature of a piece of matter is changed, several things happen to it. Its size, its electrical, magnetic, or optical properties may become different, and any such change could be used to detect and measure its change in temperature. The simplest to use, in most cases, is the change in size. Nearly all materials expand when their temperature is raised and shrink when it is lowered.

A thermometer is a common instrument that measures temperature by means of the expansion and contraction of a

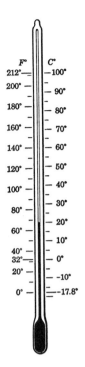

$F°$	$C°$
212°	100°
200°	90°
180°	80°
160°	70°
140°	60°
120°	50°
100°	40°
80°	30°
	20°
60°	10°
40°	
32°	0°
20°	-10°
0°	-17.8°

Fig.14.2 Fahrenheit and Celsius scales on a thermometer.

liquid, usually mercury or colored alcohol. To fix a scale for a thermometer, the number 0 is assigned to the temperature at which water freezes, and the number 100 to the temperature at which water boils. The space between is divided into 100 equal parts, called degrees; hence a thermometer so calibrated has been called a centigrade thermometer. It is now called a *Celsius* thermometer in honor of the man who first suggested the scale, the Swedish astronomer Anders Celsius.

In English-speaking countries, the number 32 is assigned to the temperature at which water freezes, and the number 212 is assigned to the temperature at which water boils. Such a scale is called *Fahrenheit*, after the German physicist G. D. Fahrenheit, who was the first to calibrate a thermometer.

Arithmetic formulas are used for converting from one temperature scale to the other and are popular in classroom exams. The probability of your having the occasion to do this task elsewhere does not merit our concern with it here. Besides, this can be very closely approximated by simply reading the corresponding temperature from the side-by-side scales in Figure 14.2.

Absolute Zero

In principle there is no upper limit of temperature; as thermal motion increases a solid body first melts and then evaporates. As the temperature is further increased molecules break up into atoms, and atoms lose some or all of their electrons, thereby forming a plasma, or cloud of electrically charged particles. This situation exists inside stars, where the temperature is many millions of degrees Celsius.

In contrast, there is a definite limit at the other end of the temperature scale. Theoretically, when thermal motion ceases, the coldest possible temperature—"absolute zero"—has been reached.* At absolute zero no more energy can be extracted from a substance, and no further lowering of its temperature is possible. This limiting temperature is 273.16° *below* zero on the Celsius scale of temperature, and 459.69° *below* zero on the Fahrenheit scale.

Low-temperature physicists customarily denote temperatures in degrees Kelvin. On this scale absolute zero is 0°K. Degrees on the Kelvin scale are calibrated with the same-sized divisions

---

*Even at absolute zero, molecules still have a small kinetic energy, called the "zero-point energy." Its presence can be explained by modern quantum theory.

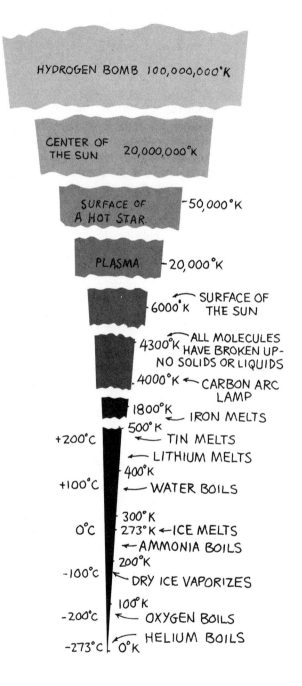

Fig. 14.3   Some absolute temperatures.

as the Celsius scale. The melting point of ice thus is $273.16°K$, and the boiling point of water is $373.16°K$.

Absolute zero is far below the normal temperatures of our environment. Air liquefies at $83°K$, and helium must be cooled to $4.2°K$ for liquefaction. Extremely low temperatures can be attained by demagnetization techniques. Certain salts become magnetized when a magnet is brought near them, and become demagnetized when the magnet is removed. The salts become warmer when they are magnetized, and cooler when they are demagnetized. If one of these salts is magnetized while in a liquid helium bath which has been cooled to $1°K$, the magnetized salt will be cooled to a temperature of $1°K$. When the salt is demagnetized its temperature falls below $1°K$. Temperatures as low as $0.001°K$ have been produced by this method. A similar method, based on demagnetized copper nuclei, has produced temperatures as low as $0.000001°K$. Physicists may be able to produce even lower temperatures, but bringing the temperatures of a substance all the way to $0°K$ is not possible. The closer one gets to absolute zero the harder it is to get closer. It is more difficult, for example, to cool a substance from $0.1°K$ to $0.01°K$ than it is to cool a substance from $100°K$ to $10°K$. It is not possible to get to absolute zero in a finite number of operations. The unattainability of absolute zero is called the third law of thermodynamics.*

Quantity of Heat

A body does not contain heat. A body contains internal energy. The internal energy that is transferred from a body to another by virtue of a temperature difference is called heat. The quantity of heat involved in such a transfer is measured by some change that accompanies the process. For example, in determining the energy value in food, the amount of internal energy that is released as heat is measured by burning. Fuels are rated on how much thermal energy a certain amount of the fuel will produce. The unit of heat is defined as the heat necessary to produce some standard, agreed-on change. The most commonly used unit for heat is the *calorie*.†

---

*The first law of thermodynamics is a restatement of energy conservation for thermal systems; the second law of thermodynamics states that heat can be made to go from a body at lower temperature to one at higher temperature only if external work is done. The principle that heat does not spontaneously flow from a cold body to a hot one is called the zeroth law of thermodynamics.

†Another common unit of heat quantity is the *British thermal unit* (Btu). *The Btu is defined as the amount of heat required to change the temperature of 1 pound of water 1°F.*

The calorie is defined as the amount of heat required to change the temperature of 1 gram of water 1°C.

Another common unit of heat is the kilocalorie, which is 1000 calories (the thermal energy required to heat 1 kilogram of water 1°C). The Calorie, used in rating the energy of foods, is actually a kilocalorie as defined here. The calorie and Calorie are units of energy. These names are historical carry-overs from the early idea that heat was an invisible fluid called caloric. This view persisted almost to the nineteenth century. Had heat been recognized as a form of energy earlier, we would probably measure the quantity of heat in terms of foot-pounds or joules. This, and other duplications in units of measurement, unfortunately cause considerable confusion in the study of physics.

Specific Heat

Have you ever noticed that some foods retain their heats much longer than others? Boiled onions and squash on a hot dish, for example, are often too hot to eat when mashed potatoes may be eaten comfortably. The filling of hot apple pie can burn your tongue while the crust will not, even when the pie has just been taken out of the oven. Evidently, different substances have different capacities for storing heat. If we heat a gallon of water on a stove we might find that it requires fifteen minutes to raise it from room temperature to its boiling temperature. But if we put an equal mass of iron on the same flame, we would find that it would rise through the temperature range in only about two minutes. For silver, the time would be less than a minute. We find that different materials require different amounts of thermal energy to raise the temperature of a given mass of the material through a specified number of degrees. Different materials absorb energy in different ways. The energy may increase the back-and-forth vibrational motion, which will increase the temperature, or it may go into potential energy, which increases the internal rotational and vibrational states within the molecules but does not increase temperature. Generally there is a combination of both.

A gram of water requires 1 calorie of energy to raise the temperature 1°C. It only takes about one-eighth as much energy to raise the temperature of 1 gram of iron by the same amount. Water absorbs more heat than iron. We say iron has a lower *specific heat* (sometimes called simply *specific heat capacity*).

The specific heat of any substance is defined as the quantity of heat required to raise the temperature of a unit mass of the substance by 1 degree of temperature.

The High Specific Heat of Water. Water has a much higher capacity for storing thermal energy than all but a few uncommon materials. A relatively small amount of water absorbs a great deal of heat for a correspondingly small temperature rise. Because of this, water is a very useful cooling agent, as, for example, in the cooling system of an automobile. If a liquid of lower specific heat were used in the cooling system, it would be heated to a higher temperature for a comparable absorption of heat (of course, if the temperature of the liquid increases to the temperature of the engine, no cooling takes place).

Water also takes a long time to cool, a fact that not only adds to the usefulness of the hot-water bottle but also appreciably improves the climate in many places. The next time you are looking at a world globe, notice the high latitude of Europe. If water did not have a high specific heat, the countries of Europe would be as cold as the northeastern regions of Canada, for both Europe and Canada get about the same amount of sunlight. The Gulf Stream holds its internal energy long enough to reach the North Atlantic off the coast of Europe, where it then cools. The energy released, a calorie per degree for each gram of water that cools, is carried by the westerly winds over the European continent. A similar effect occurs in the United States.

The winds in the latitude of the United States are westerly. Air moves from the Pacific Ocean landward. On the east coast, air moves from land seaward. Cooling of the Pacific Ocean releases thermal energy and warms the air moving over the land, raising the temperature of coastal regions. As a result, San Francisco is much warmer in the winter than Washington, D.C., which is at about the same latitude.

Islands and peninsulas that are more or less surrounded by water do not have the same extremes of temperature that are observed in the interior of a continent. The high summer and low winter temperatures common in the central United States, for example, are largely due to the absence of large bodies of water. Europeans, islanders, and people living in coastal regions should be glad that water has such a high specific heat. San Franciscans are!

Expansion

When a substance is heated, its molecules are made to jiggle faster. The increased collisions between molecules force them to move farther apart, resulting in an expansion of the substance. All forms of matter—solids, liquids, and gases—generally expand when they are heated, and contract when they are cooled.

In many cases the changes in the size of objects are not very noticeable, but careful observation will usually detect them. Telephone wires are longer and sag more on a hot summer day than they do on a cold winter day. Metal lids to glass fruit jars can often be loosened by heating them under hot water. If one part of a piece of glass is heated or cooled more rapidly than adjacent parts, the expansion or contraction that results may break the glass. This is especially true with thick glasses. Pyrex glass is specially formulated to expand very little when it is heated.

Liquids expand appreciably when heated. When you get your gasoline tank filled at a filling station and then park the car, the gasoline often overflows after it sits in the gas tank for a while. This is because the gasoline is cold when it comes from the underground gas tanks; as it sits in the gas tank of your car it warms up to the temperature of your car. As the gasoline warms it expands—its volume increases and overflows the gas tank. Similarly, an automobile radiator filled to the brim with cold water overflows when heated.

Gases also expand when heated. Hold an air-filled balloon over a hot stove and notice that the balloon gets bigger; this is because the air inside expands when heated.

Different substances expand at different rates. In most cases the expansion of liquids is greater than the expansion of solids. The gasoline overflowing a gas tank on a hot day is evidence for this. If the tank expanded at the same rate, both tank and contents would expand together and no overflow would occur. Similarly, if the expansion of the glass of a thermometer were as great as the expansion of the mercury, the mercury would not rise with increasing temperature. The mercury in a thermometer rises with increasing temperature because the expansion of liquid mercury is greater than the expansion of glass.

When two strips of different metals, say one of brass and the other of iron, are welded or riveted together, the greater expansion of one metal over the other is greatly magnified, Figure 14.4. Such a compound bar is called a *bimetallic strip*. The difference in the amounts of expansion of brass and iron

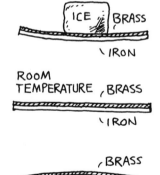

Fig. 14.4 A bimetallic strip. Brass expands (or contracts) more when heated (or cooled) than does iron, so the strip bends as shown.

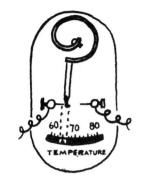

Fig. 14.5 A thermostat.

Fig. 14.6 An oven thermometer.

shows up easily because the double strip bends into a curve when its temperature changes. The movement of the strip may be used to turn a pointer, to regulate a valve, or to close a switch.

A practical application of this is the *thermostat*, Figure 14.5. The bending back and forth of the bimetallic strip opens and closes electrical circuits automatically. When the room becomes too cold, the strip bends toward the brass side, and in so doing makes contact with an electrical switch that turns on the heat. When the room becomes too warm, the strip bends toward the iron side which makes contact with a switch that turns off the heating unit. Electrical refrigerators are equipped with special thermostats to prevent them from becoming either too warm or too cold. Compound metal strips are used in oven thermometers, Figure 14.6, in electric toasters, in automatic chokes on carburetors, and in various other devices.

The expansion of substances must be allowed for in the construction of structures and devices of all kinds. A dentist uses fillings that have the same rate of expansion as teeth; the aluminum pistons of an automobile engine are made enough smaller in diameter than the steel cylinders to allow for the much greater expansion rate of aluminum. A civil engineer uses reinforcing steel of the same expansion rate as concrete. Long steel bridges are provided with rollers or rockers at the ends, Figure 14.7. Expansion joints are provided between the concrete slabs of a road or sidewalk.

The Expansion of Water

Increase the temperature of any common liquid and it will expand. But not water at temperatures near the freezing point; ice cold water does just the opposite! Water at the temperature of melting ice, 0°C or 32°F *contracts* when heated. This is most unusual. As the water is heated and its temperature rises, it continues to contract until it reaches a temperature of 4°C or 39.2°F. With further increase in temperature the water then begins to *expand*; the expansion continues all the way to the boiling point, 100°C. The result of this odd behavior is that

Fig. 14.7 One end of the steel bridge rests on rollers to allow for expansion.

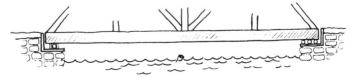

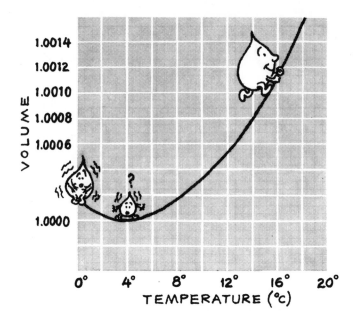

Fig. 14.8 The expansion of water with increasing temperature.

water has its smallest volume and greatest density at 4°C. This is shown graphically in Figure 14.8. A given amount of water has its smallest volume and greatest density at 4°C, and its largest volume and smallest density (neglecting steam) in its solid form, ice. *The volume of ice is not shown in Figure 14.8,* for if it were the graph would extend far beyond the top of the page if it were plotted to the same scale. After water has turned to ice, further cooling causes it to contract.

Ice has a crystalline structure. For most crystals, the orderly arrangement of the molecules in the solid state results in a smaller volume than the same molecules in the liquid state; in the case of ice, however, the angular shape of the water molecules, plus the fact that the binding forces are strongest at certain angles, results in open-structured crystals, Figure 14.9,

Fig. 14.9 Water molecules in their crystal form have an open-structured hexagonal arrangement that results in the expansion of water upon freezing. Ice therefore is less dense than water.

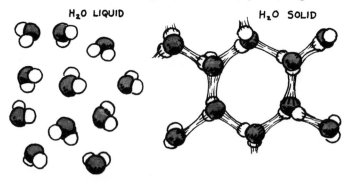

which occupy a greater volume in the solid rather than the liquid state. Consequently, ice is less dense than water and floats on water.

The reason for the dip in the curve of Figure 14.8 is because two types of volume changes are taking place. The open-structured crystals that make up solid ice also are present, to a much smaller extent, in ice cold water. They exist as a sort of microscopic slush. These crystals gradually collapse as the temperature is increased and thus reduce the volume of the water. At about 10°C all the ice crystals have dissociated. Figure 14.10a indicates how volume changes due only to the collapsing of the microscopic ice crystals. Figure 14.10b, on the

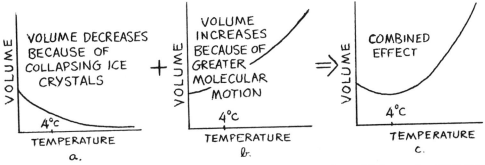

Fig. 14.10   Collapsing ice crystals plus increased molecular motion with increasing temperature produce the overall effect of water being most dense at 4°C.

other hand, shows how volume changes as a result of the increased molecular motion and its resulting expansion. Whether ice crystals are in the water or not, increased vibrational motion of the molecules and crystals increases the volume of the water. When we combine these two effects, one of contraction and the other of expansion, the curve looks like Figure 14.10c, or Figure 14.8.

This behavior of water is of great importance in nature. If the greatest density of water were at its freezing point, as is true of most liquids, then the coldest water would settle to the bottom and ponds would freeze from the bottom up, with a destruction of marine life in winter months. But this doesn't happen because the densest water that settles at the bottom of a pond is 4 degrees above the freezing temperature. Water at the freezing point, 0°C, is less dense and so ice forms at the surface.

Let us examine this in more detail. A pond of water cools when the air at its surface is colder than the water; most of the

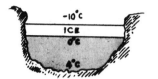

Fig. 14.11 A pond covered with ice.

cooling takes place at the surface. As the surface water is cooled, it becomes more dense, and sinks to the bottom. Water will remain at the surface for further cooling only if the water below has an equal or greater density. Consider a body of water that initially is at, say, 10°C. It cannot possibly be cooled to 0°C without first being cooled to 4°C. And water at 4°C cannot remain at the surface for further cooling unless all the water below has at least an equal density—that is, unless all the water below is 4°C. If the water below the surface is any temperature other than 4°C, any surface water at 4°C will be denser and sink before it can be further cooled. So before any ice can form, *all* the water in a pond must be cooled to 4°C. Only when this condition is met can the surface water be cooled to 3°, 2°, 1°, and 0°C without sinking. Then ice can form. We can see that the water at the surface is first to freeze. Continued cooling of the pond results in the freezing of the uppermost water against the ice, so a pond freezes from the surface downward. In a cold winter the ice will be thicker than in a milder winter.

Because all the water in a lake must be cooled to 4°C before lower temperatures can be reached, very deep bodies of water are not ice covered even in the coldest of winters. This is because the winter is not long enough for all the water to be cooled to 4°C. If only some of the water is 4°C, it lies on the bottom. Because of water's high specific heat and poor ability to conduct heat, the bottom of deep lakes in cold regions is a constant 4°C the year round.

Summary of Terms

Heat. The thermal energy that flows from a body of higher temperature to a body of lower temperature, commonly measured in calories (or Btu's).

Temperature. A measure of the average kinetic energy per molecule in a body, measured in degrees Celsius, Fahrenheit, or Kelvin.

Absolute zero. The lowest possible temperature that a substance may have—the temperature at which the molecules of a substance have their minimum kinetic energy.

Specific heat. The quantity of heat per unit mass required to raise the temperature of a substance by 1 degree; measured in units calories per gram Celsius degree (or Btu's per pound Fahrenheit degree).

Suggested Reading

Chalmers, Bruce, "How Water Freezes," *Scientific American*, February, 1959.

Davis, Kenneth S., and John Arthur Day, *Water, the Mirror of Science* (Science Study Series), Garden City, N. Y., Doubleday (Anchor), 1961.

Kelley, James B., "Heat, Cold and Clothing," *Scientific American*, February, 1956.

MacDonald, D. K. C., *Near Zero* (Science Study Series), Garden City, N. Y., Doubleday (Anchor), 1961.

Questions

1. Would you expect the temperature of water at the bottom of Niagara Falls to be slightly higher than the temperature at the top of the Falls? Why?

2. Why does the pressure of a gas which is enclosed in a rigid container increase as the temperature increases?

3. Would you or the gas company gain by having gas warmed before it passes through your gas meter?

4. A metal ball is just able to pass through a metal ring. When the ball is heated, however, it will not pass through the ring. What would happen if the ring, rather than the ball, were heated? Does the size of the hole increase, stay the same, or decrease?

5. If you measure a lot of land with a steel tape on a hot day, will your measurements of the lot be larger or smaller than they actually are?

6. If glass expanded more than mercury when heated, how would the temperature scale on a mercury thermometer appear?

7. What was the precise temperature at the bottom of Lake Superior at 12:01 A.M. on October 31, 1894?

8. A piece of metal has a temperature of 0°C. A second identical piece of metal is twice as hot. What is its temperature?

9. Suppose that water is used in a thermometer instead of mercury. If the temperature is at 4°C and then changes, why cannot the thermometer indicate whether the temperature is rising or falling?

10. If the winds at the latitude of San Francisco and Washington, D.C., were easterly rather than westerly, why might San Francisco be able to only grow cherry trees and Washington, D.C., grow palm trees?

11. If cooling occurred at the bottom of a pond instead of at the surface, would a lake freeze from the bottom up? Explain.

12. If water had a lower specific heat, would ponds be more likely to freeze or less likely to freeze?

15
Transmission of Heat

Heat always tends to pass from warmer to colder bodies. If several bodies near one another have different temperatures, those that are hot become colder, and those that are cold become warmer, until all have a common temperature. This equalizing of temperatures is brought about in three ways: by *conduction*, by *convection*, and by *radiation*.

Conduction

Hold one end of an iron nail in a flame. It will quickly become too hot to be held in the hand. The heat enters the metal nail at the end kept in the flame, and is transmitted along its whole length. The transmission of heat in this manner is called *conduction*. The fire causes the molecules at the heated end of the nail to move more rapidly. Because of this increased motion, these molecules and free electrons collide with their neighbors, causing them to move faster. These, in turn, collide with their neighbors, and so on. This process continues until the increased motion has been transmitted to all the molecules and the entire body has become hot. The conduction of heat is accomplished by electron and molecular collisions.

How well an object conducts heat depends on the electrical bonding of the molecular structure. Solids whose molecules have a "loose" outer electron conduct heat (and electricity) well. Metals are the best conductors of heat and electricity for this reason. Silver is the best, copper is next, and, among the common metals, aluminum and then iron are next in order. Wool, wood, straw, paper, cork, and styrofoam are poor conductors of heat. Poor conductors are called *insulators*.

Liquids and gases, in general, are poor conductors. Air is a very poor conductor. Porous substances that have a large number of small air spaces are poor conductors and good insulators. The good insulating properties of such things as wool, fur, and feathers are largely due to the air spaces they contain.

Snow is a poor conductor, and hence is popularly said to keep the earth warm. Its flakes are formed of crystals, which collect into feathery masses, imprisoning air, thereby interfering with the escape of heat from the earth's surface. The winter dwellings of the Eskimos are shielded from the cold by their

Fig. 15.1 The tile floor feels colder than the wooden floor even though both floor materials are at the same temperature. This is because tile is a better conductor than wood, and heat is more readily conducted from the foot that makes contact with the tile.

Fig. 15.2 Convection currents in air.

snow covering. Animals in the forest find shelter from the cold in snowbanks and in holes in the snow. The snow doesn't provide them with heat; it simply prevents the heat they generate from escaping.

Heat is transmitted from the higher to the lower temperature. We often hear people say they wish to "keep the cold out" of their homes. There is no "cold" that flows into a warm home. If the home becomes colder it is because heat flows out. A better way to put this is to say that they want to prevent the heat from escaping. Homes are insulated with rock wool or spun glass to prevent heat from escaping rather than to prevent cold from entering.

Convection

Liquids and gases are heated mainly by convection, or transmission by means of currents. Air, for example, in contact with a hot surface is heated and then ascends, and is replaced by cooler air. After the warm column rises it cools and then descends, whereupon the process is repeated. To understand convection currents in the atmosphere we must first understand why warm air rises—and then, why it cools.

Why Warm Air Rises

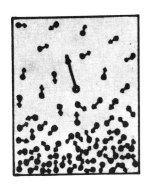

Fig. 15.3 A fast-moving molecule tends to migrate toward the region of least obstruction—upward. Warm air therefore rises.

We all know that warm air rises. From our study of buoyancy we can understand why this is so. Warm air expands and becomes less dense than the surrounding air and is buoyed upward like a balloon. It is buoyed upward because the air pressure below a region of warmed air is greater than the air pressure above. We can understand the rising of warm air from a different point of view also—by considering the motion of individual molecules. Consider a fairly large region of identical gas molecules. Because of gravity we would find more molecules near the bottom of our region than near the top; the gas is slightly denser toward the ground. Suppose the region is of uniform temperature; then each molecule, on the average, has the same kinetic energy and the same average velocity. Each molecule, then, has the same tendency to migrate throughout the region. Suppose now that we introduce a faster moving molecule—a "hot" one. Until it gives up its excess energy to slower-moving molecules, it will migrate farther and more rapidly than any of its neighbors. If our sample molecule is placed in the middle of our region, it will bump into and rebound from molecules in all directions. It will rebound, however, from a greater number of molecules whenever it happens to be moving downward than upward. This is because the density of molecules is greater below—there is more opposition to a downward migration than to an upward migration where the air is less dense. Furthermore, when our "hot" molecule is moving in an upward direction, it travels farther before making a collision than when it travels downward. We say it has a longer "free-mean path" when moving upward. So our faster-moving molecule will tend to bumble upward in its random jostling.

We have simplified the idea of rising warm air by considering the behavior of a single molecule. A single fast-moving molecule would, of course, soon share its excess energy and momentum with its less energetic neighbors, and would not rise very high. If we start with a large cluster of energetic molecules, many of these will rise to appreciable heights before their energy and momentum is dissipated.

Why Expanding Air Cools

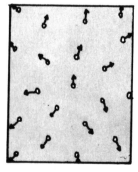

Fig. 15.4 A molecule in a region of expanding air collides more often with receding molecules than with approaching ones. Its velocity of rebound therefore is lessened with each collision, which results in a cooling of expanding air.

Because warm air rises we might expect the atmosphere to be warmer with increasing altitude; we might expect the mountain tops to be warm and green and the valleys below to be cold and snow covered. But this is not the case; the atmosphere is cooler with increasing altitude. As strange as it may seem, the principal reason for the cooling at higher altitudes has very much to do with the fact that warm air rises. Warm air rises from a region of higher atmospheric pressure at the ground to a region of less pressure above. And while it is rising to regions of less pressure it *expands*. The rapid expansion of air is a cooling process. To see why the air cools, consider a molecule in the midst of a region of expanding air. When a molecule collides with another that is approaching, its rebound velocity is increased; when a molecule collides with another that is receding, its rebound velocity is lessened. (This is easy to see: a Ping-Pong ball rebounds faster from an approaching paddle than from a receding paddle.) If the molecule is in a region of air that is expanding, then, on the average, it will collide more often with receding molecules than approaching ones. Its velocity therefore decreases. Many molecules slowing down results in a lowering of temperature. At any point within the expanding region, the thermal energy is diluted as it spreads over a wider region.

A common misconception about temperature and molecular motion is that heat is produced by the collisions of molecules against one another—that the more frequently molecules collide, the higher the temperature of the gas should be. This is not true. A pair of molecules bouncing off one another have the same total energy and momentum before and after a collision. Temperature is not a measure of their collision rates, but is a measure of their kinetic energies. The temperature of gas would be no different if all the molecules were able to move without colliding with one another. Or let's put this another way: when a gas is heated the molecules collide more often. We can say they collide more often *because* they're heated. But we can *not* say that they are heated because they collide more often.

To compress air is to heat it—to expand air is to cool it. But once compressed or expanded, it soon comes to a temperature equilibrium with its surroundings. Put your hand on a tank of compressed air and you will find that it has the same temperature as its surroundings.

Convection is a means of heat transmission in all fluids, whether liquids or gases. Whether we heat water in a pan or warm air in a room, the process is the same, Figure 15.5. If the fluid is heated from below, its molecules increase in speed and rise, permitting cooler fluid to come to the bottom. In this way convection currents keep the fluid stirred up as it heats.

Fig. 15.5 Convection currents in liquid.

Convection currents stirring the atmosphere result in winds. Some parts of the earth's surface absorb heat from the sun more readily than others, and as a result the air near the surface is heated unevenly—convection currents are created. This is most evident at the seashore. In the daytime the shore warms more easily than the water; air over the shore rises and cooler air from over the water takes its place. The result is a sea breeze. At night the process is reversed because the shore cools off more quickly than the water, and then the warmer air is over the sea. Build a fire on the beach and you'll notice that the smoke sweeps inward in the day and seaward at night.

Radiation

In the foregoing discussion of wind, heat from the sun somehow passes through the atmosphere and warms the earth's surface. This heat does not pass through the atmosphere by conduction, for air is among the poorest of conductors. Nor does it pass through by convection, for convection begins only after the earth is warmed. It is equally clear that neither convection nor conduction is possible in the empty space between our atmosphere and the sun. We can see that heat must be transmitted by another process—we call this process *radiation*.

While we usually think of heat as being transmitted in the radiation process, strictly speaking this is not true. The heat of a radiating body is transformed, at the instant of radiation, into *radiant energy*. Throughout the space between the radiating and receiving object, the radiation is a form of energy entirely distinct from heat. The heat from the sun, for example, is transformed into radiant energy and passes on to us as radiant energy; it is *retransformed into heat when it strikes an object*. So, strictly speaking, radiation is the transmission of radiant energy, and not heat. For the sake of brevity, we speak of heat radiation.

Radiant energy is carried through space by means of *electromagnetic waves*. These waves originate from vibrating electrons. Since all matter contains vibrating electrons, all matter in the universe, whether hot or cold, radiates energy. The universe is filled with a montage of electromagnetic waves. The waves emanating from the slower-moving electrons are longer and are called radio waves; those emanating from the most rapidly vibrating electrons are the shortwave X-rays and shorter gamma rays. In between are infrared, visible, and ultraviolet waves. If radiation in the wave range of infrared falls upon our skin, it may excite the sensation of warmth. Shorter waves falling upon the eye excite the sensation of light. We shall discuss electromagnetic radiation more fully in Chapter 25.

The Temperature Dependence of Radiation

The radiations that hot bodies give off are not all alike. The length of the waves depends on the temperature of the source. As the temperature of a radiating object is increased, the vibratory motion of electrons in the atoms and molecules of the source increases and vibrations of shorter wavelength are emitted. Bodies at room temperature emit only the longer waves. A steam radiator at a temperature of about 100°C emits some waves that are a little shorter, but none are short enough to affect our vision. As the temperature of a radiating body rises, it emits, in addition to the longwaves, shorter and shorter waves. At a temperature of about 500°C (932°F) iron begins to emit waves so short that they stimulate vision. They are the longest waves we can see, red light. At about 800°C (1472°F) iron gives out still shorter waves and is a bright cherry color. At about 1200°C (2192°F) it becomes "white hot" and emits all the different waves to which the eye is sensitive. At the same time it continues to emit the longwaves, thus radiating a variety of wavelengths. When these waves are absorbed by any kind of matter, they set the electrons in the matter into vibration, and heat is produced. In this way heat is transmitted from the radiating object to the receiving object.

Emission and Absorption of Heat Radiation

All bodies are continually radiating energy. Why, then, doesn't the temperature of all bodies continually decrease? The answer is that all bodies are also continually absorbing radiant energy. If a body is radiating more energy than it is absorbing, its temperature decreases; if a body is absorbing more energy than it is emitting, its temperature increases. A body that is warmer than its surroundings emits more energy than it receives, while a body colder than its surroundings is a net gainer of energy. The rate at which a body radiates or absorbs radiant energy depends in part upon its surface and its color. Black, rough surfaces are the best radiators and absorbers of radiant energy. When they are hot they are good radiators, and when they are cold they are good absorbers. Polished, shiny, and white surfaces, on the other hand, reflect heat radiation and are therefore poor absorbers.

Fig. 15.6 When the containers are filled with hot (or cold) water the blackened one cools (or warms up) faster.

Place thermometers in two metal containers of the same size and shape, one having a brightly polished surface and the other a blackened surface, Figure 15.6. Fill them with hot water and you will find that the container with the blackened surface cools faster. The blackened surface is a better radiator. Coffee will keep hot longer in a polished pot than in a blackened one. If we repeat the same experiment, only this time we fill each container with ice water, we would find that the container with the blackened surface warms up faster. The blackened surface is also a better absorber of radiant energy.

A simple relation exists between the ability of a surface to radiate heat and its ability to absorb heat radiation:

A surface that is a good absorber of radiation is also a good radiator of heat.

A surface that is a poor absorber of radiation is also a poor radiator of heat.

We can support these two statements with the following reasoning. We know that a number of bodies placed in a closed room will ultimately come to the same temperature. Upon reaching the same temperature, they will continue to radiate heat—but, because their temperature remains constant, each body must absorb as much heat as it is radiating. It follows that if one of these bodies is a good radiator, it must be a good absorber, otherwise it would be colder than its surroundings. Conversely, if one of the bodies is a poor radiator, it must also be a poor absorber; for if it were not it would absorb more radiation than it gave out, and it would be warmer than its surroundings. A good absorber of radiation must therefore be a good radiator, and a poor absorber must be a poor radiator.

Reflection and Absorption of Heat Radiation

Heat radiation is not always absorbed by a body it falls upon. It may be transmitted, in the same way that light is transmitted through glass; or it may be reflected, as light is reflected from a mirror. The brightly polished container in Figure 15.6 reflects the radiant energy incident upon it while the blackened container absorbs it. Polished metals are good reflectors and poor absorbers of heat radiation.

The heat radiation that falls on a body and is absorbed obviously cannot also be reflected; likewise, the heat radiation that falls on a body and is reflected cannot be absorbed. We can say,

A good absorber is a poor reflector of heat radiation, and a good reflector is a poor absorber of heat radiation.

Clean snow is a good reflector and therefore does not melt rapidly in sunlight. If the snow is dirty, radiant energy from the sun is absorbed and it melts faster. Dropping black soot on snowed-in mountain sides by aircraft is a technique sometimes used in flood control. Gradual melting at favorable times rather than a sudden runoff of melted snows is accomplished.

The radiant energy we receive from the sun is partly transmitted, partly absorbed, and partly reflected by the atmosphere. The amounts vary from place to place, but, as a general world average, about 46 percent of the incoming radiant energy reaches the ground; about 19 percent is absorbed by the atmosphere; and about 35 percent is reflected by the atmosphere.

Cooling at Night by Radiation

Bodies that radiate more energy than they receive become cooler. This happens at night when solar radiation is absent.

Objects out in the open radiate energy into the night and, because of the absence of warmer bodies, may receive very little in return. They give out more energy than they receive and become cooler. If the object is a good conductor of heat, like metal, stone, or concrete, heat from the ground will be conducted to it, somewhat stabilizing its temperature. But materials such as wood, straw, and grass are poor conductors, and little heat is conducted into them from the ground. These insulating materials radiate without recompensation and *get colder than the air*. On these kinds of materials it is common for frost to form even when the temperature of the air does not go down to freezing. Have you ever seen a frost-covered lawn or field on a chilly but above-freezing morning before the sun is up? The next time you see this, notice that the frost forms only on the grass, straw, or other poor conductors, while none forms on cement, stone, or good conductors.

The Thermos Bottle

Fig. 15.7 A Thermos bottle.

We can briefly summarize the ways in which heat is transmitted by considering a device that inhibits these three methods —the common vacuum or Thermos bottle. The Thermos bottle is double-walled glass, with a vacuum between the walls. The two inner glass surfaces facing each other are silvered. When a hot liquid is poured into such a bottle, it remains at very nearly the same temperature for many hours. This is because the transmission of heat by conduction, convection, and radiation is severely inhibited.

1. Heat transfer by *conduction* through the vacuum is impossible. Some heat escapes by conduction through the glass and stopper, but this is a slow process as glass and plastic or cork are poor conductors.

2. The vacuum also prevents heat loss through the walls by *convection*.

3. Heat loss by *radiation* is prevented by the silvered surfaces of the walls, which reflect heat waves back into the bottle.

Summary of Terms

Conduction. The transfer and distribution of thermal energy from molecule to molecule within a body.

Convection. The transfer of thermal energy in a gas or liquid by means of currents in the heated fluid.

Radiation. The transfer of energy by means of electromagnetic waves.

Questions

1. If you hold one end of a metal nail against a piece of ice, the end in your hand soon becomes cold. Does cold flow from the ice to your hand? Explain.

2. Why do double windows (Thermopane) keep a house warmer in winter?

3. In a still room, smoke from a cigarette will sometimes rise and then settle in the air before reaching the ceiling. Explain why.

4. Why would you expect a single helium molecule to continually rise in an atmosphere of nitrogen and oxygen? Why doesn't it "settle off" like the smoke in the preceding question?

5. If we warm a volume of air it expands. Does it then follow that if we expand a volume of air it warms? Explain.

6. Why is air leaking out of a tire cooler than the tire?

7. Why does a piston-type bicycle tire pump become hot when you pump air with it?

8. What does the high specific heat of water have to do with convection currents in the air at the seashore?

9. What would be the most efficient color for steam radiators?

10. From the rules that a good absorber of radiation is a good radiator, and a good reflector is a poor absorber, state a rule relating the reflecting and radiating properties of a surface.

16

Change of State

Evaporation and Condensation

A liquid left in an open dish will evaporate and form a gas. Molecules in the liquid state are moving at many speeds. The temperature of the liquid is a measure of the average kinetic energy of the molecules. There are as many molecules moving faster than the average speed as there are molecules moving at speeds less than the average. If the very fast molecules happen to be at or near the surface, and are moving in the right direction, they will overcome the surface tension forces and fly into the space above the liquid, thus becoming molecules of a gas. This is the process of *evaporation*. Since it is the faster or more energetic molecules that evaporate, the average kinetic energy of remaining molecules in the liquid is lowered. Hence the temperature of the liquid is lowered. We say that evaporation is a cooling process.

The cooling effect of evaporation is strikingly demonstrated when rubbing alcohol is poured on your back. The alcohol evaporates very rapidly, cooling the surface of the body quickly. The more rapid the evaporation, the faster will be the cooling.

The converse process takes place also. Gas molecules near the surface of a liquid may strike the surface and be absorbed by the liquid. This process is called *condensation*. The kinetic energy of the absorbed gas molecules is given to the liquid, thereby increasing the temperature of the liquid. We say that condensation is a warming process.

If a dish of water undergoes no apparent evaporation and no change in temperature during some period of time, we might conclude that "nothing is happening." But in this case both evaporation and condensation are taking place at the same rate. The number of molecules and amount of energy that leaves the liquid surface by evaporation is counteracted by as many molecules and as much energy returning by condensation. We say that the liquid is in equilibrium, since evaporation and condensation have canceling effects.

When we emerge from a shower and step into a dry room we feel cold. This is because evaporation is taking place at a rate to produce considerable cooling. If we remain in the shower, even with the water off, we do not feel as chilly. This is because

221

we are in a moist environment, and moisture from the air condenses upon our skin, producing a warming effect that counteracts the cooling effect of evaporation. If as much moisture condenses as evaporates, we feel no change in body temperature. We can dry ourselves with a towel much more comfortably if we remain in the shower area—to thoroughly dry ourselves we can then finish the job in a less moist area.

Both evaporation and condensation take place at the surface of liquids. If the rate of evaporation exceeds the rate of condensation, the liquid is cooled. If the rate of condensation exceeds the rate of evaporation, the liquid is warmed. We feel uncomfortably warm on a humid or muggy day for this reason. We will discuss humidity shortly.

Boiling

Under the right conditions, evaporation can take place beneath the surface of a liquid, forming bubbles of gas which are buoyed to the surface where they escape. The speed of the molecules forming gas must be great enough to exert as much pressure within the bubble as the atmosphere and water above exerts. We therefore find that boiling depends not only on temperature, but on pressure as well. Unless the molecules in the liquid are moving fast enough, atmospheric pressure acting on the surface of the liquid will collapse any bubbles that tend to form. As the atmospheric pressure is increased, the molecules

(a)   (b)   (c)   (d)

Fig. 16.1 The toy drinking bird operates by the evaporation of ether inside his body and by the evaporation of water from the outer surface of his head. The lower body contains liquid ether, which evaporates rapidly at room temperature. As it vaporizes (a), it creates pressure (b) (inside arrows), which pushes ether up the tube. Ether in the upper part does not vaporize because the head is cooled by the evaporation of water from the outer felt-covered beak and head. When the weight of ether in the head is sufficient, the bird pivots forward (c), permitting the ether to run back to the body. Each pivot wets the felt surface of the beak and head, and the cycle is repeated.

in the liquid are required to move faster to exert a vapor pressure within the bubble equal to the impressed atmospheric pressure. So increasing the pressure on the surface of a liquid raises its boiling point.

Fig. 16.2 The motion of molecules in the bubble of steam (much enlarged) creates an outward vapor pressure that counterbalances the atmospheric and water pressure pushing inward on the bubble.

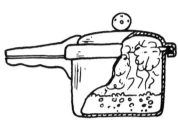

Fig. 16.3 A pressure cooker.

The pressure cooker utilizes this fact. As the evaporating vapor builds up under the lid of the pressure cooker, pressure upon the surface of the liquid is increased which prevents boiling.* This raises the boiling point. The increased boiling temperature allows the liquid to hold more heat which cooks the food faster. Conversely, if the pressure is reduced, the temperature at which boiling takes place is reduced. At atmospheric pressure, water boils at 212°F or 100°C. In regions of reduced atmospheric pressure, the mountains for example, boiling takes place at temperatures lower than 212°F and 100°C. In Denver, Colorado, the "mile-high city," water boils at 203°F or 95°C. As a result, food cooked in boiling water requires more time (a three-minute egg in Denver is "runny"). In the absence of atmospheric pressure, water would boil away at even freezing temperatures. That's why no ponds or lakes can exist on the moon.

Geysers

A geyser is a periodically erupting pressure cooker. It consists of a long, narrow, vertical hole into which underground streams seep; Figure 16.4. The column of water is heated from

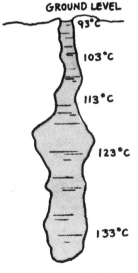

Fig. 16.4 An "Old Faithful" type geyser.

---
*The pressurized spacesuit of an astronaut similarly prevents boiling of blood by keeping oxygen and other gases dissolved in the blood. If the astronaut were exposed to pressureless space, the gases would quickly bubble from his blood, stop his heartbeat, and kill him.

volcanic heat below to temperatures exceeding 100°C. This is because the vertical column of water exerts pressure on the deeper water, thereby increasing the boiling point. The narrowness of the shaft shuts off convection currents which allows the deeper portions to become considerably hotter than the water surface. Water at the surface, of course, will boil at 100°C. Because the water is heated from below, a temperature high enough to permit boiling is reached near the bottom and boiling begins there before it does at the top. The rising bubbles push out the column of water above and the eruption starts. As the water gushes out, the pressure is reduced in the remaining water which then rapidly boils and erupts, pushing out with great force.

Boiling Is a Cooling Process

Just as evaporation is a cooling process, boiling is also a cooling process. At first thought this may seem surprising— perhaps because we always associate boiling with hot water, or because we don't make a distinction between heating and boiling. But at second thought, the fact that the temperature of water is not increased above the boiling temperature when heated supports the idea that cooling is taking place. At 212°F, water at sea level is in thermal equilibrium. It is being cooled by boiling as fast as it is being heated by the heat from the stove. If cooling did not take place, continued application of heat to a pot of boiling water would result in a continued increase in temperature. The higher temperatures in a pressure cooker are reached because cooling by boiling is prevented.

Boiling and Freezing at the Same Time

A dramatic demonstration of these ideas consists of placing a dish of water at room temperature in a vacuum jar. The pressure in the jar is slowly reduced by a vacuum pump until the water starts to boil. The vaporization of water takes heat away from the remaining water, thus cooling it to a lower temperature. Continued reduction in pressure allows more and more of the slower-moving molecules to boil away. Continued boiling results in a lowering of temperature until finally the

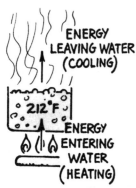

Fig. 16.5 Heating warms the water and boiling cools it.

Fig. 16.6 Apparatus to demonstrate that water will freeze and boil at the same time in a vacuum.

freezing point of approximately 0°C is reached. Continued evaporation cools the surface of the water until ice forms over the surface of the boiling water. Boiling and freezing are taking place at the same time! This must be witnessed to be appreciated. Frozen bubbles of boiling water are a remarkable sight. (A small dish of sulfuric acid is usually placed in the vacuum chamber to absorb water vapor and aid the pump in keeping the pressure low. Without the acid, a longer time would be required.)

Melting and Freezing

Suppose you held hands with someone, and each of you started jumping around randomly. The more violently you jumped the more difficult keeping hold would be. If you jumped violently enough, keeping hold would be impossible. Something like this happens to the molecules of a solid when it is heated. As heat is absorbed the molecules vibrate more and more violently. If enough heat is absorbed the attractive forces between the molecules will no longer be able to hold them together. The solid melts.

Freezing is the converse of this process. As energy is withdrawn from a liquid, molecular motion diminishes until finally the molecules, on the average, are moving slowly enough so that the attractive forces between them are able to cause cohesion. The molecules then vibrate about fixed positions and form a solid.

Just as equilibrium can take place between evaporation and condensation, equilibrium between melting and freezing can occur. This happens with ice and water together at the same temperature of 0°C. At this temperature the molecules in both the ice and the water have the same average kinetic energy. There are some molecules that move faster and some that move slower than average. Some of the faster-moving molecules of the surface of the ice crystals jostle loose from their neighboring molecules and mingle with the molecules of the liquid. As a result, some melting is taking place. Some of the slower-moving molecules in the liquid, on the other hand, are captured by the molecules in the crystals when they touch the crystal surface. Consequently, some freezing is taking place. At 0°C the rate of molecules leaving the crystals is equal to the rate returning and the proportion of ice and water remains constant.

An interesting observation demonstrating the equilibrium

between melting and freezing is shown in Figure 16.7. If a jagged piece of ice is put in ice water at 0°C, after some time the ice surface will become smooth. The protrusions melt away

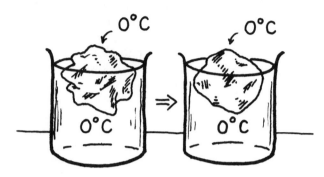
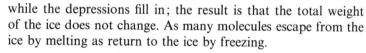

Fig. 16.7 Equilibrium between melting and freezing.

while the depressions fill in; the result is that the total weight of the ice does not change. As many molecules escape from the ice by melting as return to the ice by freezing.

Regelation

Because ice crystals are open structured, pressure applied to ice can cause melting. Ice therefore will melt at a lower temperature under pressure (the temperature of the melting point is only lowered slightly, being .0072°C for each 14.7 psi of pressure added). Sufficient pressure, however, is exerted by an ice-skate blade to melt the ice beneath it. A skater skates on the thin film of water between the blade and the ice which is produced by the blade pressure. As soon as the pressure is released, the water refreezes. This process of melting under pressure and freezing again when the pressure is reduced is called *regelation*. The making of snowballs is a good example of regelation.

An experiment that clearly shows regelation is shown in Figure 16.8. A fine wire with weights attached to its ends is hung over a block of ice. The wire will slowly cut its way through the ice, but its track will be left full of ice.

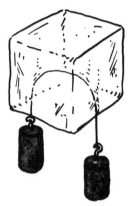

Fig. 16.8 Regelation. The wire will gradually pass through the ice without cutting it in half.

Freezing Point of Solutions

Dissolving sugar in water lowers the water's freezing temperature. This is because the sugar molecules do not enter into the hexagonal ice-crystal structure. As a result, molecules of sugar get in the way of water molecules that ordinarily would join together. As ice crystals do form, the hindrance is intensified

—the ratio of sugar to water molecules increases and connections become more and more difficult. Only when the water molecules move slowly enough for attractive forces to play an unusually large part in the process can freezing be completed. In general, adding anything to water has this result—antifreeze is a practical application of this process.

Energy of Changes of State

If we continually add heat to a solid or liquid, it will eventually change state. A solid will liquefy, and a liquid will vaporize. Energy is required for both liquefaction of a solid and vaporization of a liquid. The general behavior of many substances can be illustrated by a description of the changes that occur with water. To make the numbers easy to deal with, suppose we have a 1-gram cube of ice at a temperature of $-50°C$ in a closed container, and put it on a stove to heat. A thermometer in the container would reveal a slow increase in temperature until $0°C$. At $0°C$ the temperature stops rising, yet heat is continually being supplied. This heat melts the ice. To melt the whole gram, 80 calories of heat are absorbed by the ice. Not until all the ice melts does the temperature again begin to rise. Each additional calorie absorbed by the water increases its temperature by $1°C$ until it reaches the boiling temperature, $100°C$. Again, as heat is added the temperature remains constant, while more and more of the gram of water is boiled away, becoming steam. To vaporize the whole gram, 540 calories of heat are absorbed by the water. Finally, when all the water has become steam at $100°C$, the temperature begins to rise once more. It will continue to rise as long as we continue to add heat. This process is graphed in Figure 16.9. (Note that the

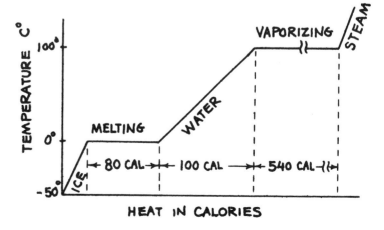

Fig. 16.9   A graph showing the energy involved in the heating and change of state of 1 gram of water.

540-calorie section of the graph could not be drawn to scale without running off the page; 540 calories is a relatively large amount of energy, much more than would be required to bring a gram of ice at absolute zero to boiling water! Steam contains a vast amount of thermal energy.)

Water can change to the vapor state by boiling or by evaporation at lower temperatures. For temperatures lower than 100°C, even more energy is required for vaporization. So whether by boiling or by evaporation, at least 540 calories of heat are needed to convert each gram of liquid water into vapor. When perspiration evaporates from your skin it draws much of this heat out of your body.

A refrigerator is cooled in a similar way. Pipes in the refrigerator contain a special liquid with a low boiling temperature. As this liquid turns into a gas in the cooling unit, it draws heat from the things stored in the food compartment.

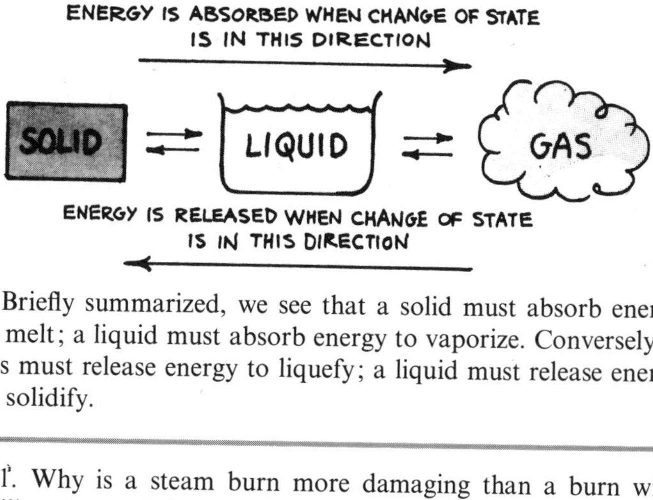

Fig. 16.10 Change of state and energy changes.

Briefly summarized, we see that a solid must absorb energy to melt; a liquid must absorb energy to vaporize. Conversely, a gas must release energy to liquefy; a liquid must release energy to solidify.

Questions

1. Why is a steam burn more damaging than a burn with boiling water of the same temperature?

2. How does snow and/or rain affect the temperature of the air?

3. Why do lakes freeze more readily after a heavy snowstorm?

4. When ice melts, how does the temperature of the surrounding environment change?

5. Some old-timers found that when they wrapped newspaper around the ice in their iceboxes, melting was inhibited. Discuss the advisability of this.

Humidity   The air always contains some water vapor; at any given temperature, however, there is a limit to the amount that the air will support. When this limit is reached we say the air is *saturated*. More water is required to saturate the atmosphere when the temperature is high than when it is low. This is because water vapor molecules, which would coalesce and liquefy upon low-speed collisions, bounce apart and remain in the gaseous state upon higher-speed collisions. This is similar to a fly making a grazing contact with flypaper. At low speed he would surely get stuck, whereas at high speed he stands a greater chance of rebounding into the air. So the faster that water vapor molecules move, the less chance there is that they will stick to one another and form droplets. Warmer air, therefore, will support a greater number of water molecules in the vapor state than cooler air.

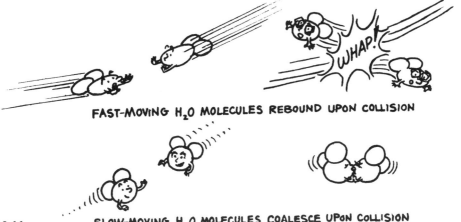

FAST-MOVING H_2O MOLECULES REBOUND UPON COLLISION

SLOW-MOVING H_2O MOLECULES COALESCE UPON COLLISION

Fig. 16.11

Usually we speak of the amount of water in the air in one of two ways. Sometimes we speak of the percentage of water vapor in a unit volume of air—this is called the *absolute humidity*. Thus we might say the absolute humidity of some sample of air is 25 percent, meaning that 25 percent of our sample is water vapor. More often, however, we speak of the amount of water vapor present as compared to the amount of vapor present in saturated air at the same temperature—this is called *relative humidity*. Thus, if the relative humidity is 50 percent, the air contains half the amount it would contain when saturated at the same temperature.

Our bodily comfort depends on the humidity, as well as the temperature. For the average person, conditions are ideal when the temperature is about 68°F and the relative humidity is about 50–60 percent. When the relative humidity is high, condensation of moist air counteracts evaporation of perspiration, and we say the weather is "muggy."

Body temperature in a rising environmental temperature is regulated by the evaporation of sweat. In dry desert air, with a well-ventilated hat and adequate salt replacement, a person can work with comfort when the air temperature is as high as 125°F. When the air is very dry, sweat is hardly noticed as it evaporates rapidly.

As the humidity rises toward the saturation point, it becomes harder and harder to evaporate sweat. Net evaporation declines as condensation of moisture from the air increases. When the air is saturated, sweat rolls off a person in streams without evaporating—vital salt (NaCl) is lost and body temperature begins to rise. This is one form of "sunstroke" (not due to the sun necessarily) where strokers may be found unconscious with a temperature of 107°F and shock due to low blood salt.*

Fog and Clouds

All fogs and clouds are produced by the cooling of moist air. Fast-moving water molecules in the vapor state coalesce into tiny droplets upon chilling. If the process takes place overhead in the atmosphere, we call the result a cloud. If it takes place near the ground, we call the result fog.

Warm air rises. As it rises it expands. As it expands it chills. As it chills water vapor molecules begin coalescing rather than bouncing off one another upon glancing collisions. Condensation takes place and we have a cloud.

Warm breezes blow over the ocean. When the moist air moves from warmer to cooler waters or from warm water to cool land it chills. As it chills water vapor molecules begin coalescing rather than bouncing off one another upon glancing collisions. Condensation takes place and we have fog.

Snowflakes are formed when water vapor condenses in the air at a temperature below freezing. When an adequate amount of

---

*The other form of "sunstroke" is usually, though not always, due to the sun and is not related to humidity: for instance, hatless exposure to a "hot sun" may result in the brain temperature rising faster than it can be cooled by the blood, and at about 104° to 105°F the heat-regulating center in the hypothalamus fails, and sweating stops. In this case a person may be unconscious with a temperature of perhaps 107°F, but not in shock. Blood is normal and he is not sweating.

vapor condenses the snowflakes become large enough to fall. Tiny flakes may have such a small rate of fall that they appear to float in the air. High cirrus and cirrostratus clouds consist of snowflakes or minute ice crystals. A haze of minute ice crystals high up in the atmosphere sometimes produces a large halo around the sun and moon.

Summary of Terms

Evaporation. The change of state at the surface of a liquid as it passes to vapor. This results from the random motion of molecules which occasionally escape from the liquid surface. Cooling of the liquid results.

Condensation. The change of state from vapor to liquid; the opposite of evaporation. Warming of the liquid results.

Boiling. A rapid state of evaporation that takes place within the liquid as well as at its surface. Like evaporation, cooling of the liquid results.

Melting. The change of state from the solid to liquid form. Energy is absorbed by the substance that is melting.

Freezing. The change of state from the liquid to the solid form; opposite of melting. Energy is released by the substance undergoing freezing.

Regelation. The process of melting under pressure and the subsequent refreezing when the pressure is removed.

Absolute humidity. A measure of the amount of water vapor in a sample of air.

Relative humidity. The ratio of the amount of water vapor in a sample of air to the amount of water vapor the sample of air is capable of supporting at a given temperature.

Suggested Reading

Westwater, J. W., "The Boiling of Liquids," *Scientific American*, June, 1954.

Questions

1. Can you heat a substance without raising its temperature? Explain.

2. Why is the freezing temperature of salt water lower than that of fresh water?

3. Why might an astronaut's blood boil if he stepped out of his capsule without his pressurized spacesuit?

4. Why does the temperature of boiling water remain the same as long as the boiling continues?

5. The human body can maintain its customary temperature of 98.6°F on a day when the temperature is above 100°F. How is this done?

6. In a nuclear submarine power plant, the temperature of the water in the reactor is above 100°C. How is this possible?

7. Why is it that in cold winters a tub of water placed in a farmer's canning cellar helps to prevent canned food from freezing?

8. On cold days the windows in your home sometimes get wet on the inside. Why?

9. What accounts for the dew found on the grass in early morning?

10. Suppose one wishes to cool a kitchen by leaving the refrigerator door open and closing the kitchen door and windows. What will happen to the room temperature? Why?

Photo by Arthur Vining Fisher.

PART 4

Sound

17

Vibrations and Waves

Many things around us vibrate. Our vocal chords vibrate when we speak; the prongs of a tuning fork vibrate and generate sound waves; electrons vibrate back and forth in electrical circuits and make up electricity, while the vibration of electrons in the atom generates light waves. We will learn that the source of all wave motion is a vibrating object.

The Pendulum

If we suspend a small massive object at the end of a length of string, we have a simple pendulum. Pendulums swing back and forth with such regularity that they have long been used to control the motion of clocks. Galileo discovered that the time a pendulum takes to swing to and fro through small distances depends neither on its mass nor on the length of the arc through which it swings. The time of swing depends only on the *length of the pendulum and the acceleration of a freely falling body.**

In addition to controlling time-keeping devices, pendulums can be used to measure the acceleration due to gravity. Oil and mineral prospectors use very sensitive pendulums to detect slight differences in this acceleration, which is affected by the densities of underlying formations.

A long pendulum swings back and forth more slowly than a short pendulum. When we walk we allow our legs to swing with the help of gravity, that is, at a pendulum rate. Just as a long pendulum takes a long time to swing to and fro, a person having long legs tends to walk with slower strides than a person having short legs. This is also evident in animals, where giraffes, horses, and ostriches run with a slower gait than dachshunds, mice, and bugs.

---

*The exact relationship for the period of a simple pendulum is $T = 2\pi\sqrt{l/g}$, where T is the time for one complete to-and-fro swing, called the *period*; l is the length of the pendulum; and g is the acceleration of a freely falling body.

237

Figure 17.1 shows the path traced by a compound pendulum that is free to swing in all directions.* Friction causes a decrease in the arc with each successive swing. A pen mounted to the bob of the pendulum traces successively smaller patterns until it finally comes to rest at the middle of the pattern.

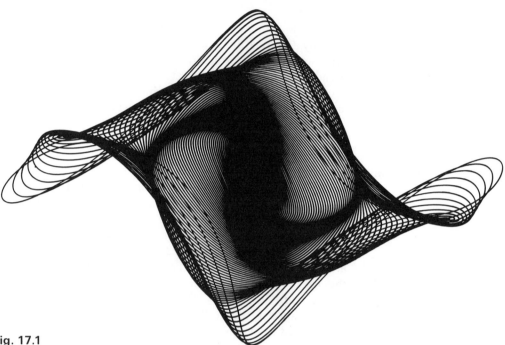

Fig. 17.1

A pendulum consisting of a suspended bag of sand will similarly trace interesting patterns if a hole is punched in the bottom of the bag. The leaking sand traces the path of the swinging bag. Interesting paintings can be made by swinging cans of leaking paint over a canvas.

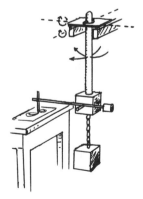

---

*The compound pendulum used to make such drawings is a double pendulum, and is not too difficult to build. The upper pendulum is suspended in a manner so that it can swing not only back and forth, but from side to side as well. It is constrained to swing about two perpendicular axes. In this way the bob to which the pen assembly is mounted doesn't twist when the pendulum is in motion. The pen is attached to the end of a balanced arm that rests on a single pivot at the side of the pendulum bob so that the pen remains in contact with paper during the swinging. The weight of the pen provides contact. A second pendulum is suspended by a rope or chain as shown. Its motion complicates the path of the upper pendulum, giving rise to an infinite variety of interesting patterns.

The Sine Curve

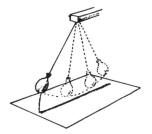

Fig. 17.2 A straight line is traced by a leaking sand-bag undergoing simple harmonic motion.

The motion of a pendulum bob swinging back and forth along a single plane in a small arc is called *simple harmonic motion*. If the sandbag just described is undergoing simple harmonic motion, it will trace out and retrace a short straight line, Figure 17.2. Suppose that we swing such a pendulum above a conveyor belt that moves in a perpendicular direction to the plane of the swinging pendulum, Figure 17.3. The trace it makes is called a *sine curve*. This curve is not itself a wave, but is a pictorial representation of a wave, and lends itself to a description of some of the technical terms used in describing wave motion.

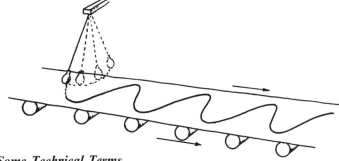

Fig. 17.3 The sandbag pendulum traces a sine curve on a moving conveyor belt.

Some Technical Terms

The terms *crest* and *trough* refer to the highest and lowest parts of the curve, or the wave it represents, Figure 17.4. The term *amplitude* refers to the distance from the midpoint (broken line) to the crest (or to the trough) of the wave. Thus amplitude is equal to the maximum displacement of the pendulum from its position of rest. The distance from the top of one crest to the top of the next one is equal to the *wavelength*. Or the wavelength is the distance between any successive identical parts of a wave.

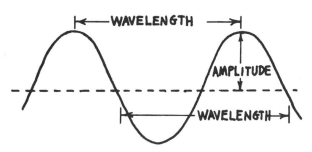

Fig. 17.4 A sine curve.

Another important term we will use to describe wave motion is *frequency*. In the case of the swinging pendulum, we can speak of its frequency in terms of how frequently it swings back and forth, or, more specifically, by the number of vibrations per second that it undergoes. We call a complete back-and-forth swing one vibration (or cycle). For example, if the pendulum swings back and forth at the rate of two complete vibrations each second, we say the frequency is 2 vibrations per second. We said earlier that the source of all waves is a vibrating object. We will see that the frequency of a wave, that is, the rate at which the crests of a wave pass by a given point, is the same as the frequency of the vibrating source.

Wave Motion   Most of the information about our surroundings comes to us in some form of wave motion. It is through wave motion that sounds come to our ears, light to our eyes, and electromagnetic signals to our radios and television sets. We define wave motion as the transfer of energy from a source to a distant receiver without the transfer of matter between the two points.

Wave motion can be most easily understood by first considering the simple case of wave motion in a horizontally stretched string. If one end of such a string is shaken up and down, a rhythmic disturbance travels along the string. Each particle of the string moves up and down, while at the same time, the disturbance moves along the length of the string. The medium returns to its initial condition after the disturbance has passed.

Perhaps a more familiar example of wave motion is a water wave. If a stone is dropped into a quiet pond, waves will travel outward in expanding circles whose centers are at the source of the disturbance. In this case we might think that water is being transported with the waves, since water is splashed onto previously dry ground when the waves meet the shore. We should realize, however, that barring obstacles, the water will run back into the pond and things will be much as they were in the beginning—the surface of the water will have been disturbed but the water itself will have gone nowhere. Again, the medium returns to its initial condition after the disturbance has passed.

Let us consider a final example of a wave to illustrate the fact that what is transported from one locality to another is a disturbance in a medium, rather than the medium itself. If you view a wheatfield from an elevated position on a gusty day, you will see waves travel across the wheat. It should be clear that the individual stems do not leave their places. Instead they swing to and fro. Furthermore, if you stand in a narrow footpath, the wheat that blows over the edge of the path, brushing against your legs, is very much like the water that doused the shore in our earlier example. While wave motion continues, the wheat swings back and forth, vibrating between definite limits but going nowhere. When the wave motion stops, the wheat returns to its initial position. It is characteristic of wave motion that the medium carrying the wave returns to its initial condition after the disturbance has passed.

Wave Velocity

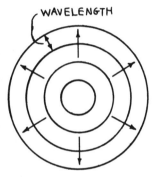

WAVELENGTH

Fig. 17.5 A top view of water waves.

The velocity of wave motion is related to the frequency and wavelength of the waves. We can understand this by considering the simple case of water waves, Figure 17.5. Imagine that we fix our eyes at a stationary point on the surface of a body of water and observe the waves passing by this point. If we count the number of crests of water passing this point each second (the frequency) and also observe the distance between crests (the wavelength), we can then calculate the horizontal distance that a particular crest travels each second. We will then know how frequently a distance equal to the wavelength is traveled. This will be the *wave velocity*.

For example, if two crests pass a stationary point each second, and if the wavelength is 10 feet, then 2×10 feet of waves pass by in 1 second. The waves therefore are traveling at 20 feet per second. We can say

$$\text{Wave velocity} = \text{frequency} \times \text{wavelength}$$

This relationship holds true for all kinds of waves, whether they be water waves, sound waves, or light waves.

Transverse Waves

Suppose we fasten one end of a long rope to a wall and hold the other end in our hand. If we suddenly jerk the end we are holding, a pulse will travel along the rope and back, Figure 17.6. In this case the motion of the rope (up and down arrows) is at right angles to the direction of wave velocity. The right-angled, or sideways, motion is called *transverse*. Since the motion of the medium is transverse to the direction the wave travels, this type is called a *transverse wave*.

Waves in the stretched strings of musical instruments and upon the surfaces of liquids are transverse; so also are electro-

Fig. 17.6 A transverse wave pulse.

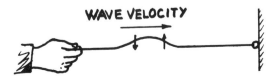

WAVE VELOCITY

magnetic waves (radio waves, visible light, X-rays, and so forth).

Standing Waves

If the rope shown in Figure 17.6 is shaken up and down, a train of waves will be sent out which will be reflected from the fixed end. By shaking the rope just right, we can cause the incident and reflected waves to form a *standing wave*, where parts of the rope, called the *nodes*, are stationary.

It is easy to make standing waves yourself. Tie a rope, or better a rubber tube, between two firm supports. Shake the tube from side to side with your hand near one of the supports. If you shake the tube with the right frequency you will set up a standing wave as shown in Figure 17.7. Shake the tube with twice the frequency and a standing wave of half the wavelength,

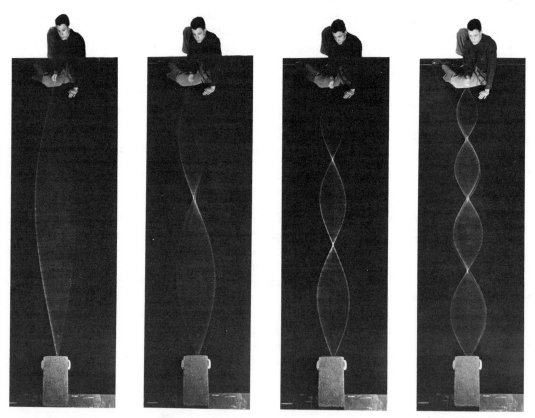

Fig. 17.7 Standing waves set up in a taut rubber tube. (From *Physics,* Physical Science Study Committee, Boston, Heath, 1960.)

two loops, will result. (The distance between successive nodes is a half wavelength—two loops comprise a full wavelength.) Triple the frequency and a standing wave with one-third a wavelength, three loops, results, and so forth. Unless you find the right frequency in shaking the tube, the waves reflecting up and down the tube will not combine to form a standing wave. But when you find a proper frequency, a very small motion of your hand will produce a standing wave of large amplitude.

Standing waves are set up in a guitar string when it is plucked, in a violin string when it is bowed, and in a piano string when it is struck. They are set up in the pipes of an organ and in the air of a soda pop bottle when air is blown over the top. Standing waves can be set up in a tub of water by sloshing it back and forth with the right frequency.

In transverse waves the medium (rope, rubber tube, water, or whatever) vibrates to and fro in a direction at right angles (transverse) to the direction in which the wave is traveling.

Longitudinal Waves

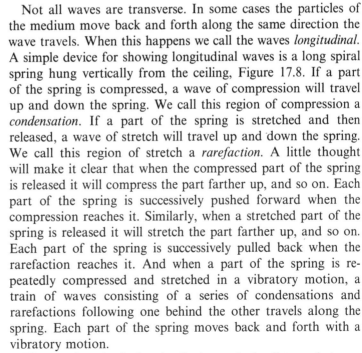

Not all waves are transverse. In some cases the particles of the medium move back and forth along the same direction the wave travels. When this happens we call the waves *longitudinal.* A simple device for showing longitudinal waves is a long spiral spring hung vertically from the ceiling, Figure 17.8. If a part of the spring is compressed, a wave of compression will travel up and down the spring. We call this region of compression a *condensation.* If a part of the spring is stretched and then released, a wave of stretch will travel up and down the spring. We call this region of stretch a *rarefaction.* A little thought will make it clear that when the compressed part of the spring is released it will compress the part farther up, and so on. Each part of the spring is successively pushed forward when the compression reaches it. Similarly, when a stretched part of the spring is released it will stretch the part farther up, and so on. Each part of the spring is successively pulled back when the rarefaction reaches it. And when a part of the spring is repeatedly compressed and stretched in a vibratory motion, a train of waves consisting of a series of condensations and rarefactions following one behind the other travels along the spring. Each part of the spring moves back and forth with a vibratory motion.

The wavelength of a longitudinal wave is the distance between successive regions of condensation or, equivalently, the distance between successive rarefactions.

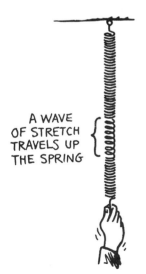

A WAVE
OF STRETCH
TRAVELS UP
THE SPRING

Fig. 17.8 A longitudinal wave.

In the case of longitudinal waves the medium vibrates to and fro along the direction in which the wave is traveling. The most common example of longitudinal waves is sound in air. Each air molecule vibrates back and forth about some equilibrium position as the waves move by.

Summary of Terms

Simple harmonic motion. A vibratory or periodic motion, like that of a pendulum, in which the force acting on the vibrating body is proportional to its displacement from its central equilibrium position and acts toward that position.

Sine curve. The wavelike path traced by an object undergoing simple harmonic motion.

Amplitude. For a body undergoing simple harmonic motion, the amplitude is the maximum displacement on either side of its equilibrium position. For a wave, the amplitude is the maximum value of the wave variable (displacement for a transverse or longitudinal wave in a solid, pressure for a wave in a liquid or gas, electric and magnetic field intensity for an electromagnetic wave, etc., depending on the nature of the wave).

Frequency. For a body undergoing simple harmonic motion, frequency is the number of vibrations it makes per unit time. For a wave the frequency of a series of waves is the number of waves that pass a particular point per unit time.

Wavelength. The distance between successive crests, troughs, or identical parts of a wave.

Wave velocity. The speed with which waves pass by a particular point:

$$\text{Wave velocity} = \text{frequency} \times \text{wavelength}$$

Transverse wave. A wave in which the individual particles of a medium vibrate from side to side perpendicular (transverse) to the direction in which the wave travels. The vibrations along a stretched string are transverse waves.

Standing waves. Stationary wave patterns formed in a medium when two sets of identical waves pass through the medium in opposite directions.

Longitudinal wave. A wave in which the individual particles of a medium vibrate back and forth in the direction in which the wave travels. *Sound* consists of longitudinal waves.

Suggested Reading

Bascom, Willard, "Ocean Waves," *Scientific American*, August, 1959.

Kock, Winston E., *Sound Waves and Light Waves* (Science Study Series), Garden City, N. Y., Doubleday (Anchor), 1965.

Questions   1. Why do short people tend to walk with quicker strides than tall people?

2. What kind of motion would you impart to a garden hose so that the resulting stream of water would approximate a sine curve?

3. How does the frequency of vibration of a small object floating in water compare to the number of waves passing it each second?

4. Clearly distinguish between wave frequency and wave velocity.

5. What kind of motion would you impart to a stretched, coiled spring (or "slinky") to provide a transverse wave? A longitudinal wave?

18
Sound

If a tree fell in the middle of a deep forest hundreds of miles away from any living being, would there be a sound? Different people will answer this question in different ways. "No," some will say, "a sound is subjective and requires a listener. If there is no listener there will be no sound." "Yes," others will say, "a sound is not something in a listener's head. A sound is an objective thing." Discussions of questions like this one often are beyond agreement because the participants fail to realize that they are arguing not about the nature of sound, but about the definition of a word. Either side is right, depending on which definition is taken, but investigation can proceed only when a definition has been agreed upon. For this reason the physicist usually defines sound as a form of energy that exists whether or not it is heard, and goes on from there to investigate its nature.

The Origin of Sound

All sounds are waves produced by the vibrations of material objects. In pianos and violins, the sound is produced by the vibrating strings; in a clarinet, by a vibrating reed. The human voice results from the vibration of the vocal chords. In each of these cases a vibrating source sends a disturbance through the surrounding medium in the form of longitudinal waves. The frequency of the sound wave is identical to the frequency of the vibrating source. The human ear can normally hear sounds made by vibrating bodies whose frequencies are between 16 and 20,000 vibrations per second. Sound waves whose frequencies are below 16 vibrations per second are called *infrasonic*—those whose frequencies are above 20,000 vibrations per second are called *ultrasonic*. We cannot hear infrasonic and ultrasonic sound waves.

The Nature of Sound in Air

When we clap our hands we produce a wave pulse that travels out in all directions. Being longitudinal, this wave pulse vibrates its medium, the air, in the same way that a similar pulse would vibrate a coiled spring. Each particle moves back and forth along the direction of the expanding wave.

For a clearer picture of this process, consider a long corridor as in Figure 18.1a. At one end is an open window with a curtain over it. At the other end is a door. If we open the door we can imagine the door pushing the adjacent molecules of air away from their initial positions. These molecules strike their neighbors; the neighbors are driven into *their* neighbors, and so on, until the curtain flaps out of the window. A pulse of compressed air has moved from the door to the curtain. This pulse of compressed air is what we call a *condensation*. Individual air molecules have tended to move first away from the door and then, after pushing against their neighbors, back toward the door. They have vibrated like points on a spiral spring.

If we close the door, Figure 18-1b, the door pushes adjacent air molecules out of the room. An area of low pressure behind the door is thus produced. Neighboring molecules then move into it, leaving a zone of lessened pressure behind them. Others, which are still farther from the door, in turn move into these rarefied regions and once again a disturbance moves across the room—only this time the disturbance is a *rarefaction*. It is important to note that it is not the air itself, but a *pulse* that travels across the room; and in both cases it travels in a direction from the door to the curtain. We know this because in both cases the curtain moves *after* the door is opened or closed.

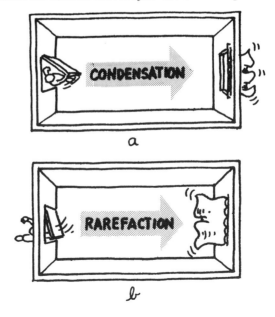

Fig. 18.1 When the door is opened a condensation travels across the room; when the door is closed a rarefaction travels across the room. (Adapted from Albert V. Baez, *The New College Physics: A Spiral Approach*, San Francisco, Freeman, 1967.)

The same idea applies to the vibrating tuning fork shown in Figure 18.2. For simplicity, we represent only the waves that travel through the air in a long tube placed in the vicinity of the vibrating fork. When the prong of the fork next to the tube moves to the right, a condensation is started through the tube; when it swings back to the left, a rarefaction follows the condensation. It is like a Ping-Pong paddle moving back and forth in a room packed full of Ping-Pong balls. The paddle strikes the neighboring balls which then in turn strike their neighbors, which in turn do the same, resulting in the transmission of a pulse through the Ping-Pong balls. In other words, as the fork vibrates back and forth, a series of compressions and rarefactions of air molecules travels through the tube.

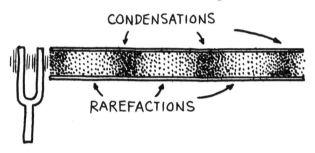

Fig. 18.2 Condensations and rarefactions traveling from the tuning fork through the tube.

Pause to reflect on the physics of sound while you are quietly listening to your radio sometime. The radio loudspeaker is a paper cone that vibrates in rhythm with an electrical signal. Air molecules that constantly impinge on the vibrating cone of the speaker are themselves set into vibration. These in turn vibrate against neighboring air molecules, which in turn do the same, and so on. As a result, rhythmic patterns of compressed and rarefied air emanate from the loudspeaker, showering the whole room with undulating motions. This resulting vibrating air sets your eardrum into vibration, which in turn sends cascades of rhythmic electrical impulses along the cochlear nerve canal and into the brain. And you listen to the sound of music.

Media That Transmit Sound

Most sounds that we hear are transmitted through the air. However, any elastic substance,* whether solid, liquid, or gas, can transmit sound. Compared to solids and liquids, air is a

---

*Recall that an elastic substance (Chapter 10) has resilience and can transmit energy with little loss, such as steel compared to putty.

relatively poor conductor of sound. The sound of a distant train can be heard more clearly if the ear is placed against the rail. Similarly, a watch placed on a table beyond hearing distance can be heard by placing your ear to the table. American Indians often placed their ears to the ground to hear sounds that were inaudible in the air. The next time you go swimming, have a friend at some distance click two rocks together beneath the surface of the water while you are submerged. You will find that liquid is an excellent conductor of sound. If you and your friend ever happen to be in a vacuum, perform your last experiment and have her click two rocks together. You won't hear a thing! Sound will not travel in a vacuum. The transmission of sound requires a medium—if there is nothing to compress and expand there can be no sound.

The Speed of Sound

If we watch a person at a distance chopping wood or hammering, we can easily see that the blow takes place an appreciable time before its sound reaches our ears. Thunder is heard after a flash of lightning. These common experiences show that sound requires a definite time to travel from one place to another. The speed of sound in air depends on wind conditions, temperature, and humidity. It does not depend on the frequency of the sound—all notes travel at the same speed. The speed of sound in dry air at 0°C (32°F) is about 1090 feet per second or 750 miles per hour. Water vapor in the air increases this speed slightly. Sound travels faster through warm air than through cold air. This is to be expected because the faster-moving molecules in warm air bump into each other more often and therefore can transmit a pulse in less time. For each degree rise in temperature above 0°C, the speed of sound in air increases by 2 feet per second. In water, sound travels about four times as fast as it does in air, while in steel, the speed of sound is about fifteen times as great as in air.

Reflection of Sound

An echo results from the reflection of sound by distant walls, buildings, and the like. If an observer in a favorable location makes a sound, in a short time that sound is reflected back to him. The time required, of course, depends on how far away the reflector is. If the reflector is 550 feet away, the sound must travel 550 feet and back, or 1100 feet. Since at normal temperatures sound travels 1100 feet in about 1 second, the echo will be heard about 1 second after the sound is produced. When in a fog, seafaring men once used this principle in reckoning distance to obstacles by timing the echo of their ship's whistle. Today's sailors still use the principle; only instead of using sound, they use the high-frequency radio waves of radar.

Where there is more than one reflecting surface, we may hear a series of echoes. Thus when a gun is fired in a canyon, the sound bounces first from one surface and then from another, reflecting many times and reaching our ears by many paths, so that it is drawn out into a long peal. We are all familiar with the same effect in the rumble of distant thunder. This prolonging of sound by reflection is called *reverberation*.

Energy in Sound Waves

All kinds of wave motion possess energy, but of varying degrees. For example, the energy in the wave motion known as sunlight is large, while the energy in the waves that produce sounds of ordinary intensity is small. We should expect this because only a small amount of energy is required to produce a sound. For example, 10,000,000 people talking at the same time would produce a sound energy equal only to the energy required to operate an ordinary incandescent lamp. Hearing is possible only because of the remarkable sensitivity of the ear.

Resonance

When someone drops a wrench on a concrete floor, you are not likely to mistake its sound for that of a baseball bat. This is because both objects vibrate at characteristic frequencies when struck. Any object composed of an elastic material will vibrate at its own special frequency when disturbed. This frequency depends on factors such as the elasticity and shape of the object. We express this fact when we speak of the body's *natural frequency*.

Resonance occurs when successive impulses are applied to a vibrating object in time with its natural frequency. The result of resonance is increased amplitude. A common experience illustrating resonance is pushing a swing. As a child you probably learned how to make someone on a swing move back and forth in a greater and greater arc. This didn't require strength nearly as much as a sense of timing—even small pushes, if delivered in rhythm with the frequency of the swinging motion, ultimately produced a large amplitude. Similarly, a tuning fork adjusted to the same frequency as a second fork will be set in vibration by the sound waves from the second fork even when twenty or thirty feet away. When a series of sound waves

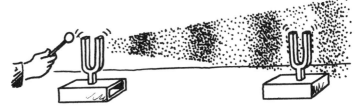

Fig. 18.3   Resonance.

impinges on the fork, each condensation gives the fork prong a tiny push. Since these pushes correspond to the natural frequency of the fork, they will successively increase the amplitude of vibration. This is because the pushes are repeatedly in the same direction as the instantaneous motion of the fork—they act in the same way as a child's pushes on a swing. This is true of the matched-frequency tuning forks shown in Figure 18.3 and is true for all elastic bodies. Submultiples ($\frac{1}{2}$, $\frac{1}{3}$, $\frac{1}{4}$, etc.) of the natural frequency will also produce resonance.

When any elastic object is struck with a sound wave of the same frequency, the succession of tiny pushes of air will set the object into resonance. Sometimes the amplitudes that result can be disastrous as can be seen from Figure 18.4.

Interphoto

Associated Press

Fig. 18.4   In November, 1940, four months after being completed, the Tacoma Narrows Bridge in the state of Washington was destroyed by wind-generated resonance. The mild gale produced a fluctuating force in resonance with the natural frequency of the bridge, steadily increasing the amplitude until destruction.

Forced Vibrations   If we strike an unmounted tuning fork, the sound from it may be rather faint. If we hold the same fork against a table and strike it with the same force, the sound is intensified. This is because the table is made to vibrate, and with its larger surface it will set more air into motion. In this exercise it is not necessary to have a tuning fork of a certain frequency. The table will be set into vibration by a fork of any frequency. This is not a case of impressing a frequency on the table which is the same as its natural frequency. This is not a case of resonance, but one of *forced vibration*. The vibration of a factory floor caused by the running of heavy machinery is an example of forced vibration. A more pleasing example is given by the sounding boards of stringed instruments.

Interference   If two stones are dropped into the water at the same time, the resulting two sets of waves cross each other producing what is called an *interference pattern*. Within the pattern, wave effects may be increased, decreased, or neutralized. When the crest of one wave coincides with the crest of another, their individual effects add together, and increased amplitude results. This is called *constructive interference*. When the crest of one wave coincides with the trough of another, their individual effects are reduced. This is called *destructive interference*. Figure 18.5 shows the interference pattern of identical water waves. You can see the regions where a crest of one wave overlaps the trough of another, producing a region of zero amplitude. At points along these regions the waves arrive "out of step." We say they are out of *phase* with one another.

Fig. 18.5   Two sets of overlapping water waves interfere. (From *Physics*, Physical Science Study Committee, Boston, Heath, 1965.)

Interference is characteristic of all wave motion whether it be water waves, light waves, or sound waves. It is characteristic of both transverse and longitudinal waves. Figure 18.6 shows the effects of superimposing identical waves when they are in phase with each other, and when they are out of phase with each other.

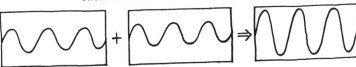

The superposition of two identical transverse waves in phase produces a wave of increased amplitude.

The superposition of two identical longitudinal waves in phase produces a wave of increased intensity.

Two identical transverse waves that are out of phase destroy each other when they are superimposed.

Two identical longitudinal waves that are out of phase destroy each other when they are superimposed.

Fig. 18.6 Constructive and destructive interference.

An interesting case of interference of sound is illustrated in Figure 18.7. If you are at equal distance from two sound speakers which both emit an identical unvarying tone, the

Fig. 18.7 (a) Waves of sound constructively interfere (condensation overlaps condensation) when the distances from the speakers to the listener are the same. (b) Destructive interference (condensation overlaps rarefaction) occurs when one speaker is farther from the listener than the other by a distance of a half wavelength (or $\frac{3}{2}$, $\frac{5}{2}$, etc.).

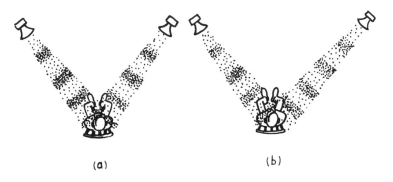

(a)   (b)

intensity of sound you receive is increased, for the condensations and rarefactions from each speaker arrive in phase. If you move to the side, however, so that the paths from the speakers to you differ by a half wavelength, then the rarefactions from one speaker will be filled in with the condensations from the other speaker producing destructive interference. If the region were devoid of any reflecting surfaces, little or no sound would be heard.

Beats

When two tones of slightly different frequencies are sounded together, a fluctuation in the loudness of the combined sounds is heard; the sound is loud, then faint, then loud, then faint, and so on. This periodic variation in the loudness of the sound is called *beats*, and is due to interference. Suppose, for example, the sources of interfering sounds are two tuning forks, each of a slightly different frequency. Because one fork vibrates faster than the other, the forks will get in step, then out, then in again, and so on. When the combined waves reaching our ears are in step, say when a condensation from one fork reaches us at the same time as a condensation from the other fork, the resulting sound is a maximum. A moment later, when the forks are out of step, a condensation from one fork will be met with a rarefaction from the other, resulting in a minimum. The sound reaching our ears will throb between maximum and minimum loudness, producing a vibrato effect.

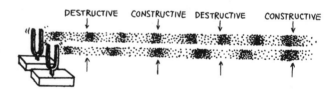

Fig. 18.8 The interference of two sound waves having different frequencies produces beats.

We can understand beats by considering the analogous case of two people with different strides walking together. At one moment they will be in step, a little later out of step, then in again and so forth. Imagine that one person, perhaps with shorter legs, takes exactly 72 steps in one minute while the taller person takes 70 steps. The shorter person then gains two steps per minute on the taller person. A little thought will show that they will momentarily be in step twice each minute. We can generalize this to the following: If two people with different strides walk together, the number of times they are in step each minute is equal to the difference in the frequencies of the steps. We may apply this to two tuning forks. If one makes 256 vibrations each second and the other 254, they will be in step twice each second, and 2 beats will be heard each second. If one fork gives 256 and the other 260 vibrations per second, they will produce 4 beats each second.

Beats are used in tuning the notes of any two sources to the same frequency. For example, if two piano strings differ in frequency they will produce beats when sounded together. When no beats are heard, the frequencies are matched.

The familiar vibrato effect of organ pipes is actually an example of beats. Two pipes tuned to different frequencies are used for each "single" note.

Summary of Terms

Reverberation. Re-echoed sound.

Resonance. The setting up of vibrations in a body at its natural vibration frequency by a vibrating force or wave having the same (or submultiple) frequency.

Forced vibration. The setting up of vibrations in a body, at frequencies other than the body's natural vibrating frequency, by a vibrating force.

Interference. The superposition of different sets of waves that produces mutual reinforcement in some places, and cancellation in others.

Beats. A series of alternate reinforcements and cancellations produced by the interference of two sets of superimposed waves of different frequencies; heard as a throbbing effect in sound waves.

Questions

1. If the speed of sound were frequency dependent, how would distant music sound?

2. Why does sound travel faster in warm air?

3. Why does sound travel faster in moist air? (*Hint*: At the same temperature, water vapor molecules have the same average kinetic energy as the heavier nitrogen and oxygen molecules in the air. How, then, do the average speeds of H_2O molecules compare to N_2 and O_2 molecules?)

4. Why can the tremor of the ground from a distant explosion be felt before the sound of the explosion can be heard?

5. How could you estimate the distance of a distant thunderstorm?

6. Apartment dwellers will testify that bass notes are most distinctly heard from music played in nearby apartments. What does this indicate about the natural frequency of the walls, floor, or ceiling?

7. Why will marchers at the end of a long parade following a band be out of step with marchers nearer the band?

8. Why do soldiers break step in marching over a bridge?

9. Why does a tuning fork eventually stop vibrating?

10. If the handle of a tuning fork is held solidly against a table, the sound from the tuning fork becomes louder. Why? How will this affect the length of time the fork keeps vibrating? Explain.

19
Musical Sounds

Noises and Musical Sounds

Most of the sounds we hear are noises. The barking of a dog, the slamming of a door, the impact of a falling object, and most of the sounds arising from the city streets are noises. Noise corresponds to an irregular vibration of the eardrum produced by the irregular vibration of some nearby object. If we make a diagram to indicate the pressure of the air on the eardrum as it varies with time, the graph corresponding to a noise might look like that shown in Figure 19.1a. The sound of music has a different character, having more or less sustained tones—or musical "notes." (Musical instruments may make noise as well!) The graph representing a musical sound has a shape that repeats itself over and over again, Figure 19.1b. Such graphs

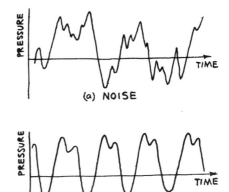

Fig. 19.1 Graphical representations of noise and music.

can be displayed on the screen of an oscilloscope, Figure 19.2. The electrical signal from a microphone is fed into the input terminal of this important instrument.

To the contemporary composer the dividing line between music and noise can be nonexistent. Some of the most radical composers feel that noise should be the basis for a totally new kind of music. The composer John Cage, for example, once wrote a piece for twenty-four radios played by twelve performers who changed the stations to the time of a stop watch.

257

The result was a strange montage of sound. This type of music is called *chance music*, or *aleatoric music*. It is not restricted to the traditional forms of structure, or to traditional sounds. The only limitations the composer has are his own imagination and perhaps the prejudices of his audience. Differentiating contemporary music from noise becomes a problem of aesthetics. Differentiating traditional music, however—that is, classical music and most types of pop music—from noise presents no real problem. A deaf person could distinguish between these with the use of an oscilloscope.

Musicians usually speak of a musical tone in terms of three characteristics—the loudness, the pitch, and the quality.

Loudness   The intensity of sound depends on pressure variations within the sound wave—it depends on the amplitude (more specifically, like any type wave, intensity is proportional to the square of the amplitude). Sound intensity is a purely objective and physical attribute of a wave, and can be measured by various acoustical instruments. This is shown in Figure 19.2. *Loudness*, on the other hand, is a physiological sensation—it depends on intensity, but in a complicated way. For example, if you turn a radio up until it seems about twice as loud as before, you would have to increase the power output, and therefore the intensity, by approximately eight times. The loudest sounds we can tolerate

Fig. 19.2   The author displays a sound signal on a cathode-ray oscilloscope.

The intensity and loudness of sound depends on the energy and pressure variations set up in the sound wave. Photo shows Joe Cocker at Woodstock.

have intensities a million million times greater than the faintest sounds. The difference in loudness, however, is much less than this amount.

The relative loudness of a sound heard by the ear is measured in *decibels*, a unit named after Alexander Graham Bell. Ordinary conversation in a room generates a noise level of about 60 to 70 decibels. A sound level higher than 120 decibels is highly discomforting.

Table 19.1 A table of approximate noise levels, in decibels, produced by various sources.

Source of Sound	Noise level (db)
Jet airplane, 100 feet away	140
Air raid siren, nearby	125
Rock music, amplified	120
Riveter	95
Busy street traffic	70
Conversation in home	65
Quiet radio in home	40
Whisper	20
Rustle of leaves	10
Threshold of hearing	0

Pitch

The pitch of a sound corresponds to frequency. We speak of the pitch of a sound in terms of its position in the musical scale. "Low" notes have a lower frequency of vibration than "high" notes. Suppose we mount a toothed wheel on an axis and spin it, Figure 19.3. If the wheel is rotating fast enough and a card is placed against it, the vibrating card will give out sound waves. If the wheel rotates at a constant speed, the pitch of the sound will not change. If the wheel is rotated faster, the pitch will rise; and if rotated slower, the pitch will fall. When the frequency rises, the pitch rises; when the frequency falls, the pitch falls.

A siren works on this principle. A metal disk has a row of holes regularly spaced near its edge. When the disk is rotated in front of a nozzle from which air is blown, a series of puffs of air passes through the disk. This gives a musical tone. The frequency of these successive puffs depends on the rotational speed of the disk, so the pitch of the tone changes as the speed of rotation of the disk is changed. If the holes in the disk were unequally spaced, the sound produced would have no pitch. Only a noise would be heard.

Fig. 19.3 The pitch of the sound emitted by the vibrating card is proportional to its vibrating frequency.

High-pitched sounds used in music are most often less than 4000 vibrations per second, but the average human ear can hear sounds up to 20,000 vibrations per second. Some people can hear tones of higher pitch than this, and most all dogs can. In general, the upper limit of hearing in people gets lower as they grow older. It is not a rare occurrence for a high-pitched sound to be inaudible to an older person and yet clearly heard by a younger one. So by the time you can really afford that high-fidelity music system, you probably won't be able to hear the difference.

Quality

When we hear a tone from a piano and a like-pitched tone from a clarinet, we have no trouble in telling the two tones apart. Each one has a characteristic sound. The difference in the two cases is called *quality*, or *timbre*. Very few musical sounds are *pure* tones; that is, very few contain only a single frequency or pitch. Most musical sounds are composed of a superposition of many frequencies. The lowest frequency, called the *fundamental*, determines the pitch of the note. The higher frequencies, called the *overtones* or *harmonics*, give the characteristic quality, Figure 19.4. The frequencies of the overtones are not haphazard, but are whole multiples of the lowest frequency.

Thus, if we strike middle C on the piano we get a tone having a pitch of about 262 vibrations per second, and at the same time we get, all blended together, tones having frequencies of two, three, four, five, etc., times the frequency of middle C.

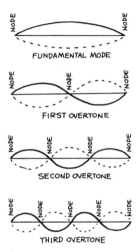

Fig. 19.4 Modes of vibration.

The number and relative loudness of the overtones produce the quality of sound associated with the piano. Sound from practically every musical instrument consists of a fundamental and overtones. Pure tones, those having only one frequency, can be produced electronically. The electronic Moog Synthesizer, for example, produces pure tones and mixtures of these to give a vast variety of musical sounds.

The quality of a tone is determined by the presence and relative intensity of the various overtones. The sound produced by a certain tone from the piano and by one of the same pitch from a clarinet, Figure 19.5, have different qualities to the ear because their overtones are not alike. Two tones of the same pitch which have different qualities either will have different overtones or the relative intensity of the overtones will be different.

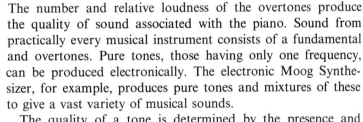

Fig. 19.5 Sounds from the piano and clarinet differ in quality.

Musical Instruments

Musical instruments can be grouped into one of two classes; those in which the sound is produced by vibrating strings, or those in which the sound is produced by vibrating air columns.

The piano, violin, cello, guitar, and sitar are stringed instruments, and the pitch of their tones depends on the vibrations of their strings. Their qualities depend on the overtones, and these depend on the way the strings are mounted, the character of the sounding boards, and the method of setting the strings into vibration. The organ, accordion, harmonica, trumpet, bugle, clarinet, flute, fife, piccolo, trombone, saxophone, and the like are all wind instruments, whose tones are produced by vibrating air columns. In the fife, piccolo, and flute, air is blown against the edge of a hole at one end of the instrument, and this fluttering stream of air sets an air column into vibration. In the trumpet, bugle, and trombone, the player's lips vibrate. In the reed organ, clarinet, saxophone, accordion, and harmonica, the stream of air sets a reed vibrating. In most wind instruments the pitch of the tone emitted is that of the fundamental of the air column or, sometimes, that of one of its overtones. The pitch is regulated by changing the length of the air column as with the trombone, or in some cases, such as the bugle, by emphasizing different overtones. In all cases of musical sounds, the quality depends on the number and relative loudness of the overtones. Often a very slight change in the construction of an instrument makes a great change in its quality.

Fourier Analysis

Did you ever look closely at the grooves in a phonograph record? And did you notice the variations in the width of the grooves—variations which cause the phonograph needle that rides in the groove to vibrate? And did you ever wonder how all the distinct vibrations made by the various pieces of an orchestra are captured into the single wave groove of the record? The sound of an oboe when captured by the groove of a phonograph record and displayed on an oscilloscope screen looks like Figure 19.7a. The high points on the wave correspond to the greatest amplitude of the electronic signal produced by the vibrating needle. They also correspond to the amplified signal which activates the loudspeaker of the sound system, and to the amplitude of air vibrating against the eardrum. Figure 19.7b shows the wave appearance of a clarinet, and Figure 19.7c shows the waveform when oboe and clarinet are sounded together.

The shape of the wave in Figure 19.7c is the net result of shapes (a) and (b) interfering with each other. If we know (a) and (b), it is a simple thing to create (c). But it is a far dif-

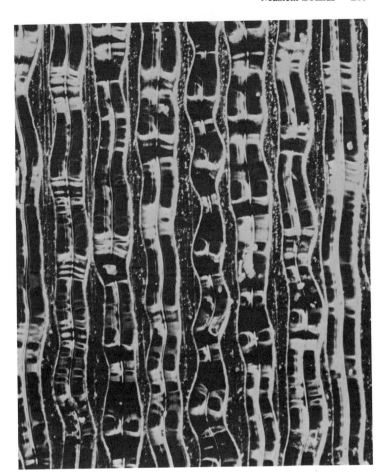

Fig. 19.6 A microscopic view of the grooves in a phonograph record.

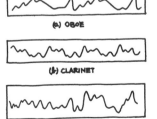

(a) OBOE

(b) CLARINET

(c) OBOE AND CLARINET TOGETHER

Fig. 19.7 Waveforms of (a) an oboe, (b) a clarinet, (c) the oboe and clarinet sounded together.

ferent problem to discern in (c) the shapes of (a) and (b) that make it up. Looking only at shape (c) we cannot unscramble the oboe from the clarinet.

But play the record on the phonograph, and our ears will at once know what instruments are being played, what notes they are playing, and what their relative loudness is. Our ears break the overall signal into its component parts automatically.

In 1822 the French mathematician Joseph Fourier discovered a mathematical regularity to the component parts of wave motion. He found that even the most complex wave motion could be broken down into simple sine waves. Recall from Chapter 17 that a sine wave is the simplest of waves, having a

Fig. 19.8 A sine wave.

single frequency, Figure 19.8. Fourier found that all rhythmic waves may be broken down into constituent sine waves of different amplitudes and frequencies. The mathematical operation for doing this is called *Fourier analysis*. We will not explain the mathematics here, but simply point out that by such analysis one can find the pure sine tones that compose the tone of, say, a violin. When these pure tones are sounded together, as by striking a number of tuning forks, or by selecting the proper keys on an electric organ, they combine to give the tone of the violin. The lowest-frequency sine wave is the fundamental and determines the pitch of the note. The higher-frequency sine waves are the overtones that give the characteristic quality. Thus the waveform of any musical sound is no more than a sum of simple sine waves.

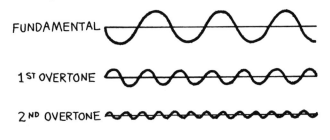

FUNDAMENTAL

1ˢᵀ OVERTONE

2ᴺᴰ OVERTONE

Fig. 19.9 The fundamental and its harmonics combine to produce a composite wave.

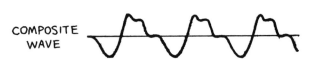

COMPOSITE WAVE

Since the waveform of music is a multitude of various sine waves, to duplicate sound accurately by radio, record player, or tape recorder, we should have as large a range of frequencies as possible. For example, the notes of a piano keyboard range in the hundreds of cycles per second, but to duplicate the music of a piano composition accurately, the sound system must have a range of frequencies into the thousands of cycles per second. The greater the range of the frequencies of an electrical sound system, the closer the music output approximates the original sound—hence the wide range of frequencies in a high-fidelity sound system.

Our ear performs a sort of Fourier analysis automatically. It sorts the complex jumble of air pulsations reaching our ear into pure notes. And we recombine various combinations of these pure notes when we listen. What combinations of notes we have learned to focus our attention to determines what we hear when we listen to a concert. We can direct our attention to the sounds of the various instruments, and discern the faintest notes from the loudest—we can delight in the intricate interplay of instruments, and still detect the extraneous noises of others around us. This is a most incredible feat.

Summary of Terms

Pitch. The "highness" or "lowness" of a tone, as on a musical scale, which is governed by frequency. A high-frequency vibrating source produces a sound of high pitch; a low-frequency vibrating source produces a sound of low pitch.

Overtones. Tones produced by vibrations which are multiples of the lowest or fundamental vibrating frequency.

Quality. The characteristic *timbre* of a musical sound, governed by the number and relative intensities of the overtones.

Fourier analysis. A mathematical method that will resolve any waveform into a series of simple sine waves.

Questions

1. How are different notes on a musical scale produced by one string?

2. The amplitude of a transverse wave in a stretched string is the maximum displacement of the string from its equilibrium position. What does the amplitude of a longitudinal sound wave in air correspond to?

3. Why do identical notes plucked on a banjo and on a guitar have distinctly different sounds?

4. When a person talks after inhaling helium gas, the voice is high pitched. This is principally because the helium gas molecules move faster past the vocal chords than molecules of air. Why do helium molecules move faster?

5. A high-fidelity sound system may have a frequency range that extends beyond the range of human hearing. Of what use is this extended range?

20

Shock Waves and the Sonic Boom

When an object travels with a speed greater than the speed of sound in that medium, the speed of the object is said to be *supersonic*. Any projectile, such as a bullet or an airplane, moving at supersonic speeds will generate a shock wave and produce a sonic boom. To understand how sonic booms are produced, we will first consider how similar "booms" result in the case of water waves.

The Doppler Effect

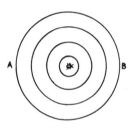

Fig. 20.1 Water waves made by a stationary bug jiggling in still water.

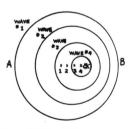

Fig. 20.2 Water waves made by a bug swimming in still water.

A pattern of water waves produced by a bug jiggling his legs and bobbing up and down in still water is shown in Figure 20.1. The bug is not going anywhere, but is merely treading water in a fixed position. Note that the waves are concentric circles, the larger circles being those produced first. The circles represent wave crests and travel at a constant speed. The circles are actually expanding, so we could consider that the figure is a "snapshot" of the moving waves. If the bug bobs in the water at a constant frequency, the distance between wave crests (the wavelength) is the same for all successive waves. Waves would encounter point A as frequently as they would point B. That is, the frequency of wave motion is the same at points A and B, or anywhere in the vicinity of the bobbing bug. And the wave frequency is the same as the bobbing frequency of the bug.

Suppose that the bug moves across the water at a speed less than the wave velocity. He in effect chases the waves he has produced. The wave pattern is distorted as shown in Figure 20.2. The waves are no longer concentric. Wave 1 was produced "longest ago" when the bug was in position 1; wave 2 was produced when the bug was in position 2, and so forth. An interesting thing to note here is that even though the bug maintains the same bobbing frequency as before in Figure 20.1, an observer at point B would encounter a *higher* frequency. This is because each successive wave has a shorter distance to travel and therefore arrives at point B more frequently than

266

would be the case if the bug were not moving toward point *B*. An observer at *A* encounters a *lower* frequency because the time between wave-crest arrivals is increased owing to the longer distance each successive wave must travel. The waves arrive less frequently, which is to say, at a lower frequency. This change in frequency due to the motion of the source (or receiver) is called the *Doppler effect*.

Water waves spread over the flat surface of the water. Sound waves, on the other hand, travel in all directions like an expanding balloon. Just as circular waves are closer together in front of the swimming bug, spherical sound waves ahead of a moving sound source are closer together and encounter a listener more frequently. The higher-frequency sound is perceived by a listener as a higher pitch. That is, as a higher "note as on a musical scale." A lower frequency is perceived as a lower pitch, or lower tone. The Doppler effect is evident to a listener standing by the side of a high-speed highway. He hears a higher-pitch sound from cars approaching and a lower-pitch sound when they recede.

The Wave Barrier

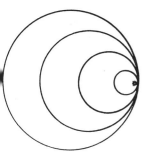

Fig. 20.3 Wave pattern made by a bug swimming as fast as the wave velocity.

Suppose the bug swims as fast as the wave velocity. Then he "keeps up" with the waves he produces. Instead of the waves moving ahead of him, they pile up or superimpose on one another directly in front of him, Figure 20.3. The bug encounters a "wave barrier." Considerable effort is required for the bug to swim over this barrier before he can swim faster than the wave velocity. An airplane traveling at the speed of sound similarly encounters a barrier of superimposed waves—wave upon wave of sound producing a barrier of compressed air along the leading edges of the aircraft. Considerable thrust is required for the aircraft to push through this barrier. But once through, no barrier exists to interrupt further acceleration. Or once the bug gets over his wave barrier, the water in front of him is smooth and undisturbed.

The Bow Wave

When the bug swims faster than the wave velocity, he produces a wave pattern as shown in Figure 20.4. He outraces the waves he produces which seem to be dragging behind him. But most important, they overlap where the X's are shown. When one wave crest overlaps another wave crest, a greater wave crest is produced. Only a few waves are shown in the figure and therefore only a few positions of overlapping waves are indicated. If more waves were indicated, there would be a

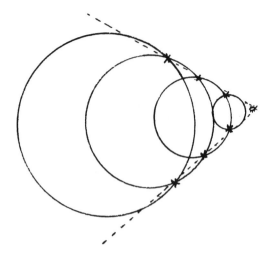

Fig. 20.4 Wave pattern made by a bug swimming faster than wave velocity.

greater number of X's. In practice the bug produces many waves; so many that the X's form a solid V-shape called a *bow wave*. The familiar bow wave generated by a speedboat knifing through the water is actually the superposition of many circular waves!

Figure 20.5 summarizes some wave patterns made by sources of various velocities. Note that after the velocity of the wave source exceeds the wave velocity, increased velocity produces a narrower V-shape.

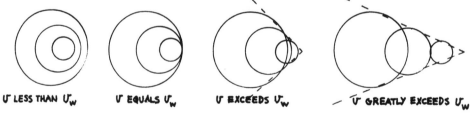

U LESS THAN U_w U EQUALS U_w U EXCEEDS U_w U GREATLY EXCEEDS U_w

Fig. 20.5 Summary of wave patterns.

The Shock Wave   Just as overlapping circular waves form a "V," overlapping spherical waves produced by a supersonic aircraft form a cone. And just as the bow wave of a speedboat spreads until it reaches the shore of a lake, the conical wake generated by a supersonic aircraft grows in size until it reaches the ground, Figure 20.6. This cone of sound is called a *shock wave*. It is a thin conical shell of compressed air which is "dragged" behind the aircraft just as a bow wave of water is "dragged" behind a

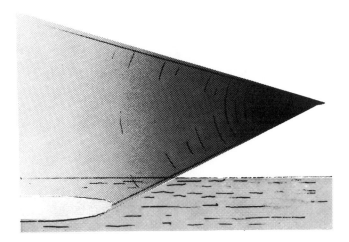

Fig. 20.6   A shock wave.

swimming bug or speeding boat. Suppose you were floating in tranquil water and a speedboat happened by. After the boat passed, its bow wave would soon reach you. You might describe your dousing as being hit by a "water boom." In the same way, when the shock wave of a supersonic aircraft is incident upon a listener, he hears a sharp crack—which we call the *sonic boom.*

The Sonic Boom

The sound reaching our ears produced by a slower moving or subsonic aircraft is encountered one wave at a time and is perceived as a continuous tone. Encountering a shock wave, however, is receiving many sound waves in a single burst. The sudden increase in pressure is much the same in effect as the sudden expansion of air produced by an explosion. Both processes direct a burst of high-pressure air to the listener. Pressure from an explosion results from rapidly expanding air, while for the sonic boom the pressure results from the superposition of many waves. The ear is hard put to tell the difference between the two!

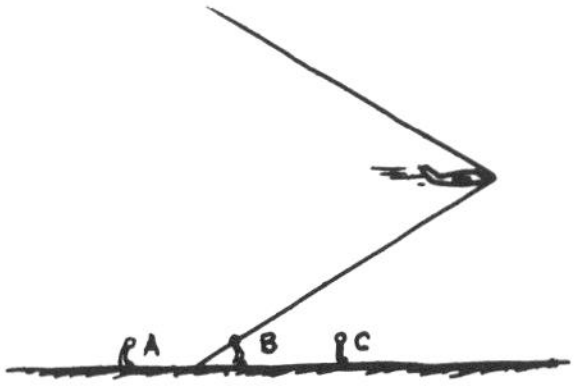

A common misconception is that sonic booms are produced *when* an aircraft breaks through the sound barrier—that is, just as the aircraft surpasses the speed of sound. This would be equivalent to saying that a boat produces a bow wave *when* it overtakes its own waves. This is not so. The fact is that a shock wave and its resulting sonic boom are "dragged" continuously behind an aircraft traveling *faster* than sound, just as a bow wave is dragged continuously behind a speedboat. In Figure 20.7, listener *B* is in the process of hearing a sonic boom, while

Fig. 20.7 The shock wave has already encountered listener *A*, is now encountering listener *B*, and will very soon encounter listener *C*.

listener A has already heard it. Listener C will hear it shortly
The aircraft generating this shock wave may have broken
through the sound barrier hours ago!

More on Shock Waves

Shock waves are often visible to the naked eye. Since a shock
wave is a conical shell of overlapping condensations of sound,
the density of air in this region is higher than the density of
surrounding air. The outline of the cone is visible because light
is distorted when passing through the dense air. Such distortion
of light is commonly evident above a hot surface. In such cases
we say that we see "heat waves," which are actually distortions
of light traveling through air of different densities. Figure 20.8
shows a photograph of a shock wave traveling with a bullet.

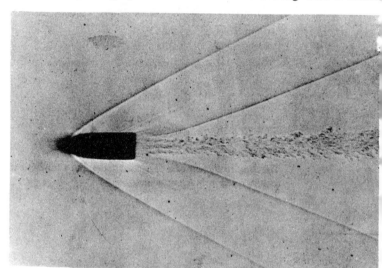

Fig. 20.8 Photograph of
a shock wave produced by
a bullet.

Note that there are actually two shock waves. The outer wave
is the superposition of the condensed regions of sound waves
while the inner wave is the superposition of the rarefied regions
of sound waves. In the analogous case of water waves, the outer
cone corresponds to the superposition of wave crests and the
inner cone corresponds to the superposition of wave troughs.
The outer wave exceeds atmospheric pressure and the inner
wave is less than atmospheric pressure. With a sonic boom,
there is first a rapid increase of pressure, then a slow decrease
to below atmospheric pressure, and finally a quick return to
normal. The usual measure of the boom's intensity is the peak
overpressure of the outer cone—how much the air pressure

generated by the sonic boom rises above the normal atmospheric pressure.

Peak overpressure of the boom is measured in pounds per square foot (psf). A boom produced by a small fighter plane (F-104) at a few thousand feet altitude may measure only 1 psf. Flying the plane at lower altitudes would make the intensity of the boom greater. In general, a sonic boom is louder when the aircraft is larger, when the craft flies closer to the ground, and when it passes directly overhead. The weather, the wind, and the conditions of the atmosphere also influence sonic-boom intensity, at times focusing the wave and leading to abnormally large booms.

Supersonic aircraft are rated by Mach numbers (rhymes with "sock"). Mach number is the ratio of the speed of motion to the speed of sound in air. The term is named after the Austrian physicist and philosopher Ernst Mach (1838–1916). An aircraft traveling at the speed of sound is traveling at "Mach 1.0"; at twice the speed of sound, "Mach 2.0," and so on. A subsonic aircraft would have a Mach number less than 1.

The speed of a supersonic aircraft can be determined from the shape of the shock wave as follows. Consider any point along the shock wave, say point *S* in Figure 20.9. Sound at point *S* originated some time ago when the aircraft was at point *O*. During the time spent for the sphere of sound to

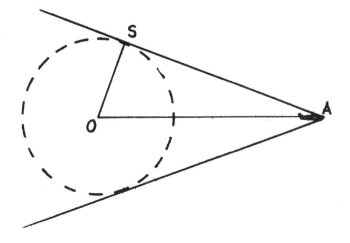

Fig. 20.9 The aircraft at *A* has traveled three times as far from point *O* as sound *S* has in the same time. The aircraft therefore has traveled at three times the speed of sound, Mach 3.

expand from *O* to *S*, the aircraft has traveled from *O* to *A*. If the aircraft has traveled three times the distance sound has traveled in the same time, as is the case in the figure, then it is traveling at three times the speed of sound, Mach 3. We can say,

$$\text{Mach number} = \frac{\text{distance aircraft travels, } O \rightarrow A}{\text{distance sound travels, } O \rightarrow S}$$

This ratio will be the same for any position of S along the wave edge.

It is not necessary that the moving object emit sound to produce shock waves. Once an object is moving faster than the speed of sound, it will *make* sound. A bullet passing overhead produces a cracking sound, which is a small sonic boom. If the bullet were larger and disturbed more air in its path, the crack would be more boomlike. When the lion tamer cracks his circus whip, the cracking sound is actually a sonic boom produced by the tip of the whip which travels faster than the speed of sound! Both the bullet and whip are not in themselves sound sources; but when traveling at supersonic speeds, they produce their own sound as waves of air are generated to the sides of the moving objects.

Shock waves also occur in the case of light. At first one might think that nothing can move faster than the speed of light. This is true for light in a vacuum, but the speed of light in a transparent medium is less than the speed of light in a vacuum. In water, for example, light travels at only 75 percent its speed in a vacuum. Why this is so will be discussed in Chapter 28. A charged particle such as an electron can travel faster in water than the speed of light *in water*. The particle produces a cone of bluish light. By measuring the angle of the cone, the speed of the particle can be determined, a useful technique in high-energy nuclear research and cosmic-ray research. This light is called Cerenkov radiation.

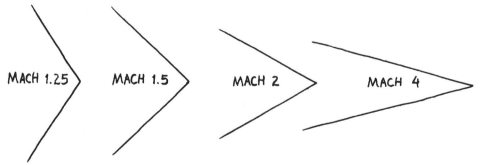

Fig. 20.10   Shock waves for various speeds.

Summary of Terms

Doppler effect. The change in frequency or pitch of sound waves, heard when the source of sound and/or the listener are moving toward or away from each other.

Bow wave. The V-shaped wave made by an object moving across a liquid surface at a speed greater than the wave velocity.

Shock wave. The cone-shaped wave made by an object moving at supersonic speed through a fluid.

Sonic boom. The loud sound resulting from the incidence of a shock wave.

Mach number. The ratio of the speed of an object to the speed of sound; for example, an aircraft traveling at the speed of sound is rated Mach 1.0; at twice the speed of sound, Mach 2.0, etc.

Suggested Reading

Green, David M., "Sonic Booms," *Psychology Today*, November, 1968.
Wilson, Herbert A., Jr., "Sonic Boom," *Scientific American*, January, 1962.

Questions

1. Does the pitch of a factory whistle vary on a windy day?

2. Does a sonic boom occur at the moment when an aircraft exceeds the speed of sound? Explain.

3. Will a Mach 0.5 aircraft produce a sonic boom? Explain.

4. Draw a shock wave for a Mach 5.0 aircraft, showing the proper angle.

5. As an example of sonic-boom damage, one of the scenic old Indian cliff dwellings in Mesa Verde National Park now lies under 80 tons of granite rubble as a result of a supersonic military jet flying overhead. Some of the purveyors of commercial supersonic aircraft argue, however, that such unfortunate incidents are the cost of progress. Discuss this in light of technological progress as discussed in Chapter 1.

Photo by Madison Devlin

PART 5

Electricity and Magnetism

21
Electricity at Rest

Electrical Forces

Consider a universal force like gravitation which varies inversely as the square of the distance, but which is about a *billion-billion-billion-billion* times stronger. If there were such a force, and if it were attractive like gravity, the universe would be pulled together into a tight sphere with all the matter in the universe pulled as close together as possible. But suppose this force were a repelling force, where every particle repelled every other particle. What then? The universe would be an ever-expanding gaseous cloud. Suppose, however, that the universe consisted of both attractive and repulsive particles, say positives and negatives. Suppose that positives repelled positives, but attracted negatives; and negatives repelled negatives, but attracted positives. Like kinds repel and unlike kinds attract. And suppose that there were equal numbers of each. What would the universe be like? The answer is simple: It would be like the one we are living in. For there is such a force. We call it the electrical force.

Clusters of positives and negatives have been pulled together by the enormous attraction of the electrical force. The result is that the huge forces have balanced themselves out almost perfectly by forming tight, fine mixtures of evenly mixed bunches of positives and negatives. Furthermore, between two separate bunches of such mixtures, there is practically no electrical attraction or repulsion at all. Any electrical forces between the earth and moon, for example, have been balanced out. In this way the much weaker gravitational force, which only attracts, is the predominant force between these two bodies.

The positives and negatives refer to the protons and electrons of which all matter is made. Atoms, molecules, and the matter they make up are mixtures of positive protons and negative electrons which are attracting and repelling with this huge force. The balance between attraction and repulsion is so perfect that when we stand near someone else we don't feel any force at all. If there were even a little bit of unbalance we would know it. If a person stood at arm's length from someone and each had *1 percent* more electrons than protons, the repelling force would be incredible. How great? Enough to lift the Golden

Gate Bridge? Enough to lift Mount Everest? The repulsion force would be much greater—it would be enough to lift a "weight" equal to that of the entire world!

It is electrical forces that hold atoms together, and the chemical forces that hold molecules together are really electrical forces acting in small regions where the balance of charge is not perfect. Recall from our study of atoms that:

1. Every atom is composed of a positively charged nucleus, around which is distributed a number of negatively charged electrons.

2. The electrons of all atoms are identical—that is, each has the same quantity of negative charge and the same mass.

3. The nucleus is composed of protons and neutrons. (The common form of hydrogen which has no neutrons is the only exception.) Protons are almost 2000 times more massive than electrons, but carry an amount of positive charge equal to the negative charge of the electron. Neutrons are slightly more massive than protons and have no net charge.

4. All normal atoms have exactly as many electrons surrounding the nucleus as there are protons within the nucleus. Thus a normal atom has no net charge.

Why don't protons pull the oppositely charged electrons into the nucleus? Fifty years ago the answer offered was that the electrons are not pulled into the nucleus by electrical force for the same reason the earth is not pulled into the sun by gravitational force—the electrons are held in orbit by the pull of the protons. This oversimplified explanation serves as a starter for understanding the electrical nature of the atom, but must be modified upon further study. The answer today has to do with the wave nature of matter, the quantum effects, which we will discuss in Chapter 32.

Why is it that the protons in the nucleus don't fly apart? What holds the nucleus together? The answer is that in addition to electrical forces in the nucleus, there are even greater non-electrical nuclear forces which are able to hold the protons together in spite of the electrical repulsion. The nuclear forces, however, have a short range—they diminish with distance much more rapidly than the inverse-square electrical forces—which has an important consequence: If a nucleus has too many protons in it, it gets too big, and it will not stay together. This is because some of the protons in a big nucleus are far apart—those on opposite sides of the nucleus, for example.

Consider uranium with 92 protons. The short-range nuclear forces act mainly between each proton (or neutron) and its nearest neighbor, while the electrical forces act over larger distances. The electrical force of repulsion between protons close together is overpowered by the huge attractive nuclear force. The electrical force of repulsion between protons far apart, however, may not be overpowered by the attractive nuclear force, which is weak for larger distances. For protons that are far apart, the electrical force of repulsion becomes a significant factor. The more protons in a nucleus, the stronger is the electrical repulsion, until, as in the case of uranium, the balance is so delicate that the nucleus is almost ready to fly apart from the repulsive electrical force. If such a nucleus is just "tapped" lightly (as can be done by sending in a slow neutron), it may break into two pieces, each with a positive charge, and these pieces fly apart by electrical repulsion. The energy that is liberated is the energy of the atomic bomb. This energy is usually called "nuclear" energy, but it is primarily "electrical" energy released when electrical forces have overcome the attractive nuclear forces. We will discuss nuclear forces further in Chapter 34.

We have said that the electrical force, like gravitational force, decreases inversely as the square of the distance between charges. This relationship is called *Coulomb's Law*. It states that the force between two charges varies directly as the product of the charges and inversely as the square of the separation. Coulomb's Law can be expressed as

$$F \sim \frac{qq'}{d^2}$$

where q represents the quantity of charge of one particle, and q' the quantity of charge* of the other particle, and d is the distance between them. The force between like charges is repulsive, and that between unlike charges is attractive. Notice the similarity to Newton's law of gravitation.† In the eighteenth century, Charles Coulomb correctly guessed that the relationship between electrical forces and the charges was similar to the relationship between gravitational forces and mass. He verified his hunch experimentally.

---

*The common unit of charge is called the *coulomb*. It is the charge associated with six and a quarter billion-billion electrons.

†Recall Newton's law of gravity is $F \sim mm'/d^2$.

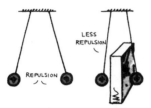

Fig. 21.1 The electrical force between charged objects diminishes when any material is placed between the objects.

The obvious difference between gravitational and electrical forces is that where gravity only attracts, electrical forces may be either attractive or repulsive. Another important difference is that in the case of electricity the force depends on the medium between the charges. All material media placed between the charges produces a *shielding* effect and decreases the force, Figure 21.1. The amount of shielding is characteristic of the medium between the charges. Air, for example, diminishes the force between two charges slightly more than a vacuum, while oil placed between the charges diminishes the force by about one-eightieth. Metal will completely shield the electrical forces, Figure 21.2.

Fig. 21.2 The car is struck by "lightning," but the man inside is shielded from the electricity. Electrons from the lightning bolt are mutually repelled to the outer metal surface of the car. They then arc to the ground near the front end. (Courtesy of Westinghouse Electric Corp.)

The electrical forces between bodies are the results of a very slight disturbance in the normally perfect balance of protons and electrons. Electrical forces hold atoms and molecules together, prevent the dissolution of solid matter, and provide the source of all chemical energy.

Conductors and Insulators

All substances can be arranged in order of their ability to conduct electrical charges. Those at the top of the list are referred to as *conductors* and those at the bottom as *insulators*. But the ends of the list are very far apart. Nearly all metals are relatively good conductors, and most nonmetals are poor ones. The conductivity of a metal, for example, can be more than a billion-billion times greater than the conductivity of an insulator such as glass. In a power line, for example, charge flows much more easily through hundreds of miles of metal wire than through the few inches of insulating material separating the wire from its supporting tower. In a common appliance cord in the home, charge moves through several feet of wire to the appliance, then through the electrical network in the appliance, and then back through the other wire in preference to flowing across from one wire to the other through a small fraction of an inch of rubber insulation.

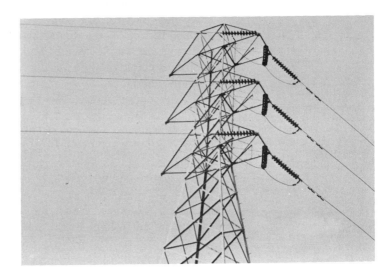

Fig. 21.3 It is easier for electricity to flow through hundreds of miles of metal wire than through a few inches of insulating material. (Photo by Johnny Wong.)

Whether a substance is classified a conductor or insulator depends on the interatomic bonding and on how tightly the atoms of a substance hold their electrons. Each atom in a metal, for example, contributes one or more electrons to a general sea of electrons attached to no particular atom. These *conduction electrons* are free to wander long distances throughout the material. On the other hand, all the electrons in an insulating material are attached to particular atoms. Small differences in the bonding between atoms account for very large differences in conductivities.

Semiconductors

The interatomic bondings in some materials, such as germanium and silicon, are intermediate between ionic and metallic. These materials are called *semiconductors*. They are good insulators in their pure crystalline form, but increase tremendously in conductivity when even one atom in ten million is replaced with an impurity which adds or removes an electron from the crystal structure. In an "*n*-type" semiconductor (*n* for negative), added electrons are easily made to jump from atom to atom and carry negative charge through the crystals. In "*p*-type" semiconductors (*p* for positive) where the added impurities remove electrons, "holes" move through the crystal, effectively carrying positive charge. Transistors, used for control and amplification of electric signals in radios and other devices, are composed of both *n*-type and *p*-type semiconductors. These tiny solids require very little power and in normal use last indefinitely. Solid-state circuitry is far superior to circuits employing the less dependable and power-consuming vacuum tubes.

A semiconductor can also be made to conduct by shining light of the proper color on it. A pure silicon plate is normally a good insulator, and any electrostatic charge built up on its surface will remain for extended periods in the dark. If the plate is exposed to light, however, the charge will leak away almost immediately. If a charged silicon plate is exposed to a pattern of light, such as the pattern of light and dark that makes up this page, the charge will leak away only from the areas exposed to light. If a black plastic powder were brushed across its surface, the powder would stick only to the charged areas—where the plate was not exposed to light. Now if a piece of paper were put over the plate and electric charge put on the back, the black plastic powder would be drawn to the paper to form the same pattern as, say, this page. If the paper were then heated to melt the plastic and fuse it to the paper, you might pay a dime for it and call it a Xerox copy.

Charging by Friction

We are all familiar with the electrical effects produced by friction, as when we stroke a cat's fur and hear the crackle of sparks that are produced, or comb our hair, especially in front of a mirror in a dark room so we can see as well as hear the sparks of electricity. Or when we scuff our shoes across a rug and then produce a spark when we reach for a door knob, or do the same when sliding across plastic seat covers in an automobile. In all these cases electrons are being transferred by the friction of contact from one material to another.

Although the innermost electrons in an atom are bound very tightly to the oppositely charged nucleus, the outermost electrons of many atoms are bound very loosely and can be easily dislodged. The force with which the outer electrons are held in the atom varies for different substances. The electrons are held more firmly in rubber than in fur, for example. Hence, when a rubber rod is rubbed by a piece of fur, electrons transfer from the fur to the rubber rod. The rubber therefore has an excess of electrons and is said to be negatively charged. The fur, in turn, has a deficiency of electrons and is said to be positively charged. If we rub a glass or plastic rod with silk, we find that the rod becomes positively charged. The silk has a greater affinity for electrons than the glass or plastic rod. Electrons are rubbed off the rod and onto the silk. We can say:

An object which has an imbalance of electrons and protons is electrically charged. If it has more electrons than protons, the object is said to be negatively charged. If it has fewer electrons than protons, then it is positively charged. Because no electrons are created or destroyed, but are simply transferred from one material to another, we say that charge is conserved.

Charging by Contact

Electrons can be transferred from one material to another by simply touching. A charged rod placed in contact with a neutral body, for example, will transfer charge to the neutral body. If the body is a good conductor, the charge will spread to all parts of its surface, for the like charges repel one another. If it is a poor conductor, it may be necessary to touch the rod to several points on the body in order to get a more or less uniform distribution of the charge. This method of charging is called *charging by contact.*

Charging by Induction   A suspended, positively charged rod is repelled by another positively charged rod, and attracted by a negatively charged rod, Figure 21.4. But how can a charged rod attract an uncharged or neutral object such as a bit of paper? And why is it that the paper will be attracted to both a positively and negatively charged rod? What happens is that as a charged rod is brought near the paper, the charges in the molecules making up the paper are redistributed. For example, if a positively

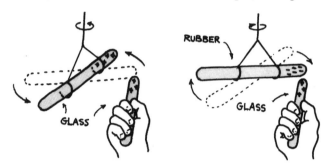

Fig. 21.4 Like charges repel and unlike charges attract.

charged rod is brought near the paper, it attracts the electrons in each paper molecule to the side of the molecule nearest the rod, Figure 21.5. No electrons have been added or removed. The paper is electrically neutral, but the surface layer nearest the charged rod contains the negative sides of molecules on

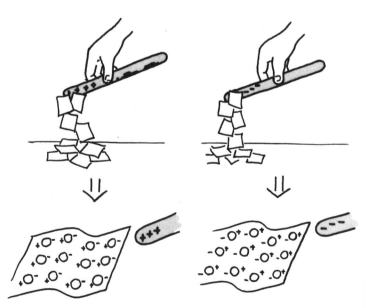

Fig. 21.5   In the presence of the charged rod, charges of the individual molecules in the paper are reoriented. As a result, the force of attraction is greater than the force of repulsion.

that surface, while the far surface contains the positive sides of molecules on that surface. The negative surface is closer to the charged rod than is the positive surface. Therefore the force of attraction is greater than the force of repulsion and the piece of paper is attracted toward the charged rod. If the rod is negatively charged, then the charges within the paper are oriented with the positive surface of the paper nearest the rod and negative surface farthest away, again resulting in an attraction between the paper and the rod.

The bits of paper are electrically neutral, but their charges have been redistributed. This redistribution of atomic and molecular charges is called *charge polarization*. This inducement of charge polarization has occurred without there being any contact between the rod and the paper. The surface of the paper has been *charged by induction*. When the charged rod is removed, the induced surface charge disappears. Sometimes a charged rod attracts a piece of paper in this way and the paper clings to the rod. Suddenly the paper flies off the rod. What happens in this case is that the paper touching the rod may acquire a charge by contact, where electrons on the rod repel one another and transfer onto the paper. The paper then has the same sign charge as the rod and is repelled.

When we rub an inflated balloon against our hair we charge the balloon by contact. Electrons are rubbed from our hair onto the balloon, which is then negatively charged. We find that the charged balloon easily sticks to the wall or any insulating surface. This is because the charged balloon induces an opposite charge on the surface of the wall. The molecules in the wall become polarized, like the pieces of paper in the previous example. If the balloon is negative, a layer of positive charge is induced in the wall, and both balloon and wall attract each other. Since both the wall and balloon are good insulators, very little charge transfers from the balloon to the wall.

Charging by induction takes place during thunderstorms. The bottoms of negatively charged clouds induce a positive charge on the surface of the earth beneath. Benjamin Franklin was the first to demonstrate this when he proved during his famous kite-flying experiment that lightning was an electrical phenomenon.* Lightning is an electrical discharge between

*In addition to being a great statesman, Benjamin Franklin was a first-rate scientist. He introduced the terms "positive" and "negative," as they relate to electricity, and established the "one fluid" theory of electricity. He contributed to an understanding of induction, grounding, and insulation.

the clouds and oppositely charged ground, or between oppositely charged clouds. Franklin also found that charge leaks off sharp points, and fashioned the first lightning rod. If the rod is placed above a structure and connected to the ground, charge induced by the clouds leaks off the rod and prevents an electrical discharge from occurring. If for any reason sufficient charge does not leak off the rod and lightning strikes anyway, it will be attracted to the rod and directed through the metal path to ground, thereby sparing the structure.

Electric Field

Electrical forces, like gravitational forces, act between bodies that are not in contact with each other. A conceptual way to describe such forces involves the concept of a force *field*. The properties of space surrounding any mass can be considered to be so altered that another mass introduced to this region will experience a force. The "alteration in space" caused by a mass is called its *gravitational field*. We can think of any other mass as interacting with the field and not directly with the mass producing it. For example, when an apple falls from a tree, it is interacting with the mass of the earth, but we can also think of the apple as interacting with the gravitational field of the earth. It is common to think of distant rockets and the like as interacting with gravitational fields rather than with the masses of the earth and other bodies responsible for the fields. Similarly, an electric charge produces an *electric field* around it that interacts with any other charges present.

We can pictorially represent fields with arrows. Fields have both magnitude and direction, so the arrows are vector representations of fields. In Figure 21.6 the vectors represent the gravitational field about the earth. The arrowheads point in the direction of force that an object in the region would experience. All the vectors point to the center of the earth because gravitational force pulls objects in that direction. The vectors farther away from the earth are shorter, showing that the pull on any object is less as it moves away from the earth.

Fig. 21.6 Two ways to represent the earth's gravitational field.

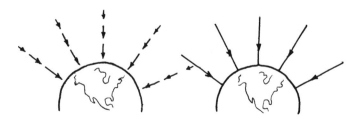

Ideally we could think of a vector drawn at every point in space. A more simplified representation of a field is simply lines in the direction of the vectors. Where the lines are farther apart, the field is weaker.

The electric field around a charge is very similar to the gravitational field around the earth, Figure 21.7. Like the gravitational field, the electric field has both magnitude and direction, and is a vector quantity. The arrows in any region represent the force that would be exerted on a positive charge if placed in that region. Again, continuous lines simplify the picture. The electric field lines point toward a negative charge, and away from a positive charge. This is because a positively charged sample placed in the field will be forced toward a negative charge and away from a positive charge.

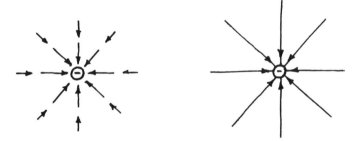

Fig. 21.7 Electric field representations of an electron.

It may seem that the field concept is an unnecessary construct at this point. But it is easier to visualize an electron beam interacting with the uniform field between two oppositely charged plates, as in a television picture tube, than to think

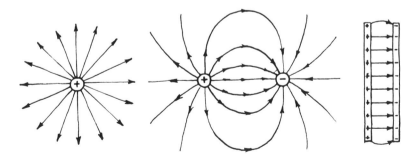

Fig. 21.8 Some electric field configurations. *Left:* field lines emanate from a positive charge; *middle:* field lines emanate from a positive charge and terminate on a negative charge; *right:* field lines are uniform between two equally and oppositely charged parallel plates.

of the electrons in the beam interacting with each charge on the plates. But more important, we will learn that the field itself is a storehouse of energy, and that energy can be transported over long distances in an electric field. Electric fields may be directed through and guided by metal wires or through empty space. We will discuss this further in the next chapter and again in Chapter 25 when we learn about electromagnetic radiation.

Electrical Potential

When we studied energy in Chapter 6, we learned that an object may have gravitational potential energy because of its position in a gravitational field. Similarly, a charged object can also have potential energy by virtue of its position in an electric field. Just as work is required to push a massive object against the gravitational field of the earth, work is required to push an electron against the electric field of a positively charged body. This work increases the electric potential energy of the electron. This potential energy will convert into kinetic energy if the electron is released and allowed to fall toward the positive charge, just as the gravitational potential energy of a raised object will be converted into kinetic energy if it is released in the gravitational field. The amount of energy a falling object can impart to the floor depends on its change in elevation—or the change in its potential energy as it moves from one position to another in the gravitational field. Likewise, the amount of energy an electric charge can deliver to a system depends on the change in its potential energy as it moves from one position to another in an electric field.

Much more useful than the electric potential energy of a charged body is the electric potential energy *per charge* on that body. This is a very important concept, and we call the electric potential energy per charge *electric potential*; or, more briefly,

$$\text{Electric potential} = \frac{\text{energy}}{\text{charge}}$$

The unit of measurement for electric potential is the *volt**— hence electric potential is often called *voltage*. Both names are common, so we will use the names electric potential and voltage interchangeably.

In a high-voltage power line, the charges making up the

---

*One volt is equal to one joule of energy per coulomb of charge.

current in the wire have been raised to high potential energies. In a 10,000-volt line, for example, each unit of charge making up the current carries 10,000 units of energy.

Electric potential differs from electric potential energy just as temperature differs from heat. Recall from our study of heat that we found it useful to distinguish between the energy of total molecular motion in a body and the average kinetic energy per single molecule. We distinguished between heat and temperature. Similarly, in the study of electricity we distinguish between the total electric potential energy of a body and the potential energy per single unit of charge. We distinguish between electric potential energy and electric potential or, equivalently, between electrical potential energy and voltage.

The Van de Graaff Generator

A common laboratory device for building up high voltages is the Van de Graaff generator. This is the lightning machine used by evil scientists in old science fiction movies. A simple model of the Van de Graaff generator is shown in Figure 21.9. A large hollow metal sphere is supported by a cylindrical insulating stand. A motor-driven silk or rubber belt inside the supporting stand carries charge gathered by friction of the belt against a glass cylinder below to the conducting sphere above.

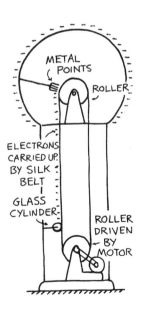

Fig. 21.9 A simple model of the Van de Graaff generator.

Electrons leak off the belt onto sharp metal points (tiny lightning rods) and are deposited to the inside of the sphere. The electrons mutually repel each other to the outer surface of the conducting sphere. Static charge always lies on the outside surface of any conductor. This leaves the inside uncharged and able to receive more electrons as they are brought up the belt, which in turn are continuously transferred to the outside surface of the sphere. In this way a giant charge builds up, establishing a high electric potential. Millions of volts are stored on the sphere.

The huge voltages generated by practical Van de Graaff generators are useful in producing X-rays for medical research. They are also useful in accelerating charged particles used as projectiles for penetrating the nuclei of atoms.

Fig. 21.10 A $5\frac{1}{2}$ million volt Van de Graaff generator in a sparkling demonstration. (Photo by Fritz Goro, Black Star.)

Summary of Terms

Coulomb's Law. The relationship between electric force, charge, and distance:

$$F \sim \frac{qq'}{d^2}$$

If the charges are alike in sign, the force is repelling; if the charges are unlike, the force is attractive.

Conductor. Any material through which charge easily flows when subject to an impressed electrical force.

Insulator. Any material through which charge resists flow when subject to an impressed electrical force.

Semiconductor. A normally insulating material such as crystalline silicon or germanium which becomes conducting when made with certain impurities or when energy is added.

Charging by contact. The transfer of charge from one body to another by physical contact between the bodies.

Charging by induction. The redistribution of charge in an object which is caused by the electrical influence of a charged body close by, but not in contact.

Electric field. The energetic region of space surrounding a charged body; about a charged point the field decreases with distance according to the inverse-square law, like the gravitational field. Between oppositely charged parallel plates the electric field is uniform. A charged object placed in the region of an electric field experiences a force.

Electric potential. The electrical potential energy per unit of charge, measured in volts, and often called "voltage,"

$$\text{Voltage} = \frac{\text{electrical energy}}{\text{unit of charge}}$$

Questions

1. We do not feel the gravitational forces between ourselves and the objects around us because these forces are extremely small. Electrical forces, in comparison, are extremely huge. Since we and the objects around us are composed of charged particles, why don't we feel electrical forces?

2. Why does touching a metal door knob often produce a spark after we have just walked across a rug?

3. At automobile toll-collecting stations a thin metal wire sticks up from the road and makes contact with cars before they reach the toll collector. What is the purpose of this wire?

4. Why is a good conductor of electricity also a good conductor of heat?

5. If you rub an inflated balloon against your hair and place it against a wooden door it will stick. Explain.

6. A gravitational field vector points toward the earth; an electric field vector points toward an electron. Why do electric field vectors point *away* from protons?

7. What is the difference between electric potential energy and electric potential?

8. Can we say that a body with twice the electric potential energy of another has twice the electric potential? Why or why not?

9. Can we say that a body with twice the electric potential of another has twice the electric potential energy? Why or why not?

10. Would you feel any electrical effects if you were inside the charged sphere of a Van de Graaff generator? Why not?

22

Current Electricity

Flow of Charge   When the ends of a conductor are placed between two bodies of different temperatures, heat is transmitted from the higher temperature to the lower temperature. Heat "flows" through the conductor when a difference in temperature exists across its ends. When both ends reach the same temperature, the "flow" of heat ceases. In a similar way, when two bodies of different electric potential are joined with an electrical conductor, charge flows from the higher potential to the lower potential. Charge flows when there is a *potential difference* across the ends of a conductor. This flow of charge persists until both bodies reach a common potential. When there is no potential difference, no flow of charge will occur. For example, if one end of a wire were connected to the ground and the other end placed in contact with the sphere of a Van de Graaff generator that has been charged to a high potential, a surge of charge would flow through the wire. The flow of charge would be brief, however, for the sphere would quickly reach a common potential with the ground.

To attain a sustained flow of charge in a conductor, some arrangement must be provided to maintain a difference in potential while charge flows from one end to the other. The situation is analogous to the flow of water from a higher reservoir to a lower one, Figure 22.1a. Water will flow in a pipe connecting the reservoirs only as long as a difference in water level exists. The flow of water in the pipe, like the flow of charge in the wire connecting the Van de Graaff generator and ground, will cease when the pressures at each end are equal. A continuous

Fig. 22.1 Water flows from the reservoir of higher pressure to the reservoir of lower pressure. (*a*) The flow will cease when the difference in pressure ceases. (*b*) Water continues to flow because a difference in pressure is maintained with the pump.

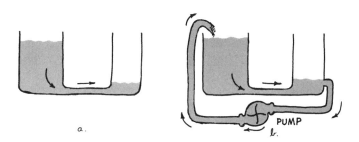

a.

PUMP
b.

flow is possible if the difference in water levels, and hence water pressures, is maintained with the use of a suitable pump, Figure 22.1b.

Electromotive Force and Current

There are many kinds of electric pumps, usually called "seats" of *electromotive force* (emf). If we charge a rubber rod by rubbing it with fur, we can develop a large difference in electrical potential between the rod and fur. Such a combination does not make a good electrical pump because when connected by a conductor the potentials equalize in a single brief surge of moving charges. Such a combination cannot maintain a sufficient flow of charge to be of practical importance. Chemical batteries or generators, on the other hand, are capable of maintaining a steady electrical flow. Any seat of emf such as a battery or generator is a source of energy. In chemical batteries, the disintegration of zinc or lead in acid results in a separation of electric charge, and the energy stored in the chemical bonds is converted into electrical energy.* Both batteries and generators convert their stores of energy into electrical energy by piling up negative charge on one of their terminals and positive charge on the other. The electrical potential energy stored in the oppositely charged battery or generator terminals provides the difference in potential, or voltage, responsible for the flow of the electrons in the circuit joining the terminals.

Electric current is simply the flow of electric charge. In solid conductors, it is the electrons that flow through the circuit, while in fluids, ions as well as electrons may comprise the flow of electrical charge. The *rate* of electrical flow is measured in *amperes*, or simply amps. An ampere is the rate of flow of one unit of charge per second.† In a wire carrying 5 amperes, for example, 5 units of charge pass any cross section in the wire each second. In a wire carrying 10 amperes, twice as many charges pass any cross section each second.††

---

*How this is done can be found in almost any chemistry text.

†The electrical charge of $6\frac{1}{4}$ billion-billion electrons is the standard unit of charge, called the *coulomb*. One coulomb of charge passing a point in one second is called an *ampere*.

††This may be accomplished by twice as many charges moving at the same speed as those in the 5-amp case, or by just as many charges moving twice as fast, or by some combination of the number of charges and their speed.

Electrical Resistance   A battery or generator of some kind is the prime mover and source of voltage in an electrical circuit. There is another equally important factor, however, controlling the rate at which charge flows—*resistance*. As the rate of water flow in a pipe depends upon the amount of pressure behind the water, it is also governed by the amount of resistance offered to the flow. Smooth-walled pipes, for example, offer less resistance than rough-walled ones. Pipes of small cross section offer greater resistance than pipes of large cross section, and long pipes offer greater resistance than short ones. These factors also

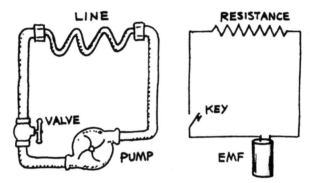

Fig. 22.2 Analogy between a simple hydraulic and an electrical circuit.

enter into electrical considerations. We have already discussed the fact that different substances conduct electricity differently. It is also a fact that the electrical resistance of a wire depends upon its thickness and length. Electrical resistance is less in thick wires. The longer the wire, of course, the greater the resistance. In addition, electrical resistance depends on temperature. The greater the jostling about of atoms within the conductor, the greater resistance the conductor offers to a flow of charge. For most conductors, increased temperature is accompanied by increased resistance.*

Ohm's Law   Voltage, current, and resistance are related by a statement called *Ohm's Law*. It states that the amount of current in a circuit is directly proportional to the voltage (emf) impressed

*Carbon is an interesting exception. At high temperatures extra electrons are shaken from the atom which increases electric current. Its resistance, in effect, is lowered with increasing temperature. This is the principal reason for its use in arc lamps.

across the circuit, and is inversely proportional to the resistance of the circuit. In short,

$$\text{Current} = \frac{\text{voltage}}{\text{resistance}}$$

For example, if we double the voltage across the ends of a circuit, the current will double; if we instead double the resistance of a circuit, the current will be reduced by half—the greater the voltage, the more current; the greater the resistance, the less current. The unit of resistance is called the *ohm*, after George Ohm who discovered the above relationship in 1826. We can say that if a potential difference of 1 volt is impressed across a circuit having a resistance of 1 ohm, a current of 1 ampere will be produced. The resistance in a typical lamp cord is much less than 1 ohm, while a typical light bulb has a resistance of about 100 ohms. From Ohm's Law, we see that 100 volts impressed upon such a bulb draws about 1 ampere of current. An iron or electric toaster has a resistance of 15 to 20 ohms. The low resistance permits a large current which produces considerable heat. Inside radio and television receivers, current is regulated by circuit elements called *resistors* whose resistance varies from a few ohms to millions of ohms.

Electric Shock and Ohm's Law

What causes electric shock—current or voltage? The damaging effects of shock are the result of current passing through the body. From Ohm's Law, we know that this current depends upon the voltage applied, as well as the electrical resistance of the human body. The resistance of the body depends on the body's condition. It can range from 100 to 500,000 ohms according to circumstances. The resistance of a man touching two electrodes with dry fingers is about 100,000 ohms, and with both hands immersed in salt water the resistance is about 700 ohms. Salt water is rich in ions and therefore is a very good conductor. Ordinary water also contains ions and is a good conductor. Therefore the very moist internal flesh is a good conductor of electricity, while the dry outer layers of skin are fair insulators. Usually the resistance of dry skin is enough to limit current to a safe intensity if the voltage is not too great. With normally dry skin you cannot even feel 12 volts, and voltage of twice that just barely tingles. But if the skin is moist, even such a low voltage can produce an uncomfortable shock. Every year many people are killed by common 110-volt electric circuits. If you touch a faulty 110-volt light fixture with your hand while your feet are on the ground, there is a 110-volt "electrical pressure" between your hand and the ground. Resistance to current flow is usually greatest between your feet and the ground, so the current usually isn't great enough to do serious harm. But if your feet and the ground are wet, there is a low-resistance electrical bond between you and the ground. Your overall resistance is so lowered that the 110-volts potential difference between your hand and your feet may produce a current greater than your body can withstand. Currents as low as 0.05 ampere can be fatal, while a current of 0.10 ampere in the heart is nearly always fatal. Often the victims of electrocution are standing in a bathtub, or are holding a faucet with wet hands, or standing with wet shoes on a wet floor, when the accident occurs. Although distilled water is a good insulator, the ions in ordinary water greatly reduce the electrical resistance. Even if you step into a pan of distilled water with bare feet, material from your feet will dissolve into the water in the form of ions. Distilled water is easily contaminated. Especially with dirty feet!

In order to receive a shock there must be a *difference* in electrical potential between one part of your body and another part. Current will pass along a path in your body connecting these two points. Suppose you fell from a bridge and managed to grab onto a high-voltage power line halting your fall. So long as you touch nothing else of different electrical potential, you will receive no shock at all. Even if the wire is a few thousand volts above ground potential and even if you hang by it with two hands, no current will flow from one hand to the other. This is because there is no difference in potential between your hands. If, however, you reach over with one hand and grab onto a wire of different potential . . . *zap*! We have all seen birds perched on high-voltage wires. Every part of their bodies is at the same high potential as the wire, and they feel no ill effects.

Electric shock, in addition to upsetting nerves in general, upsets the nerve center that controls breathing. In rescuing a victim, the first thing to do is clear him from the electric supply and then apply artificial respiration.

Direct Current and Alternating Current

Electric current may be dc or ac. By *dc* we mean *direct current*, which refers to the flowing of charges in *one direction*. A battery produces direct current in a circuit because the electrodes of the battery always have the same sign of charge. Electrons move from the repelling negative electrode and toward the attracting positive electrode, always moving through the circuit in the same direction. Even if the current moves in unsteady pulses, but in one direction only, it is dc.

Alternating current, or *ac*, is as the name implies. Electrons in the circuit are moved first in one direction and then in the opposite direction, alternating back and forth about relatively fixed positions. This is accomplished by alternating the direction of voltage at the energy source. The overwhelming majority of commercial ac circuits involve voltages and currents that alternate back and forth at a frequency of 60 cycles per second (cps). This is commonly referred to as 60-cycle ac. In a few places 25-cycle, 30-cycle, or 50-cycle current is used. The popularity of ac arises from the fact that electric energy in the form of ac can be transmitted great distances without large heat losses in the wires. Why this is so will be discussed in Chapter 24. The primary use of electric current, whether dc or ac, is to transfer energy quietly, flexibly, and conveniently, from one place to another.

The Speed and Source of Electrons in a Circuit

When a switch in an electric-light circuit is closed and the circuit is completed, the lamp appears to glow immediately. When we make a long-distance telephone call the electrical signal carrying our voice travels through the connecting wires at seemingly infinite speed. Actually, electric energy is transmitted through conductors at a speed approaching the speed of light.

Electrons themselves, however, do not move at the speed of light in a circuit.* Although electrons inside metal at room temperature have an average speed of about a couple of million miles per hour, they form no current because they are moving in all possible directions. There is no net flow in any preferred direction. When a battery or generator is connected, an electric field is established inside the conductor; the electrons continue their random motion but are also accelerated by this field in the direction of the positive terminal. It is the *electric field* that travels through a circuit at about the speed of light. The conducting wire acts as a guide to the electric-field lines established at the voltage source, Figure 22.3. If the source is dc, the

---

*Much effort and expense is expended in building cyclotrons and the like to accelerate electrons to speeds near that of light. If electrons in a common circuit traveled that fast, one would only have to bend a wire at a sharp angle and electrons traveling through the wire would possess so much momentum that they would fail to make the turn and fly off, providing a beam comparable to that produced by the expensive accelerators!

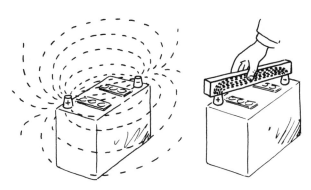

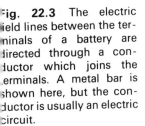

Fig. 22.3 The electric field lines between the terminals of a battery are directed through a conductor which joins the terminals. A metal bar is shown here, but the conductor is usually an electric circuit.

electric-field lines are maintained in one direction in the wires and free electrons encountering the field are accelerated along the direction of the field lines. Before they have speeded up very much they encounter the anchored metallic ions in their paths and lose some of their kinetic energy to them, causing the wires to undergo an increase in temperature. These collisions continually interrupt the motion of the electrons so that their net average speed in the direction in which they are pushed by the field is extremely slow. So in a typical dc circuit, the electric system of an automobile, for example, electrons have a net average speed of less than a half-inch per second. At this rate it would take years for an electron to travel across a transcontinental circuit. Long-distance telephone calls would be most arduous.

A common misconception regarding electrical currents is that the current is propagated through the conducting wires by electrons bumping into one another—that an electrical pulse is transmitted in a manner similar to the way the pulse of a tipped domino is transferred along a row of standing, closely spaced dominoes. This simply isn't true! The domino idea is a good model for the way sound is transmitted, but not for electrical energy. Electrons which are free to move in a conductor are accelerated by the electric field impressed upon them, not because they bump into each other. True, they do "bump into" each other and other atoms, but this slows them down and offers resistance to their motion. In an ac circuit the conducting electrons don't go anywhere. They jiggle back and forth about relatively fixed positions. It is the *pattern* of jiggling motion that is carried across the country at nearly the speed of light when you talk to someone by a transcontinental telephone call. The electrons already along the wires vibrate to the rhythm of the traveling pattern.

This brings up another misconception regarding electricity. Many people think that the electrical outlets in the walls of their homes are the source of electrons—that electrons flow from the power company through the power lines and into the home via these outlets. The fact is that no electrons flow from the power lines or the wall sockets into electrical appliances plugged into these outlets. The outlets in your home are ac. When you plug a lamp into an outlet, *energy* flows from the outlet into the lamp, not electrons. This energy is carried by the electric field and causes vibratory motion of the electrons that already exist in the lamp filament. If 110 volts are impressed on the lamp, then 110 units of energy are given to each unit of charge in the current. Most of this electrical energy is transformed into heat while some of it takes the form of light.

When you are jolted by an electrical shock, the electrons making up the current in your body originate in your body. Electrons do not come out of the wire and through your body and into the ground. Energy does. The energy simply causes free electrons in your body to vibrate in unison, which can be fatal.

Electric Power

When a charge moves in a circuit it does work. Usually this results in heating the circuit or in turning a motor. The rate at which work is done, or the rate at which energy is dissipated, is called *power*. Electric power is equal to the product of current and voltage across a circuit.*

$$\text{Power} = \text{current} \times \text{voltage}$$

If the voltage is measured in volts and the current in amperes, then the power is expressed in watts. This becomes a practical matter when we want to know the cost of electrical energy, which varies from 1 cent to 10 cents per kilowatt-hour depending upon the locality and other circumstances. A *kilowatt* is 1000 watts, and a *kilowatt-hour* represents the amount of energy consumed in 1 hour at the rate of 1 kilowatt. Thus at a place where electric energy costs 10 cents per kilowatt-hour, a 100-watt electric light bulb can be run for 10 hours at a cost of 10 cents, or 1 cent for each hour. A toaster or iron, which draws more current and therefore more energy, costs several times as much to operate.

*Note that the units check: $\text{Power} = \dfrac{\text{charge}}{\text{time}} \times \dfrac{\text{energy}}{\text{charge}} = \dfrac{\text{energy}}{\text{time}}$.

Electrical Circuits

Electrical appliances and other devices having electrical resistance are usually connected in a circuit in two ways, *series* or *parallel*. When they are connected in series, they form a single pathway for current flow between the terminals of the battery, generator, or wall socket which is simply an extension of these terminals. When they are connected in parallel, they form branches, each of which is a separate path for the flow of electrons. Both the series and parallel connections have their own distinctive characteristics. We shall treat circuits using these two types of connections briefly.

Series Circuit

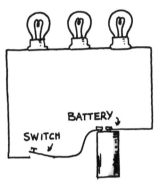

A simple series circuit is shown in Figure 22.4. Three lamps are connected in series with a battery. Electrons leave the negative terminal of the battery, pass through each of the resistive filaments in the lamps in turn, and then return to the positive terminal of the battery. This is the only path the electrons have through the circuit. A break anywhere in the path results in an open circuit and the flow of electrons ceases. Such a break might be simply opening the switch, or the burning out of one of the lamp filaments.

The circuit shown in Figure 22.4 illustrates the following important characteristics of series connections:

Fig. 22.4   A simple series circuit.

1. Since the electrons can follow only a single pathway through the circuit, the current passing through the resistances in the electrical devices and all other parts of the circuit is the same.

2. This current is resisted by the resistance in the first device, the resistance in the second, and in the third in turn so that the total resistance to current flow in the circuit is the sum of the individual resistances along the circuit path.

3. From Ohm's Law, the current flowing in the circuit is numerically equal to the voltage supplied by the battery divided by the total resistance of the circuit.

4. The total voltage applied to the circuit divides among the individual electrical devices in the circuit, so that the sum of the "voltage drops" across the resistance of each individual device is equal to the impressed voltage supplied by the emf. This follows from the fact that the energy used to move each unit of charge through the entire circuit is simply the sum of the energies used to move that unit of charge through each of the resistors in turn.

5. The voltage applied to the circuit divides among the individual electrical devices so that the voltage drop across each device is proportional to its resistance. This follows from the fact that more energy is used to move a unit of charge through a large resistance than through a small resistance.

Questions

1. What happens to other lamps if one of the lamps in a series circuit burns out?*

2. What happens to the light intensity of each lamp in a series circuit when more lamps are added to the circuit?†

It is easy to see the chief disadvantage of the series circuit; that is, that all the devices must be operating at the same time, for if any one device is turned off, the circuit is broken and all current flow ceases. Most circuits are wired such that it is possible to operate electrical devices independently of each other. In the home, for example, a lamp can be turned on or off without affecting the operation of other lamps or electrical devices. This is because these devices are connected not in series, but parallel to one another.

Parallel Circuit

A simple parallel circuit is shown in Figure 22.5. Three lamps are connected to the same two points, A and B, in the electrical circuit. Electrical devices connected to the same two points of an electrical circuit are said to be connected in parallel. Electrons leaving the negative terminal of the battery need travel through only *one* lamp filament before returning to the positive terminal of the battery. In this case there are three separate pathways over which the electrons can travel through the circuit. A break in any one path does not interrupt the flow of charge in the other paths. Each device operates independently of the other devices connected in the circuit.

This circuit illustrates the following major characteristics of parallel connections:

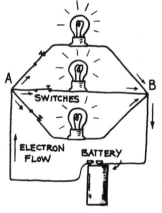

Fig. 22.5 A simple parallel circuit.

Answer: If one of the lamp filaments burns out, the path connecting the terminals of the emf is broken and no current will flow. All lamps will go out.

†*Answer*: The addition of more lamps in a series circuit results in a greater circuit resistance, which decreases the current in the circuit and therefore in each lamp, causing dimming; energy is divided among more lamps so the voltage drop across each lamp is lessened.

1. Since the devices connect the same two points A and B of the circuit, they have the same voltage across them.

2. The total current in the circuit divides among the parallel branches. Current flows more readily into devices of low resistance, so the amount of current in each branch is inversely proportional to the resistance of the branch.

3. The total current flowing in the circuit is equal to the sum of the currents flowing in its parallel branches.

4. As the number of parallel branches is increased, the overall resistance of the circuit is decreased. The resistance to current flow is lowered with each added path between any two points of a circuit. It follows that the combined resistance of resistors in parallel to the flow of current between the two points of the circuit which they connect is less than the resistance of any one of the branches.

Questions

1. What happens to other lamps if one of the lamps in a parallel circuit burns out?*

2. What happens to the light intensity of each lamp in a parallel circuit when more lamps are added in parallel to the circuit?†

Parallel Circuits and Overloading. Electricity in the home is usually supplied by two lead wires called *lines* which are connected to the wall outlets in each room. A voltage of about 110 volts is maintained across these lines by generators in the power company. Appliances, lamps, and the like are supplied with current by connecting each end of the wire leads of the

---

*Answer: If one lamp burns out the other lamps will be unaffected. The current in each branch, according to Ohm's Law, is equal to (voltage/resistance), and since neither voltage nor resistance is affected in the branches, the current in those branches is unaffected. The total current in the overall circuit, however, is lessened by an amount equal to the current drawn by the lamp in question before it burned out. But the current in any other single branch is unchanged.

†Answer: The light intensity for each lamp is unchanged as other lamps are introduced (or removed). The only change that occurs is the total resistance and total current in the total circuit. As lamps are introduced, more paths are available between the battery terminals which effectively decreases total circuit resistance. This decreased resistance is accompanied by an increased current flow, the increase of which supplies the lamps as they are introduced. Although changes of resistance and current occur for the circuit as a whole, no changes occur in any individual branch of the circuit.

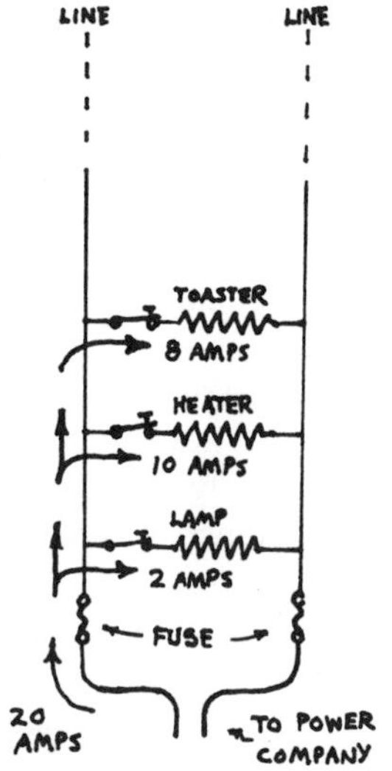

LINE   LINE

TOASTER
8 AMPS

HEATER
10 AMPS

LAMP
2 AMPS

← FUSE →

20
AMPS   TO POWER
            COMPANY

Fig. 22.6 Circuit diagram for appliances connected to a household supply line. The resistances of the appliances are indicated by the sawtooth lines.

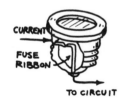

Fig. 22.7 A safety fuse.

appliance to the lines as shown in Figure 22.6. This is accomplished when the plug of the appliance is inserted into the wall outlet. The appliances are then connected in parallel. As more electrical devices are connected to the lines, the combined resistance of the circuit is lowered and a greater amount of current flows in the supply lines. Lines that carry more than a safe amount of current are said to be *overloaded*. The heat generated in them may then become intense enough to melt the wires or start a fire.

We can see how overloading occurs by considering the circuit of Figure 22.6. The supply line is connected to an electric toaster that draws 8 amperes, to an electric heater that draws 10 amperes, and to an electric lamp that draws 2 amperes. When only the toaster is turned on, the current in the lines is 8 amperes. When the heater is also turned on, the current in the supply lines increases to 18 amperes, where 8 amperes go to the toaster and 10 amperes go to the heater. Turning on the lamp increases the line current to 20 amperes, and connecting any more electrical devices draws still more line current. Connecting too many devices into the same line results in dangerous overheating that may cause fires.

Safety Fuses. To prevent overloading in circuits, fuses are connected in series along the supply line. In this way the entire line current flows through the fuse. A fuse is constructed with a ribbon of wire having a low melting point, Figure 22.7. If the current in the line becomes dangerously large, both line and fuse become hot. The fuse then melts or "blows out" and breaks the circuit.

Fuses are constructed to melt or blow out as soon as the current reaches a certain limit. Thus a "20-ampere fuse" blows out when the current in the circuit exceeds 20 amperes. Before the blown fuse is replaced, the cause of the overloading should be determined and remedied. Often insulation separating the wires in a circuit wears away and allows the wires to touch, in effect shortening the path of the circuit. This is called a *short circuit*. The decreased resistance results in an increase in current.

Circuits may also be protected by circuit breakers which use magnets or bimetallic strips to open the switch.

Summary of Terms

Electric current. The flow of electric charge which transports energy from one place to another. Measured in amperes, where 1 ampere is the flow of $6\frac{1}{4}$ billion-billion electrons (or protons) per second.

Potential difference. The difference in voltage between two points, which can be compared with a difference in water level between two containers. If two containers having a different water level are connected by a pipe, water will flow from that with the higher level to that with the lower level until the two levels are equalized. Similarly, if two points with a difference in potential are connected by a conductor, a current will flow from that with the greater potential to that with the smaller potential until the potentials are equalized. Measured in volts.

Electromotive force (emf). An energy source that maintains a potential difference across an electric circuit; the source of voltage, measured in volts.

Electric resistance. That property of a material to resist the flow of an electric current through it; measured in ohms.

Ohm's Law. The statement that the current in a circuit varies in direct proportion to the potential difference or emf, and in inverse proportion to resistance:

$$\text{Current} = \frac{\text{voltage}}{\text{resistance}}$$

A potential difference of 1 volt across a resistance of 1 ohm produces a current of 1 ampere.

Electric power. The rate of energy transfer, or the rate of doing work; the ratio of energy per time which electrically can be measured by the product of current and voltage:

$$\text{Power} = \text{current} \times \text{voltage}.$$

Measured in watts (or kilowatts) where 1 ampere $\times$ 1 volt = 1 watt.

Direct current (dc). An electric current flowing in one direction only.

Alternating current (ac). Electric current that rapidly reverses in direction—the electric charges vibrate about relatively fixed points, usually at the vibrational rate of 60 cycles per second.

Series circuit. An electrical circuit with resistances arranged such that the electric current flows through each of them in turn.

Parallel circuit. An electric circuit having two or more resistances arranged in such a way that any single one completes the circuit independently of all the others.

Questions   1. If a conductor is placed in contact with two separated bodies charged to different electrical potential energies, can you say for certain which way charge will flow in the conductor? How about if the two bodies are charged to different electric potentials?

2. Why are thick wires rather than thin wires usually used to carry large currents?

3. Will a lamp with a thick filament or thin filament draw the most current?

4. Is a current-carrying wire charged?

5. The damaging effects of electric shock result from the amount of *current* that flows in the body. Why, then, do we see signs that read, "Danger—High Voltage," rather than, "Danger—High Current"?

6. Why is the wing span of birds a consideration in determining the spacing between parallel wires in a power line?

7. Estimate the number of electrons that a power company delivers annually to the homes of a typical city of 50,000 people.

8. Why is the speed of electricity so much greater than the speed of sound?

9. In some cheap sets of Christmas-tree lights, one burned-out bulb will cause all the bulbs to go out. Explain.

10. Why will too many electrical devices operating at one time often blow a fuse?

23

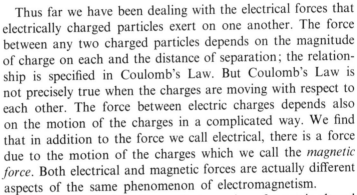

Magnetism

The Nature of Magnetism

Thus far we have been dealing with the electrical forces that electrically charged particles exert on one another. The force between any two charged particles depends on the magnitude of charge on each and the distance of separation; the relationship is specified in Coulomb's Law. But Coulomb's Law is not precisely true when the charges are moving with respect to each other. The force between electric charges depends also on the motion of the charges in a complicated way. We find that in addition to the force we call electrical, there is a force due to the motion of the charges which we call the *magnetic force*. Both electrical and magnetic forces are actually different aspects of the same phenomenon of electromagnetism.

We stated in the last chapter that a region of space is altered when an electrical charge is introduced. It is altered in that the space contains energy; this energy is contained in the electric field which originates from the electrical charge. Every electrical charge is surrounded by an electric field. If the charge is moving, the region of space surrounding the charge is altered still. We say a moving charge is surrounded by both an electric *and* a magnetic field. Like the electric field, the magnetic field is a storehouse of energy. The greater the motion of the charge, the greater is the magnitude of the magnetic field surrounding the charge. A magnetic field is produced by the motion of electrical charge.

We are all familiar with the common iron horseshoe magnet, Figure 23.1. The magnetic field between the ends is extremely strong, as evidenced by its interaction with paper clips, nails, and other iron substances. But if a magnetic field is produced by the motion of electrical charges, where is the electrical motion in a solid stationary magnet? Although the magnet as a whole may be stationary, the atoms making up the magnet are in constant motion. More important than the motion of the atoms is the motion of electrons within the atoms. The electrons move in an orbital-like motion about the atomic nuclei. This movement of electrons produces a magnetic field. In addition to this orbital-like motion, electrons spin about their own axes like a top. A spinning electron constitutes a charge in

Fig. 23.1 A horseshoe magnet.

307

motion and therefore creates a magnetic field. In every atom, twice as many magnetic fields exist as electrons, since each electron produces two fields, one for orbital motion and one for spinning. The field due to the spinning of the electron is most predominant.*

Every electron is a tiny *electromagnet*. A pair of electrons spinning in the same direction makes up a stronger electromagnet. A pair of electrons spinning in opposite directions, however, is not magnetic. The magnetic fields of each cancel one another. This is why most substances are not magnets. In most atoms the various fields cancel each other because the electrons spin in opposite directions. In materials such as iron, nickel, and cobalt, however, the fields do not cancel each other entirely. Each iron atom has four electrons whose spin magnetism is uncanceled. Each iron atom, then, is a tiny magnet. The same is true to a slightly lesser degree for the atoms of nickel and cobalt.

Magnetic Domains

The magnetic field of individual iron atoms is so strong that interaction among adjacent atoms causes large clusters of them to line up with each other. These clusters of aligned atoms are called *magnetic domains*. Each domain is perfectly magnetized, being made up of millions of aligned atoms. The domains are extremely small and a crystal of iron contains many of them. It is interesting to listen with an amplified stethoscope to the clickity-clack of domains undergoing alignment in a piece of iron' when a strong magnet is brought nearby.

Every piece of iron, however, is not a magnet. This is because the domains in the material are not aligned. Consider a common nail: the domains in the nail are randomly oriented—they can be induced into alignment, however, by bringing a magnet nearby. The domains align themselves much as electrical charges in a piece of paper align themselves in the presence of a charged rod. When we remove the nail from the permanent magnet, ordinary thermal motion causes most or all of the domains of the nail to return to a random arrangement. If the field of the permanent magnet is very strong, the nail may retain some permanent magnetism of its own even after the two are separated. Magnets are made in this way by simply placing pieces of

---

*Most common magnets are made from alloys containing Fe, Ni, or Co. In these the electron spin contributes virtually all the magnetic properties. In the rare-earth metals like Gd, the orbital motion is more significant.

iron in strong magnetic fields. It helps to tap the iron and nudge any stubborn domains into alignment. Another way of making a permanent magnet is to stroke a piece of iron with a magnet. The stroking motion aligns the domains in the iron. If a permanent magnet is dropped or heated, some of the domains are jostled out of alignment and the magnet becomes weaker.

Magnetic Poles

Magnets exhibit both attractive and repulsive forces. In electricity we have positive and negative charges, whereas in magnetism we have north and south poles. The Chinese were perhaps the first to discover that a suspended magnet will line up in a north-south direction. Such a magnet, called a *compass*, has obvious navigational advantages. In suspending a permanent magnet, it is found that one end always points northward. This shows that there is something different about the two ends.

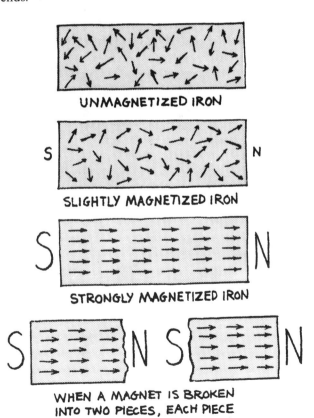

UNMAGNETIZED IRON

SLIGHTLY MAGNETIZED IRON

STRONGLY MAGNETIZED IRON

WHEN A MAGNET IS BROKEN INTO TWO PIECES, EACH PIECE IS AN EQUALLY STRONG MAGNET

Fig. 23.2 Pieces of iron in successive stages of magnetism. The arrows represent domains, the head being a north pole, the tail a south pole. Poles of neighboring domains neutralize each other's effects, except at the ends.

The end that points northward is called the *north-seeking pole*, and the end that points southward is the *south-seeking pole*. For the sake of simplicity, these are called the *north* and *south* poles. Figure 23.3 shows the magnetic field about a bar magnet. Iron filings which have been sprinkled on a piece of paper covering the magnet reveal the magnetic-field configuration.* We say the magnetic-field direction exterior to the magnet is from the north pole to the south pole. The magnetic-field lines form closed loops, emanating from the north pole and entering the south pole where they are directed through the magnet and out the north pole again.

If the north pole of one magnet is brought near the north pole of another magnet, repulsion occurs. The same is true of

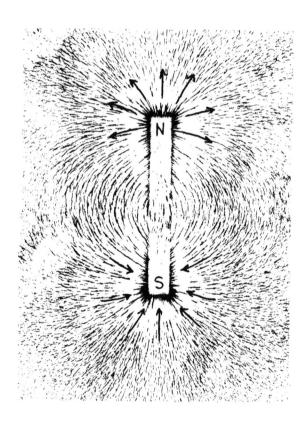

Fig. 23.3 The magnetic field configuration about a bar magnet.

---

*Domains align in the individual filings causing them to act like tiny compasses. The poles of each "compass" are pulled in opposite directions, producing a torque that twists each filing into alignment with the external magnetic field.

a south pole near a south pole. If opposite poles are brought together, however, attraction occurs.* We can say:

Like poles repel; unlike poles attract.

The Earth's Magnetic Field

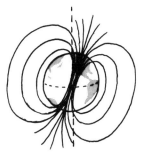

Fig. 23.4   The earth is a magnet.

A suspended magnet or compass points northward because the earth itself is a huge magnet. The compass aligns with the magnetic field of the earth. The magnetic poles of the earth do not coincide with the geographical poles, nor are they very close to the geographical poles. The magnetic pole in the northern hemisphere, for example, is located 1100 miles from the geographical pole, somewhere in the Hudson Bay region of northern Canada. The other pole is located south of Australia, Figure 23.4.

It is of some interest to note that the south pole of the earth's magnet is near the northern geographical pole, while the north pole of the earth's magnet is near the southern geographical pole. Since unlike poles attract each other, the north poles of compasses are attracted toward the northern part of the world where the south magnetic pole is located. Hence the north pole of a compass points in a northerly direction.

Since a compass points toward the earth's magnetic pole rather than to its geographical pole, the compass direction generally deviates from the true north. Mariners and others who use compasses must allow for this deviation in determining the true north. The discrepancy between the orientation of a compass and true north is known as the *magnetic declination.*

It is not known for sure exactly why the earth itself is a magnet. The earth is not a magnetized chunk of iron like a bar magnet. It has an outer rocky mantle about 1800 miles deep. Below that is the liquid part of the core, about 1300 miles thick, which surrounds the solid center. Most scientists think that the motion of charges in the liquid part of the earth's core creates the magnetic field. Because of its great size, the speed of moving charges looping around within the earth need only be somewhat less than a thousandth of a foot per second. Some scientists think that these currents are caused by the earth's rotation. This idea is supported by the following facts: Jupiter, which has a 10-hour day, has a much stronger magnetic field than the earth. The moon which rotates once in 27 days, has

---

*The force of interaction between unit magnetic poles is given by $F \sim pp'/d^2$, where p and p' represent magnetic-pole strengths, and d represents the distance between. Note the similarity of this relationship with Coulomb's Law.

a very weak magnetic field. Venus, which rotates slower still, has no measurable magnetic field, according to instruments on the space probe Mariner II, in December, 1962.

Part of the earth's magnetism may be caused by electric currents high in the atmosphere. Ultraviolet rays and X-rays from the sun split some atoms in the air into charged particles. These are the ions that make up the outer layer of the atmosphere which we call the ionosphere. Like the lower layers of air, the ionosphere is churned by the winds. A wind of charged particles is an electric current, and it is surrounded by a magnetic field.

Another possible source of the earth's magnetism may be heat rising from the earth's central core. This heat may be the cause of convection currents of molten material in the liquid part of the earth's core. The motion of ions and electrons in this molten material would produce a magnetic field. In geologic history an unsteady flow of heat might have caused a subsiding and momentary ceasing of convection currents—resulting in a collapse of the earth's magnetic field. Regeneration of heat would have again caused convection currents, but not necessarily in the same direction. This would account for prior magnetic fields reversed from those that exist today.

Whatever the cause, the magnetic field of the earth is not stable, but has wandered throughout geologic time. This is known from analysis of the magnetic properties of rock strata. Iron atoms in a molten state tend to align themselves with the magnetic field of the earth. Upon solidifying, the direction of the earth's magnetic field is recorded by the orientation of domains in the rock. The slight magnetism resulting can be measured with sensitive instruments. As samples of rock are tested from different strata formed throughout geological time, the magnetic field of the earth for different periods can be charted. This evidence shows that there have been times when the magnetic field of the earth has diminished to zero and then reversed itself. The last known reversal of the earth's magnetic field took place 700,000 years ago. Prior reversals are dated at 870,000 and 950,000 years ago.

Magnetic Forces on Moving Electrically Charged Particles

A charged particle at rest will not interact with a magnetic field. But a charged particle in motion produces its own magnetic field which does interact with another magnetic field. A charged particle, therefore, experiences a force when moving through a magnetic field. The force is greatest when the particle moves perpendicular to the magnetic field lines. At other angles the force lessens and becomes zero when the charged particle moves along the magnetic field lines. In any case, the direction of the force is always perpendicular to the magnetic field lines and the velocity of the charged particle, Figure 23.5. A moving charge experiences a sideways deflection when it crosses through a magnetic field. Traveling along the field direction, no deflection occurs.

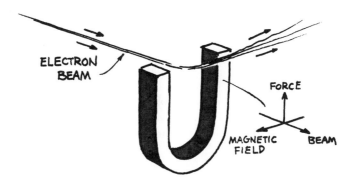

Fig. 23.5 A beam of electrons is deflected by a magnetic field.

The universe is a shooting gallery of charged particles. They are called cosmic "rays" and are the nuclei of atoms that are stripped bare of their electrons. Their origin is uncertain—perhaps they are boiled off stars, or are nuclei that did not condense to form stars. In any event, they travel through space at fantastic speeds and make up the cosmic radiation that is hazardous to astronauts. Fortunately for those of us on the earth's surface, most of these charged particles are deflected away by the magnetic field of the earth. Some of them are trapped in the outer reaches of the earth's magnetic field. These regions are the Van Allen radiation belts, Figure 23.6.

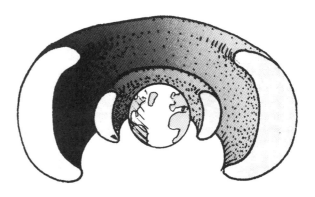

Fig. 23.6 The Van Allen radiation belts.

The Van Allen radiation belts, named after James Van Allen, who suggested their existence from data gathered by the U.S. satellite Explorer I in 1958, consist of two doughnut-shaped rings. The inner ring is about 2000 miles from the earth, and the outer ring, which is a larger and wider doughnut, is about 10,000 miles from the earth. Most of the charged particles, protons and electrons, trapped in the outer belt probably come from the sun. Storms on the sun hurl charged particles out in great fountains. Those that pass near the earth are trapped by its magnetic field. The trapped particles follow corkscrew paths around the magnetic field lines of the earth. Along these magnetic paths the particles bounce between the earth's magnetic poles high above the atmosphere. Disturbances in the earth's field often allows the ions to dip into the atmosphere, causing it to glow like a fluorescent lamp. This is the *aurora borealis* (northern lights).

The particles trapped in the inner belt probably originated from the earth's atmosphere. This belt is now masked by electrons that were produced by high-altitude hydrogen-bomb explosions in 1962.

In spite of the earth's protective magnetic field, many cosmic rays are incident upon the earth. Cosmic-ray bombardment is maximum at the poles, as charged particles incident there do not travel *across* the magnetic field lines, but *along* the field lines and therefore are not deflected. Incidence decreases away from the poles and is minimum in equatorial regions. At sea level, the number of cosmic particles per square inch each minute is about 10 to 20; this number increases rapidly with altitude. So cosmic rays are penetrating your body as you are reading this (and even when you aren't reading this!). You are somewhat less healthy every second because of this. (Perhaps we could extend our lifespan a few weeks or months by spending our lives deep beneath the earth in thick lead vaults.)

Magnetism and Evolution

The magnetic changes of the earth may have played an important role in the evolution of life forms. When life was passing through its earliest phases, some 1500 million to 500 million years ago, the magnetic field of the earth was strong enough to hold off cosmic and solar radiations that were violent enough to destroy life. The field has reversed itself several times since. During these reversals cosmic radiation upon the earth's surface increased and the Van Allen belts spilled their cargo of radiation, resulting in increased mutation of the primitive life forms then existing. Sudden bursts of radiation must have been as effective in changing life forms as X-rays have been in the famous heredity studies of fruit flies. The coincidences of the dates of increased life changes and the dates of the magnetic-pole reversals lend support to this theory.

Summary of Terms

Magnetic field. The region of "altered space" that will interact with the magnetic properties of a magnet; located mainly between the opposite poles of a magnet, or in the energetic space about an electric charge in motion.

Magnetic domains. Clustered regions of aligned magnetic atoms. When these regions themselves are aligned with each other, the substance containing them is a magnet.

Magnetic force. (1) Between magnets: The attraction of unlike magnetic poles for each other and the repelling between like magnetic poles. (2) Between a magnetic field and a moving charge: A moving charge is deflected from its path in the region of a magnetic field; the deflecting force is perpendicular to the motion of the charge and perpendicular to the magnetic-field lines. This force is maximum when the charge moves perpendicular to the field lines, and is minimum (zero) when moving parallel to the field lines.

Suggested Reading

Becker, Joseph J., "Permanent Magnets," *Scientific American*, Dec. 1970.

Bitter, Francis, *Magnets, The Education of a Physicist* (Science Study Series), Garden City, N. Y., Doubleday (Anchor), 1959.

Questions

1. Since every iron atom is a tiny magnet, why are not all iron materials themselves magnets?

2. Why will a magnet attract an ordinary nail or paper clip, but not a wooden pencil?

3. If a bar magnet is carefully broken in half as shown in Figure 23.2, each piece will be an equally strong magnet. If the magnet is carefully broken in half along its long axis, how would the strengths of the pieces compare to that of the original magnet?

4. One way to make a compass is to stick a magnetized needle into a piece of cork and float it in a wooden bucket full of water. The needle will align itself with the magnetic field of the earth. Since the north pole of this compass is attracted northward, will the needle float toward the northward side of the bucket?

5. Why will a magnet placed in front of a television picture tube distort the picture? (*Note*: Do NOT try this with a color set. If you succeed in magnetizing the metal mask in back of the glass screen, you will have picture distortion even when the magnet is removed!).

6. Why is a piece of iron attracted by either pole of a magnet? (*Hint*: See Figure 21.5 in Chapter 21.)

7. Magnet *A* has twice the magnetic field strength as magnet *B*, and at a certain distance pulls on magnet *B* with a force of 20 pounds. With how much force, then, does magnet *B* pull on magnet *A*?

8. A cyclotron is a device for accelerating charged particles in ever-increasing circular orbits to high speeds. The charged particles are subjected to both an electric field and a magnetic field. One of these fields increases the speed of the charged particles and the other field holds them in a circular path. Which field performs which function?

9. Inside a laboratory room there is said to be either an electric field or a magnetic field, but not both. What experiments might be performed to establish what kind of field exists in the room?

10. Residents of northern Canada are bombarded by more intense cosmic radiation than are residents of Mexico. Why is this so?

24
Electromagnetic Interactions

Magnetic Field Around a Current-Carrying Wire

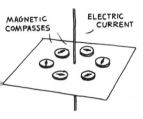

Fig. 24.1 The compasses show the circular shape of the magnetic field surrounding the current-carrying wire.

A moving charge produces a magnetic field. A current of charges, then, produces a magnetic field. The magnetic field surrounding a current-carrying conductor can be demonstrated by arranging an assortment of magnetic compasses around a wire, Figure 24.1, and passing a current through it. The compasses line up with the magnetic field produced by the moving charges. Magnetic field lines form concentric circles about the wire. When the current reverses direction, the compasses turn completely around, showing that the direction of the magnetic field changes also.

If the wire is bent into a loop, the magnetic field lines that surround the wire are bunched up inside the loop, Figure 24.2. If the wire is bent into another loop, overlapping the first, the concentration of magnetic field lines inside the double loop is twice as much as in the single loop. It follows that the magnetic field intensity in this region is increased as the number of loops are increased. The magnetic field intensity is appreciable for a

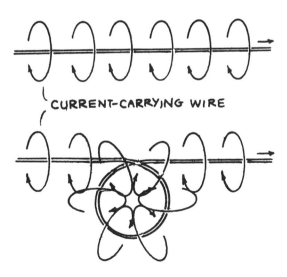

CURRENT-CARRYING WIRE

Fig. 24.2 Magnetic field lines about a current-carrying wire crowd up when the wire is bent into a loop.

current-carrying coil of wire with many loops. If a piece of iron
is placed in such a coil, the magnetic domains in the iron are
induced into alignment, which further increases the magnetic
field intensity. And we have an electromagnet!

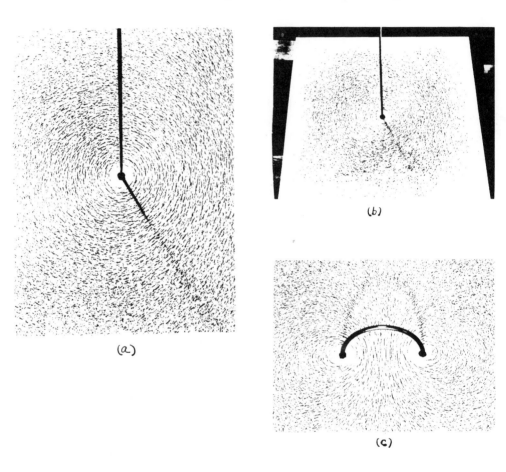

(a)

(b)

(c)

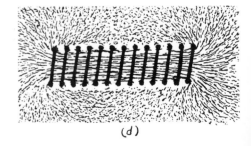

(d)

Fig. 24.3 Iron filings
sprinkled on paper reveal
the magnetic field con-
figurations about (a) and
(b) a current-carrying wire;
(c) a current-carrying loop;
(d) a coil of loops. (From
College Physics, Physical
Science Study Committee,
Boston, Raytheon, 1968.)

Deflecting Force on a Current-Carrying Wire in a Magnetic Field

A charge moving through a magnetic field experiences a deflecting force. A current of charges, then, moving through a magnetic field experiences a deflecting force. If the moving charges are trapped inside a wire, as they respond to the deflecting force they also move the wire, Figure 24.4. This was first discovered by a Danish physicist, Hans Christian Oersted, in 1820.

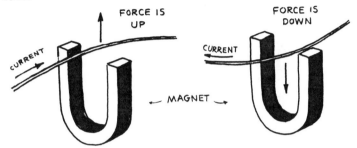

Fig. 24.4 A current-carrying wire experiences a force in a magnetic field. (Compare this figure with Figure 23.5.)

If we reverse the direction of current, the deflecting force acts in the opposite direction. The force is maximum when the current is perpendicular to the magnetic field lines. The direction of the force is not along the magnetic field lines nor along the direction of current, but is perpendicular to both field lines and current. It is a sideways force.

Oersted's discovery created much excitement, for almost immediately people began designing methods to harness this force for useful purposes. Electric motors marked the beginning of a new era. The principle of the electromagnetic motor is shown in bare outline in Figure 24.5. A permanent magnet is used to produce a magnetic field in two slots. Across each slot there

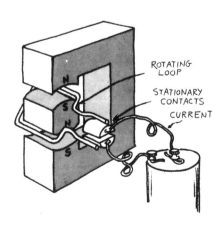

Fig. 24.5 A simplified motor.

Fig. 24.6 A galvanometer. This instrument may be calibrated to measure current (amperes), in which case it is called an ammeter; or to measure electric potential (volts), in which case it is called a voltmeter.

is a north and south pole. A rectangular loop of wire is mounted so that it can turn about an axis and pass between the two slots as shown. When a current flows through the loop, it flows in opposite directions in the two slots, resulting in opposite forces on the wire. The portion of wire in the upper slot is forced to the left while the portion of the wire in the lower slot is forced to the right, causing the loop to turn. To maintain rotation, the current is reversed during each half-revolution by means of stationary contacts on the shaft. In this way the current in the loop alternates so that the forces in each slot do not change directions as the loop rotates. Small dc motors are made this way. Larger motors, dc or ac, are usually made by replacing the permanent magnet by an electromagnet that is energized by the power source.

Electrical meters work in this fashion. A wire loop is mounted on a core so that it can rotate in a magnetic field, Figure 24.6. A spring holds it in a "zero" position. When current flows in the loop, the core is forced to rotate. If a needle is attached to the core, its deflection (which is proportional to the amount of current) can be readily observed. Such instruments are called *galvanometers*. Voltmeters and ammeters are modified galvanometers.

Electromagnetic Induction

Fig. 24.7 When the magnet is plunged into the coil, voltage is induced, as shown on the meter.

The discovery that magnetism could be produced with electrical wires was a technological turning point. The question arose as to whether electricity could be produced from magnetism. When this question was answered, the world was never again the same. That discovery began the industrial revolution. Both Joseph Henry of America and Michael Faraday of Scotland independently in 1831 discovered that when a magnet was plunged into a coil of wire, a voltage was induced. Electric current could be made to flow in a wire by simply moving a magnet in or out of a coil of wire, Figure 24.7. This phenomenon is called *electromagnetic induction*.

Electromagnetic induction in a conductor depends only on the relative motion between the conductor and the magnetic field. Voltage is induced whether the magnetic field of a magnet moves by a stationary conductor, or the conductor moves in a stationary magnetic field, Figure 24.8. The results are the same whether either or both move.

The greater the number of loops of wire moving relative to a magnetic field, the greater the induced voltage, and the greater the current in the wire, Figure 24.9. Twice as many loops will induce twice as much voltage; ten times as many loops will

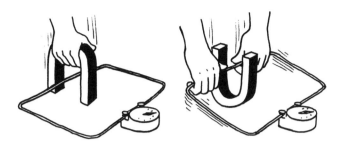

Fig. 24.8 Charges in the wire are set in motion whether the magnetic field moves through a stationary wire, or the wire moves through a stationary magnetic field.

induce ten times as much voltage, and so on. The amount of voltage induced also depends on how quickly the magnetic field lines are traversed by the wire. Very slow motion produces hardly any voltage at all. Quick motion induces a greater voltage. If a magnet is plunged in and out of a coil of wire, the voltage induced in the coil alternates in direction. As the magnetic field strength inside the coil is increased (magnet entering), the induced voltage in the coil is directed one way, and when the magnetic field strength diminishes (magnet leaving), the voltage is induced in the opposite direction. The greater the frequency of field change, the greater is the induced voltage. The frequency of the changing magnetic field within the loop is equal to the frequency of alternating voltage induced.

Electromagnetic induction can be summarized in the statement:

The induced voltage in a coil is numerically equal to the product of the number of loops and the rate at which the magnetic field intensity changes within those loops.

This statement is called Faraday's Law.

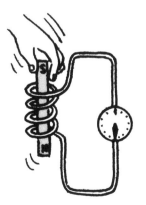

Fig. 24.9 When a magnet is plunged into a coil having twice the number of loops as another, twice as much voltage is induced. If the magnet is plunged into a coil with three times as many loops, then three times as much voltage is induced.

The amount of current produced by electromagnetic induction depends not only on the induced voltage, but also on the resistance of the coil.* For example, we can plunge a magnet in and out of a closed loop of rubber and in and out of a closed loop of copper. The voltage induced in each is the same, providing each intercepts the same number of magnetic field lines. The current in each is quite different, however. The electrons in the rubber feel the same voltage as those in copper, but their bonding to the fixed atoms prevents a current such as that which so freely ensues in copper.

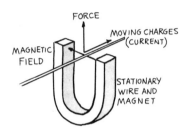 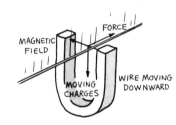

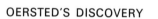

Fig. 24.10 Can you see the relationship between these phenomena?

OERSTED'S DISCOVERY

When a current moves to the right there is a perpendicular upward force on the electrons. Since there is no conducting path upward, the wire is tugged upward along with the electrons.

FARADAY'S DISCOVERY

When a wire with no initial current is moved downward, the charges in the wire experience a deflecting force perpendicular to their motion. There *is* a conducting path in this direction and the electrons follow it, thereby constituting a current.

Oersted's discovery that electric currents in a magnetic field are deflected, and Faraday's and Henry's discovery of induced voltages both stem from the same single fact: that moving charges experience a force that is perpendicular to their motion and perpendicular to the magnetic field lines they traverse, Figure 24.10. On the one hand motion is provided by some emf that drives electrons along the wire, while on the other hand

---

*Current also depends on the "reactance" of the coil. Reactance is similar to resistance, and depends on the number of loops in the coil and on the rate at which the magnetic field changes. We will not treat this complication here.

motion is provided by some mechanical force that pushes electrons, wire and all, across magnetic field lines. In Oersted's case the force on the moving charges is perpendicular to the wire; in Faraday's case the force on the moving electrons is along the wire. In both cases the force is perpendicular to both the electron motion and the magnetic field.

So far, we have considered induction with the use of permanent magnets. In the foregoing examples and diagrams, the permanent magnets may be replaced with current-carrying coils of wire—electromagnets. And furthermore, it is not even necessary to have "motion" in the ordinary sense of the word. It is the field, rather than the magnet, that must move. In the case of the electromagnet, we can cause the field to expand and collapse by simply opening and closing an electric switch, Figure 24.11. A coil connected to a battery is placed alongside another coil connected to a galvanometer. It is customary to refer to the coil connected to the source of power as the *primary*, and the other as the *secondary*. The instant the switch is closed in the primary, and current begins to flow, a current flows in the secondary even though there is no material connection between the two coils. Only a brief surge of current occurs in the secondary, however. When the switch in the primary is opened, a surge of current is again registered in the secondary, but in the opposite direction.

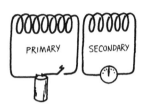

Fig. 24.11 When the primary switch is opened or closed, voltage is induced in the secondary circuit.

This is the explanation: A magnetic field builds up around the primary when the current begins to flow through the coil. This means that the magnetic field is growing (that is, *changing*) about the primary. But since the coils are near to each other, this changing field extends to the secondary coil, thereby inducing a voltage in the secondary. This induced voltage is only temporary, for when the current and the magnetic field of the primary reach a steady state, that is, when the magnetic field is no longer changing, no further voltage is induced in the secondary. But when the switch is turned off, the current in the primary drops to zero—the magnetic field about the coil collapses, thereby inducing a voltage in the secondary coil which senses the change. We see that a voltage is induced whenever a magnetic field is *changing* around the conductor, regardless of the reason.

In short, we can say that voltage can be induced in a wire in three different ways: by moving the wire near a magnet, by moving a magnet near the wire, or by changing a current in a nearby wire. In each case we have the important ingredient—

there is relative motion between the magnetic field and the charges in the wire.*

The Transformer

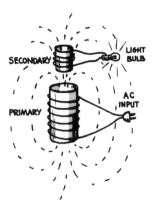

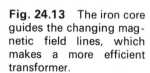

Fig. 24.12 A simple transformer arrangement.

If we opened and closed the switch of a primary circuit in rapid succession, we would induce an alternating voltage in a neighboring secondary circuit. But better than go through the task of opening and closing a switch, we could use alternating current to power the primary circuit. If we insert iron in the coils, the magnetic fields will be intensified by the alignment of the magnetic domains in the iron. The continually changing current produces a continuously changing magnetic field. This varying field induces an alternating voltage in the secondary coil, which may be sufficient, for example, to light an electric bulb, Figure 24.12.

The induced voltage in the secondary coil alternates at a frequency equal to the frequency in the primary. The induced voltage in the secondary, however, may be larger or smaller than the voltage in the primary. How much voltage is induced depends upon the intensity of the magnetic field intercepted by the secondary coil and the number of loops of wire in the secondary coil. If we wind the primary and secondary coils on an iron core as shown in Figure 24.13, then the secondary coil intercepts all the field lines produced by the primary. This is because the iron core guides the magnetic field lines, much as copper wire guides electric field lines. Greater efficiency can be obtained in transferring power from one coil to the other with such a core. We call such a device a *transformer*.

Fig. 24.13 The iron core guides the changing magnetic field lines, which makes a more efficient transformer.

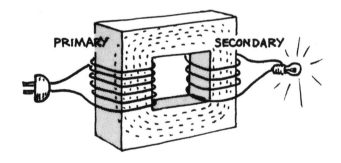

*Relative motion must be such that "new" magnetic field lines are intercepted by the wire. Back and forth motion of the wire along its length, for example, or motion along and parallel to magnetic field lines will induce no voltage. Maximum voltage is induced when motion is such that a maximum number of field lines are "cut" by the wire (as in Figure 24.8).

Since a voltage is induced in each loop of wire making up the secondary coil, a greater number of loops results in a greater voltage. The induced voltage in the secondary can be many times greater or less than the input voltage to the primary.

To see how voltages can be stepped up in a transformer, consider the simplest case possible, Figure 24.14. Suppose our primary coil consists of one double loop of wire and we attach it to a 1-volt alternating source. Further suppose that our secondary also consists of a similar double loop. Since the iron core guides the magnetic field lines produced by the primary, the secondary intercepts all of these. The change in magnetic field intensity in the secondary is equal to the change in magnetic field intensity in the primary. Therefore 1 volt is induced in the secondary.

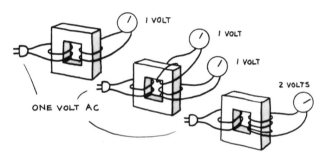

Fig. 24.14 Voltage is stepped up when the number of loops of wire in the secondary is increased.

Also suppose that we wrap a third loop around the core, effectively having two secondary coils. Since this loop intercepts as many changing magnetic field lines as the first secondary intercepts, a voltage of 1 volt will be induced in it too. There is no need to keep both the secondaries separate, for we could join them together and still have a total induced voltage of $1 + 1 = 2$ volts. This is equivalent to saying that 2 volts will be induced in a single secondary which has twice the number of loops as the primary. If the secondary is wound with three times as many loops, then 3 volts will be induced. If the secondary has a hundred times as many loops as the primary, then the induced voltage in the secondary will be a hundredfold that in the primary. How much the induced voltage differs from the primary voltage depends on the relative number of loops in each coil. This is expressed in the following relationship:

$$\frac{\text{Primary voltage}}{\text{Number of primary loops}} = \frac{\text{secondary voltage}}{\text{number of secondary loops}}$$

It might seem that we are getting something for nothing with a transformer that steps up the voltage, for we can supply a small voltage to the primary and take a large voltage off the secondary. But this is not without recompensation. The transformer actually transforms energy from one coil to the other. The rate at which energy is transferred is called *power*. The power into the primary is simply transferred to the secondary. Power from the secondary can never exceed the power input. That would violate the law of energy conservation and that's a definite no-no! If we neglect slight power losses (heating of the core), we can say:

Power into primary = power out of secondary

Since electrical power is equal to the product of voltage and current, we can say

$$(\text{Voltage} \times \text{current})_{\text{primary}} = (\text{voltage} \times \text{current})_{\text{secondary}}$$

This is analogous to mechanical energy conservation, where the product of $(\text{force} \times \text{distance})_{\text{input}} = (\text{force} \times \text{distance})_{\text{output}}$. Recall that by increasing the distance through which the input force acts, the output force is increased proportionally. The increased output force is compensated by a decreased output distance—such that the product of force and distance is the same for both input and output. In the same way, a step-up in voltage is compensated by a decrease in current. The product of voltage and current is the same for both primary and secondary coils, Figure 24.15.

Fig. 24.15 Except for small heating losses, power input = power output. Since power equals voltage × current, the product of voltage and current is the same in both primary and secondary coils. If voltage is stepped up, current is correspondingly stepped down; if voltage is stepped down, current is correspondingly stepped up.

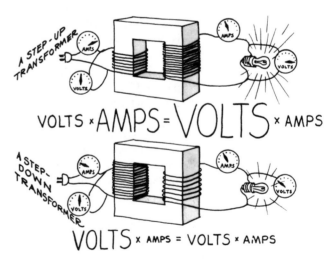

VOLTS × AMPS = VOLTS × AMPS

VOLTS × AMPS = VOLTS × AMPS

In a step-up transformer, then, voltage is stepped up and current is stepped down. This sometimes causes confusion, for according to Ohm's Law, an increase in voltage corresponds to an increase in current. And it does. The current is stepped down in comparison to the current drawn by the primary. A high voltage in the secondary might very well be accompanied by a huge current in the secondary—but the current drawn by the primary is huger still. And more power therefore is drawn. It is the voltages that are fixed. The primary voltage is fixed, and the secondary voltage is determined by the ratio of loops in the secondary and primary coils. The variable is current. The current in the secondary obeys Ohm's Law and is determined by the induced voltage and the load. By load we mean the electrical resistance of lamps, appliances, etc., to which the secondary is connected.* The product of this current and the induced voltage equals the power in the secondary, which in an efficient transformer is equal to the power in the primary—which then determines the current drawn by the primary, and hence the electric bill.

We can summarize this with a specific example: Consider a transformer with twice as many secondary loops as primary loops, powered by a 100-volt source. The induced voltage in the secondary then is 200 volts. Suppose the load to which the secondary is connected is a floodlamp having a resistance of 50 ohms. Then according to Ohm's Law, the current in the secondary is 200 volts/50 ohms = 4 amperes. The power in the secondary then is voltage × current, or 200 × 4 = 800 watts. This power must be supplied by the primary, which must then draw a current of 800 watts/100 volts = 8 amperes. From this, we see

$$100 \text{ volts} \times 8 \text{ amps} = 200 \text{ volts} \times 4 \text{ amps}$$

and power input = power output. Note that voltage is stepped up and current is stepped down from the primary to the secondary, and the amount of power drawn depends on the load connected to the secondary.

For sake of simplicity we have shown the windings on opposite sides of the transformer core. In practice the core is shaped with a middle core piece, Figure 24.16, and the secondary coil is wound on top of the primary.

Fig. 24.16 A practical transformer.

---

*When the load consists of coils and capacitors, which have "reactances" as well as resistances, the situation is more complicated than we have suggested here.

Self-induction   Current-carrying loops in a coil interact not only with loops of other coils, but also with loops of the same coil. Each loop in a coil interacts with the magnetic field produced by other loops in the same coil. This is called *self-induction*. A self-induced voltage is produced. This voltage is always in a direction opposing the changing voltage that produces it, and is commonly called the "back emf."* We won't treat self-induction and back emf's here, except to acknowledge a common and dangerous effect. A coil with a large number of turns has a large self-inductance. Suppose such a coil is used as an electromagnet and is powered with a dc source, perhaps a small battery. Current in the coil is then accompanied by a strong magnetic field. When we disconnect the battery by opening a switch, we had better be prepared for a surprise. When the switch is opened, the current in the circuit falls rapidly to zero and the magnetic field in the coil undergoes a sudden decrease. What happens when a magnetic field suddenly changes in a coil—even if it is the same coil that produced it? The answer is that a voltage is induced. The rapidly collapsing magnetic field with its store of energy induces an enormous voltage which may be large enough to develop an arc across the switch—or you, if you are opening the switch! For this reason, electromagnets are connected to a circuit that provides a bypass for this induced voltage.

Fig. 24.17 When the switch is opened the magnetic field of the coil collapses. This sudden change in the field can induce a huge voltage.

---

*This opposing direction of induction is called Lenz's Law and is a consequence of the conservation of energy.

Power Transmission   Almost all electric energy sold today is in the form of alternating current because of the ease with which it can be transformed from one voltage to another. Power is transmitted great distances at high voltages and correspondingly low currents, which otherwise would result in large energy losses owing to the heating of the wires. Power may be carried from the power plant to the cities at about 120,000 volts or more, stepped down to about 2200 volts in the city, and finally stepped down to 110 or 115 volts for safe home use.

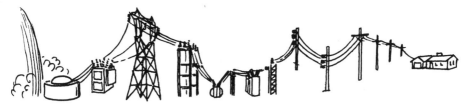

Fig. 24.18   Power transmission.

Energy, then, is transformed from one system of conducting wires to another by electromagnetic induction. It is but a short step further to find that these same principles account for sending energy from a radio-transmitter antenna to a radio receiver many miles away, and just a tiny step further to the transformation of energy of vibrating electrons in the sun to life energy on earth. The effects of electromagnetic induction are far-reaching. As far as is conceivable!

Field Induction   We have discussed electromagnetic induction thus far as the production of voltages and currents. Actually, the more fundamental fields underlie both voltages and currents. The modern view of electromagnetic induction holds that electric and magnetic *fields* are induced, which in turn give rise to the voltages we have considered. Induction takes place whether or not a conducting wire or any material medium is present. In this general sense Faraday's Law states:

An electric field is induced in any region of space in which a magnetic field is changing with time. The magnitude of the induced electric field is proportional to the rate at which the magnetic field changes. The direction of the induced field is at right angles to the changing magnetic field.

There is a second effect, which is the inverse of Faraday's Law. This was advanced by James Clerk Maxwell in about 1860 and states:

A magnetic field is induced in any region of space in which an electric field is changing with time. The magnitude of the induced magnetic field is proportional to the rate at which the electric field changes. The direction of the induced magnetic field is at right angles to the changing electric field.

These statements are two of the most important statements in physics. They underlie electromagnetic radiation.

In Perspective*   The ancient Greeks discovered that when a piece of amber (a natural plasticlike mineral) was rubbed, it picked up little pieces of papyrus. They found strange rocks on the island of Magnesia that attracted iron. Probably because the air in Greece was relatively humid, they never noticed and studied the static electrical-charge effects common in dry climates. Further development of electrical and magnetic phenomena did not take place until four hundred years ago. The world of man shrank as more was learned about electricity and magnetism. It became possible to signal by telegraph over long distances, and then to talk to another person miles away through wires, and then to not only talk, but also to send pictures over many miles with no connections in between.

Energy, so vital to civilization, could be transmitted over hundreds of miles. The energy of elevated rivers was diverted into pipes that fed giant "waterwheels" connected to assemblages of twisted and interwoven copper wires that rotated about specially designed chunks of iron—revolving monsters called generators. Out of this, energy was pumped through thick copper rods, approximately the thickness of your wrist, and sent to huge coils wrapped around transformer cores, boosting it to high voltages for efficient long-distance transmission to the cities. Then the transmission lines split into branches . . . then to more transformers . . . then more branching and spreading, until finally the energy of the river was spread throughout whole cities—turning motors, making heat, making light, working gadgetry. There was the miracle of hot lights from cold water hundreds of miles away—all done with specially designed bits of copper

*This section is drawn from parts of Volume II of Feynman's *Lectures on Physics*.

and iron—all turning because man discovered the laws of electro-magnetism. These laws were discovered at about the time the American Civil War was being fought.

From a long view of the history of mankind, there can be little doubt that the American Civil War will pale into provincial insignificance in comparison with the more significant event of the nineteenth century, man's discovery of the electromagnetic laws.

Summary of Terms

Electromagnetic induction. The induction of voltage when a magnetic field changes with time. If the magnetic field within a closed loop changes in any way, a voltage is induced in the loop.

$$\text{Voltage induced} = -(\text{number of loops}) \times \frac{\text{magnetic field change}}{\text{time}}$$

which is called Faraday's Law. The induction of voltage is actually the result of a more fundamental phenomenon: the induction of an electric *field*. We will define Faraday's Law for this more general case:

Faraday's Law. An electric field is induced in any region of space in which a magnetic field is changing with time. The magnitude of the induced electric field is proportional to the rate at which the magnetic field changes. The direction of the induced field is at right angles to the changing magnetic field.

Maxwell's counterpart to Faraday's Law. A magnetic field is induced in any region of space in which an electric field is changing with time. The magnitude of the induced magnetic field is proportional to the rate at which the electric field changes. The direction of the induced magnetic field is at right angles to the changing electric field.

Transformer. A device for transforming electrical power from one coil of wire to another, by means of electromagnetic induction. A changing magnetic field in the core of the transformer is provided by alternating current in the primary coil. Voltage in the secondary coil may be stepped up or stepped down according to the relation:

$$\frac{\text{Primary voltage}}{\text{Number of primary loops}} = \frac{\text{secondary voltage}}{\text{number of secondary loops}}$$

If the voltage is stepped up, the current is correspondingly stepped down in such a way that the product of current and voltage (power) is no greater in the secondary coil than in the primary coil; that is,

$$(\text{Voltage} \times \text{current})_{\text{primary}} = (\text{voltage} \times \text{current})_{\text{secondary}}$$

Questions

1. Why does an iron core increase the inductance of a coil of wire?

2. Why are the armature and field windings of an electric motor usually wound on an iron core?

3. Two separate but similar coils of wire are mounted vertically a few inches apart, as in Figure 24.11. The first coil is connected to a battery and has a direct current flowing through it. The second coil is connected to a galvanometer. What does the galvanometer read when the current in the first coil is increasing, decreasing, or remaining steady?

4. How could the motor in Figure 24.5 be used as a generator of electricity?

5. How is the current induced in a coil affected by a change in the speed or frequency of the changing magnetic field?

6. What is the principal advantage of ac over dc?

7. Why would long-distance transmission of electric power, if done at low voltages, incur heavy losses?

8. Note the similarities in the electric motor shown in Figure 24.5 and the do-it-yourself-paper-clip motor illustrated on the following pages. Both motors are powered with a dc source, yet the current in the rotors of each motor is ac. Explain.

Project: A Do-It-Yourself Recipe for a Simple Homemade Motor*

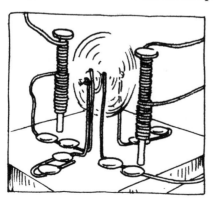

The finished motor shown to the left can be built with the following commonplace tools and materials: eight thumbtacks, three 2-inch paper clips, two $3\frac{1}{2}$-inch nails, needle-nosed pliers, electrical or adhesive tape, a wooden board about five inches square, about seven feet of No. 20 insulated copper wire, and a knife to scrape the ends with. Two $1\frac{1}{2}$-volt dry cells provide an adequate power supply.

*Courtesy of Time-Life Inc.

Step 1. The first step in making the motor is straightening the smaller loop of one of the paper clips, and then twisting it so that it stands upright at right angles to the larger loop. Then use the pliers to bend a tiny loop in the upright end. Do the same with a second paper clip.

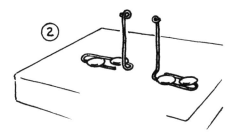

Step 2. Next, attach the paper clips to the board with tacks as shown. The upright ends of the clips should be about an inch apart. The tacks should be loose enough for final adjustment later. These clips are the supports for the axle of the motor's rotor.

Step 3. Next make the rotor. With pliers, bend the ends of the third paper clip perpendicular to the clip's midpoint as shown. The ends, which will serve as the rotor's axle, should each be about a half-inch long.

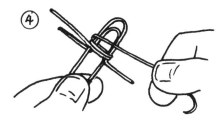

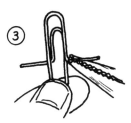

Step 4. Leaving one inch free, wrap the copper wire tightly around the rotor clip, working out from the middle. Wind the turns of wire closely together, but not so tightly that the clip is bent out of shape.

Step 5. Wrap about 20 coils out toward the end of the rotor clip. Then take the wire back to the center and wrap—in the same direction—an equal number of turns around the other half. These coils will make the clip an electromagnet.

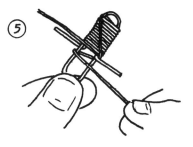

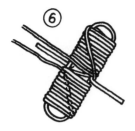

Step 6. When the copper wire has been wound around the second half of the rotor clip as shown, it is brought back to the center of the clip. The ends of the wire will serve as the rotor's *commutator*, which reverses its current with each rotation.

Step 7. The next step is to cut the ends of the wire so that they are slightly shorter than the projecting end of the clip. Then scrape the coating off the ends of the wires making sure to expose the bare copper.

Then take two strips of electrical or adhesive tape—each about $\frac{1}{4}$ inch wide and 2 inches long—and wrap them around the axle next to the clip as shown. This tape keeps the rotor-clip axle in the paper-clip supports. The center of gravity of the finished rotor should be along the axle so that it will twirl without wobbling.

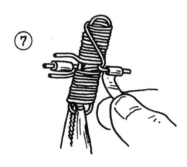

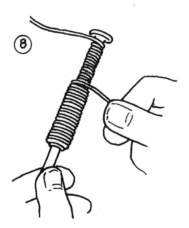

Step 8. Make two stationary electro-magnets by wrapping each nail with wire, leaving about 9 inches of wire free close to the head. Wind the wire evenly for about $2\frac{1}{2}$ inches down from the top, then about half-way back up again. Both nails should be wound in the same direction.

Leave about 6 inches of wire sticking out from the middle of each nail and cut it. Each nail should now have a 9-inch and a 6-inch tail. Scrape about $\frac{3}{4}$ inch of insulation from the end of each tail, exposing the bare copper.

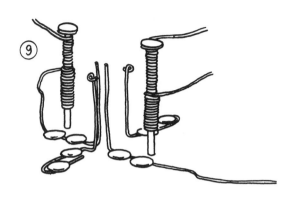

Step 9. Hammer the nails into the board just far enough apart to make room for the rotor. Tack the 6-inch tail from one nail to the board. Lead it to within $\frac{1}{4}$ inch of either support and bend it up so its tip is slightly higher than the support. Do the same with an unattached 12-inch length of wire. These form the *brushes*. About $\frac{3}{4}$ inch of insulation should be thoroughly scraped from each end of the 12-inch length of wire. Now all loose ends of wire are scraped free of insulation.

Step 10. Fit the axle of the rotor into the loops of each support so that the rotor's commutators, when twirling, will make contact with the brushes. Twist the end of the 6-inch tail from the second nail around the 9-inch wire from the first nail. The 9-inch wire from the second nail will connect with the dry-cell terminal. Link the free end of the 12-inch wire to the opposite dry-cell terminal and the circuit is complete.

It is important to make final adjustments so that the rotor will spin freely. As the rotor spins, both commutators should touch the brushes simultaneously. Only then will current be established in the entire circuit, making the rotor and nails electromagnets. Each time the rotor makes a half-turn, the direction of current in the rotor alternates, changing its magnetic-field polarity. It may be necessary to give the rotor a gentle nudge for the motor to operate, just as you sometimes have to do with some types of electric shavers.

Utilizing the fact that like magnetic poles repel each other and unlike poles attract, can you explain the operation of this motor?

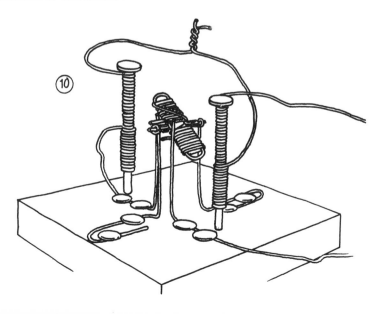

25

Electromagnetic Radiation

Electromagnetic-Wave Velocity

The existence of electromagnetic waves was first deduced by James Clerk Maxwell in about 1860 in conjunction with his theoretical work in linking electricity and magnetism. His highly mathematical ideas about the nature of electromagnetic waves are among the most abstract in physics. Nevertheless, it is possible to understand his ideas conceptually.

Consider an isolated electric charge vibrating back and forth at a certain frequency. The moving charge constitutes an electric current that changes in direction with the frequency of the vibrating charge. Surrounding this electric current, then, is a magnetic field which also changes direction with each oscillation of the vibrating charge. The law of induction tells us that a changing magnetic field will induce an electric field. Hence there are induced magnetic and electric fields about the vibrating charge. These fields mutually induce each other, the changing magnetic field inducing a changing electric field which in turn induces a changing magnetic field and so on. These fields are not localized, however, but emanate outward from the vibrating charge. The intensity of the induced fields is very much dependent on this speed of emanation. Let's see why this is so.

Consider first the initial magnetic field induced by the moving charge. This changing magnetic field induces a changing electric field, which in turn induces a magnetic field. The magnitude of this further induced magnetic field depends not only on the vibrational rate of the electric field but also on the *motion* of the electric field, or the speed at which the induced field emanates from the vibrating charge. The higher the speed, the greater the magnetic field it induces. At low speeds, electromagnetic regeneration would be short-lived because a slow-moving electric field would induce a weak magnetic field, which would induce in turn a weaker electric field. The induced fields would become successively weaker, causing the mutual induction to die out. But what of the energy in such a case? The fields contain energy given to them by the vibrating charge—if the fields disappeared with no means of transferring energy to some other form, energy would be destroyed. We see that low-speed emanation of electric and magnetic fields is incompatible with the law of energy conservation. At emanation speeds too high, on the other hand, the fields would be induced to ever-increasing magnitudes, with a crescendo of ever-increasing energies—again clearly in contradiction of the conservation of energy. At some critical speed, however, mutual induction would continue indefinitely, with neither a loss or gain in energy.

From his equations of electromagnetic induction, Maxwell calculated the value of this critical speed—186,000 miles per second. But this was the velocity of light! Maxwell at once realized that he had discovered the solution to one of the greatest mysteries of the universe—the nature of light. For if the electric charge is set into oscillation within the incredible frequency range of 4.3×10^{14} to 7×10^{14} vibrations per second, the resulting electromagnetic wave will activate the "electrical antennae" in the retina of the eye. Light is simply electromagnetic radiation in this range of frequencies! The lower frequency appears red and the higher frequency appears violet.

The Electromagnetic Spectrum

All electromagnetic waves travel at the same speed in a vacuum. They differ from one another in their frequency and wavelength. The frequency of the wave as it vibrates through space is identical to the frequency of the oscillating electric charge generating it. The differences in wavelength are due to the differences in frequency. For example, since the speed of the wave is 186,000 miles per second, an electric charge oscillating once per second will produce a wave with a wavelength 186,000 miles long. This is because only one wavelength is generated in one second. If the frequency of oscillation is 10 vibrations per second, then 10 wavelengths are generated and the corresponding wavelength would be 18,600 miles long. A frequency of 10,000 vibrations per second would produce wavelengths 18.6 miles long. So the higher the frequency of the vibrating charge, the shorter the wavelength of radiation.*

The wavelength of standard AM radio waves range around 1000 feet; and FM and television waves around 10 feet. The wavelength of visible light waves ranges from 35 to 70 millionths of a centimeter. The shortest waves detected are cosmic rays of

---

*The relationship is $c = f\lambda$, where c is the wave velocity (constant), f is the frequency, and λ is the wavelength.

wavelength 10^{-31} cm, about one billionth of a billionth the size of a proton (cosmic rays consist of electromagnetic radiation as well as nuclear particles).

Electromagnetic waves in principle can have any frequency from zero to infinity. The classification of electromagnetic waves according to frequency is called the *electromagnetic spectrum*, Figure 25.1. Low-frequency electromagnetic waves of several vibrations per second are of no practical importance and are not generated intentionally. Electromagnetic waves with frequencies on the order of several thousand cycles per second (kilocycles) are classified as radio waves. The VHF (very high frequency) television band of waves starts at about 50 million cycles per second (megacycles). Still higher frequencies are called microwaves, followed by infrared waves, often called "heat waves." Further still is visible light, which makes up about 1 percent of the measured electromagnetic spectrum. Beyond light, the higher frequencies extend into the ultraviolet, X-ray, and gamma-ray regions. There is no sharp distinction between these regions which actually overlap each other. The spectrum is simply broken up into these arbitrary regions for classification.

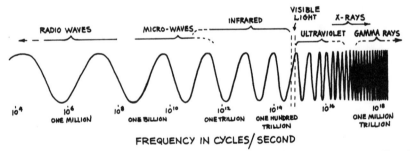

Fig. 25.1 The electromagnetic spectrum is a continuous range of radiation extending from radio waves to gamma rays. The descriptive names of the sections are merely a historical classification. In all sections the waves are the same in nature, differing only in frequency and wavelength—all have the same speed.

Production of Electromagnetic Waves

Of considerable interest is the way in which the oscillating frequency of the electric charges that produce these waves is controlled. Consider the oversimplified antenna in Figure 25.2. The rotating device in the middle alternately charges the upper and lower halves of the antenna positively and negatively. Electric charges accelerate up and down in the antenna, and send out electromagnetic waves which have a frequency equal to the rotational frequency of the rotor. If there is another wire antenna

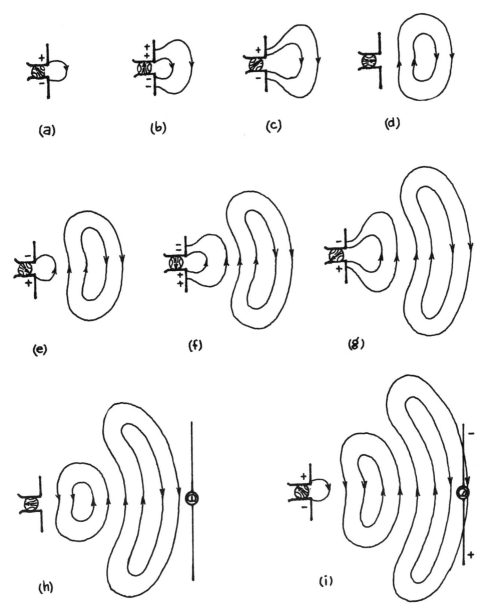

Fig. 25.2   The rotating device alternately charges the upper and lower parts of the antenna positively and negatively. Successive views, (a) through (i), indicate how acceleration of the charges up and down the antenna transmits electromagnetic waves. Only sample electric field lines of the waves are shown—the magnetic field lines are perpendicular to the electric field lines and extend into and out of the page. When the waves are incident upon a receiving antenna, (h) and (i), electric charges in it vibrate in rhythm with the field variations.

at some distance from the transmitting antenna, the electric charges in that wire will vibrate up and down in response to the variation in the electric and magnetic fields impinging on the wire. A very sensitive galvanometer in the middle of the receiving wire will register a pulsating current.

The frequency of commercial broadcasts ranges from 550 kilocycles to 1500 kilocycles per second. No mechanical device can rotate that rapidly. In place of such a rotor a small crystal is used. Small crystals vibrate naturally at these high frequencies, much as a bell vibrates at its own frequency when struck. The vibration frequency of a crystal depends on the elastic properties of its material and on its size and shape, much as the frequency of a bell depends on its material, size, and shape. Small crystals of quartz and other materials are ground to the proper size and shape, and used to control the frequency with which the electric charge is sent up and down in the transmitting antenna. Each radio station has its own crystal, usually a quartz wafer the size of a nickel, which vibrates hundreds of thousands of times each second, ensuring a constant frequency of radiation.

Smaller crystals vibrate at higher frequencies, just as smaller bells emit higher-pitched tones. Smaller crystals are used to transmit higher-frequency radio and television waves. Radar waves require crystals as small as 0.02 cm. Beyond this point crystals become too small to manipulate.

The crystal size necessary to generate frequencies corresponding to infrared or heat waves is approximately the size of molecules. This suggests that heat waves are produced by vibrating atoms and molecules carrying electric charges. To obtain frequencies corresponding to visible light, we need particles still smaller than molecules and atoms. These particles turn out to be the electrons within the atom. High-frequency vibrating electrons emit light. Higher electron frequencies produce ultraviolet radiation.

At still higher electron frequencies X-rays are emitted. X-rays are produced not only by the acceleration of vibrating electrons, but by the rapid deceleration of high-speed electrons as they hit a target. They undergo a tremendous acceleration by being stopped or deflected very suddenly. These positive and negative accelerations are accompanied by radiation of extremely high frequency.

Beyond the X-ray region of the spectrum lies the gamma-ray region. These rays accompany radioactive disintegration of the atomic nucleus. Their production indicates that within the nucleus there are extremely strong electric fields in which electric charges are accelerated at inconceivably high rates. Many of these high-frequency gamma rays originate in the cosmos and are called cosmic rays. There seems to be no upper limit to their frequencies.

All of these electromagnetic radiations are fundamentally alike in that they are produced by accelerating electric charges. All have the same speed in a vacuum. They differ only in their frequencies of vibration and in their corresponding wavelengths. As the frequency increases, the wavelength decreases such that the product of frequency and wavelength is a constant—the velocity of light.

An interesting property of radiation is penetrability. Radio waves go through air but not through metals. Lower-frequency radio waves bounce off the ionic layers high in the atmosphere while higher-frequency waves pass through and out into space. At night when this ionic layer is out of the sunlight and more settled, radio reception is improved, as distant signals are reflected from the layer and are picked up by local radio receivers. Higher-frequency radiation carrying television signals penetrates the ionic layer, however, and transmission must be accomplished on a "line of sight" basis. Infrared radiation goes through dry air but not through water vapor. Most things, like people, absorb radiation in the infrared—that is why we call them "heat waves"—because they heat us up with the energy which we absorb from them. Visible light goes through glass while ultraviolet does not. X-rays go through any kind of matter, but with some absorption. Any given material, depending on its structure, absorbs, reflects, or transmits a given radiation selectively.

Electromagnetic Waves Are Everywhere

Accelerating electric charges, then, radiate energy in waves of electric and magnetic fields. Atoms in every substance are continually being bounced and jostled about—as a result the electrons of these atoms vibrate and radiate vibrations of electromagnetic energy. Every physical object in the universe—the stars, the planets, rocks, trees, your body—radiates electromagnetic waves at a frequency proportional to the rate of molecular and atomic vibratory motion, which is to say in proportion to the temperature. If the temperature is high enough, part of the radiation is visible as light. At lower temperatures the bulk of the radiation falls in the infrared portion of the spectrum, with some amounts in the microwave-radio region. Though invisible, these radiations can be detected and measured by various detectors.

Photographic film made with an emulsion sensitive to the infrared region of the spectrum shows different temperatures as different colors. High-altitude photos of the earth do more than detect forest fires. Subterranean lava channels not visible on the surface of the earth, underground geothermal springs, and anything having a higher or lower temperature than the surrounding environment can be detected by infrared photography. A heat picture of a person can reveal regions slightly warmer or cooler than normal that may hide a malignancy. Different rocks and minerals radiate infrared waves that differ slightly for different minerals. This fact enables geologists to chart the mineral makeup of the earth from airplanes. Spacecraft can analyze the composition of soils on various parts of the moon and planets. Diseased vegetation radiates a slightly different frequency of radiation than healthy vegetation, which shows up clearly on infrared film. This knowledge is valuable to farmers.

Cooler substances radiate lower-frequency electromagnetic waves. Icebergs, for example, radiate microwaves. Although icebergs radiate a lower-frequency radiation than water, they emit slightly more radiation than water. Ice-patrol fleets take advantage of this fact, and microwave-detection devices have become highly efficient iceberg spotters along the shipping lanes of the North Atlantic. Microwaves are also used to map heavy rain-bearing clouds in weather studies, and soil-moisture and water-distribution patterns in hydrological and agricultural surveys.

We tend to think of space as being empty. But this is only because we cannot see the montages of electromagnetic waves that permeate every part of the universe. We see some of these waves, of course, and we call them light. These waves make up less than 1 percent of the range of measurable waves of the electromagnetic spectrum. We are unconscious, for example, of the radio waves that engulf us every moment. Free electrons in every piece of metal on the earth's surface continually dance to the rhythms of these waves. They jiggle in unison with the electrons being driven up and down along radio- and television-transmitting antennae. A radio or television receiver is simply a device to sort out and amplify these tiny currents. There is radiation everywhere. It is this radiation that links us to the rest of the universe. Without it we would surely feel alone.

Suggested Reading   Fink, Donald G., and David M. Lutyens, *The Physics of Television* (Science Study Series), Garden City, N. Y., Doubleday (Anchor), 1960.

"Remote Sensing," *National Geographic*, January, 1969.

Questions   1. What bearing does the conservation of energy have on the speed of light?

2. How do sound waves and radio waves differ?

3. If you charge a comb by rubbing it through your hair, and then shake it up and down, are you producing electromagnetic waves? With what frequency would you have to shake the comb to produce visible light?

4. Why is radio reception better at night than in the day?

5. A rattlesnake can see infrared radiation. Can a rattlesnake, then, see in the dark? Discuss.

6. If all objects radiate energy, why can't we see objects in a darkened room?

PART 6

Light and Quantum Theory

26

The Wave and Quantum Nature of Light

The nature of light had been a mystery for thousands of years. Theories about the nature of light ranged from showers of particles to waves of some sort. Then in 1862 Maxwell announced that light is energy carried in the electric and magnetic fields of electromagnetic waves, which was experimentally confirmed twenty-five years later by Hertz. The mystery was no more. The last word on the nature of light was not, however, the electromagnetic waves of Maxwell. We will see that the nature of light involves a strange mixture of wave and particle properties. Light does not travel in continuous waves as envisioned by Maxwell, but in tiny packets of electromagnetic radiation called *light quanta*. In this chapter we shall briefly discuss some of the whos, whens, and hows of the developments that led to our present understanding of light. A more thorough treatment of the topics mentioned can be found in the books listed at the end of the chapter.

A Prequantum History of Man's Understanding of Light

Early Concepts

One of the earliest recorded views on the nature of light is that of Plato, who thought that light consisted of streamers or filaments emitted by the eye. Plato believed that seeing takes place when these streamers, acting like antennae, make contact with an object. Euclid argued for the same view, asking "how else can we explain that we do not see a needle on the floor until we seek it out and our eyes have fallen upon it?" As late as 1644, Descartes, the great French mathematician and philosopher, published a book elaborating on a similar theory.

Not all the ancients, however, held such views. The Pythagoreans believed that light traveled from a luminous body to the eye in the form of very fine particles, while Empedocles taught that light is some kind of high-speed wavelike disturbance. It is interesting that these two apparently contradictory views were destined to play the role of rival theories down through the centuries to the present time.

The ancient Greeks knew that light travels in straight lines, and from this they deduced the inverse-square law. This law states that the intensity or brightness of light decreases as the square of the distance. They also knew that when a beam of light is reflected from a mirror, the angle of incidence is equal to the angle of reflection.

The Greeks were also aware of refraction (the bending of a light beam in traveling from one medium to another) as evidenced by a partly immersed stick in water that seems to be bent when seen from the side. It was not until 1621, however, that a quantitative law of refraction was worked out by Wellebrord Snell, a Dutch astronomer and mathematician.

The Speed of Light

Whether light travels instantaneously or with finite speed was not known until almost the end of the seventeenth century. Galileo had tried to measure the time a light beam takes to travel to a distant mirror and back, but the time interval, if one existed at all, was too short. Members of the Florentine Academy tried the experiment with longer distances. They had two groups of observers with covered lanterns on two distant mountain tops. The first group then attempted to measure the time between the uncovering of their lantern and viewing the light of the other lantern. The time was extremely short and they soon realized that they were only measuring their reaction times.

The first successful measurement of the speed of light was probably made by the Danish astronomer Olaus Roemer about 1675. Roemer studied the periods of Jupiter's moons, four of which are visible through a small telescope. The innermost moon, Io, revolves around Jupiter in about 42.5 hours. It is eclipsed by Jupiter, disappearing almost instantaneously behind the shadow of the planet so that its period (time for one complete revolution) can be measured with precision. Roemer was puzzled to find an irregularity in the periods of Io. He found that as the earth moved away from Jupiter, say from position B to C, Figure 26.1, the measured periods of Io were all somewhat longer than average; and when moving toward Jupiter, say from position E to F, the periods were shorter than average. The cumulative discrepancy between positions A and D amounted to 1000 seconds. That is, when the earth was at position D the eclipse of Io seemed to be 1000 seconds late with respect to

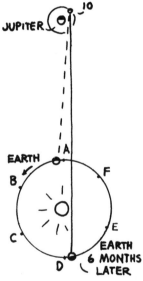

Fig. 26.1 Roemer's method of measuring the velocity of light. Light coming from the moon Io takes a longer time to reach the earth when the earth is in position D than when it is in position A. The extra distance that the light has to travel divided by the extra time of travel gives the velocity of light.

observations at position *A*. Roemer correctly interpreted this discrepancy. When the earth was farther away from Jupiter, it was the light that was late and not the moon. The eclipses still occurred at the predicted time, but the light carrying the message did not reach Roemer until it had traveled the extra distance across the diameter of the earth's orbit, 186,000,000 miles. There is some doubt as to whether Roemer knew the value of this distance. In any event, the calculation is extremely simple:

$$\text{Velocity of light} = \frac{\text{extra distance traveled}}{\text{extra time measured}}$$

$$= \frac{186,000,000 \text{ mi}}{1000 \text{ sec}} = 186,000 \text{ mi/sec}$$

Our treatment here is a bit oversimplified, as no account was taken of the motion of Jupiter, which is also revolving in its orbit about the sun. This motion is an additional complication, which does not affect our computation appreciably, because Jupiter's speed is much less than that of earth. It takes almost twelve years for Jupiter to make one revolution around the sun.

The most famous experiment measuring the speed of light was performed by Albert Michelson in 1880. Figure 26.2 is a simplified diagram representing his experiment. Light from an intense source is directed by a lens to an octagonal mirror which, for the moment, is at rest. The mirror is adjusted so that a beam of light is reflected to a distant stationary mirror which reflects it back to the octagonal mirror and finally to the eye of an observer. Michelson placed his stationary mirror on Mount San Antonio and the octagonal mirror on Mount Wilson, in California. The 22-mile distance between the mirrors was carefully surveyed. After careful alignment the octagonal mirror was set into rapid rotation. Each time one of the eight sides passed position (*A*), as indicated in the figure, a flash of light was sent to the stationary mirror atop Mount San Antonio and

Fig. 26.2 The mirror arrangement used by Michelson to measure the velocity of light.

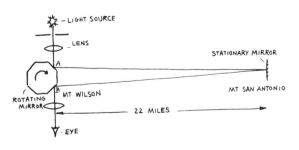

returned. If the mirror was in some different position when the light returned, it was reflected in some direction other than to the eye. However, when the speed of rotation of the mirror was made great enough so that the mirror rotated through exactly one-eighth of a revolution while the light made the trip to Mount San Antonio and back, the light was reflected from position (*B*) to the eye and observed. Then the time for the mirror to make one-eighth of a revolution was exactly equal to the time for the light to travel 44 miles. He calculated the speed of light to be 186,364 miles per second.* Michelson received the Nobel Prize for this experiment. He was the first American physicist to receive the prize.

From a Particle to a Wave Nature of Light

The velocity of light is one thing—the nature of light is another. A wave theory of light was proposed by the English physicist Robert Hooke in 1665, and improved twenty years later by the Dutch scientist and mathematician Christian Huygens. Huygens stated that light waves spreading out from a point source could be regarded as the superposition of tiny secondary wavelets and that every point on any wavefront may be regarded as a new point source of waves, Figure 26.3. This idea is called Huygens' Principle and is useful in explaining diffraction, the bending of light around sharp corners.

Fig. 26.3 Huygens' principle—every point on a wave behaves as if it were a new source of waves. Secondary wavelets starting at *b,b,b,b*, form a new wavefront *d-d*; secondary wavelets starting at *d,d,d,d*, form still another new wavefront *DCEF*. (From *Treatise on Light* by Christian Huygens.)

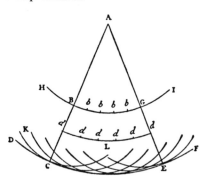

In 1704 Isaac Newton described light in a different way—as a stream of particles or corpuscles. Newton had observed that sunlight passing through a prism broke into the colors of the rainbow. He explained this by assuming that white light was

---

*Throughout the rest of this book we round this off to 186,000 miles per second.

composed of many kinds of tiny particles—atoms of light if you will—all mixed together. Newton reasoned that these different particles traveled at different speeds in the glass, bending at different angles and spreading out into overlapping groups forming the spectrum. He showed that when this spectrum was projected onto a second prism the particles recombined and emerged as white light. Experimenting with light reflected from glass plates, he noticed fringes of brightness and darkness ("Newton's rings") and recognized that particles of light have some sort of wave nature about them. He described this wave nature in terms of "fits of easy reflection and easy transmission." He did not study this further, made no hypotheses, and let the matter rest. His authority was so compelling, however, that the corpuscular theory of light held sway for a century, his successors adhering to the corpuscular view more so than Newton himself.

In 1801 Huygens' wave theory was given new life when Thomas Young performed his now famous interference experiment. Young found that light directed through two closely spaced thin slits recombined to produce fringes of brightness and darkness on a screen behind. The bright fringes of light resulted from light waves from the two slits arriving crest to crest, while the dark areas resulted from light waves arriving trough to crest. The effect is quite analogous to the phenomena of two waves on the surface of water canceling each other in certain places, as discussed in Chapter 18. It is also analogous to the production of "beats" in sound, where sound waves combine to reinforce or cancel one another. We shall treat the interference of light further in Chapter 29. Interference patterns cannot be explained in terms of particles. Young's experiment is now regarded as the first definite proof that light has wave properties.

How light waves are produced was developed mathematically by the Scotch physicist James Clerk Maxwell in 1862. Maxwell formulated four fundamental equations which are the basis of electricity and magnetism. The equations describe how energy can be propagated through space in the form of vibrating electric and magnetic fields, as was discussed in Chapter 25. A remarkable achievement of this theory is that the radiation velocity is 186,000 miles per second, which is the speed of light. According to Maxwell's theory, light is one type of electromagnetic wave which is radiated by vibrating electrons within the atom.

A wave seems to imply a medium—some continuous substance in which the wave disturbance takes place. The waves of sound are *in* air, the waves of the ocean are *in* water. If light is an electromagnetic wave, then what are these waves *in*? To satisfy this rational demand for a medium, *ether* was invented. It had to be a fluid that fills all space, from the space between stars to the space between the atoms. It had to be made of extremely fine particles, far finer than the atoms of ordinary matter, and had to flow through matter unhindered.

In 1887, two American scientists, Michelson and Morley, attempted to measure the presumed motion of the earth through the ether. Michelson invented an ingenious instrument, the *interferometer*, for this purpose. The interferometer is one of the most precise measuring instruments yet developed. It utilizes the interference of light waves to measure distances as small as the wavelength of light. We will discuss this instrument in more detail in Chapter 33. With this sensitive instrument they attempted to measure the effect of the "ether wind" on the velocity of light. The surprising results were that no change was detected in the velocity of light traveling either in the same direction or in the direction perpendicular to that of the earth with respect to the ether. The experiment showed that the velocity of light is a constant independent of the motion of the observer. No ether wind was detected. This indicated that whatever the ether was imagined to be, it does not in fact exist. Maxwell's electromagnetic waves travel through empty space, an etherless space.

Nevertheless, the idea of the all-pervading ether persisted until 1905 when Albert Einstein reconciled the results of the Michelson and Morley experiment with a new theory, a theory that was to change the course of physics—special relativity. We will discuss special relativity in Chapter 33.

Birth of the Quantum Theory

The continuous spectrum of light emitted by incandescent solids was the phenomenon that led to the birth of the quantum theory. Before the turn of the twentieth century it was known that light of all frequencies was emitted by an incandescent solid, regardless of the material. The relative brightness of the different colors depended solely on the temperature of the material. The hotter the solid, the greater the electron motion in the solid, and hence the higher the frequency of resulting radiation—the visible frequencies ranging from a dull red through orange to white, and then for extremely high temperatures, violet. Much experimentation was done finding the brightness at various frequencies for various temperatures. A typical result is the radiation curves shown in Figure 26.4.

Finding a mathematical formula describing the radiation curves proved to be a tough nut to crack. All mathematical expressions based on classical physics failed to account for the shape of the experimental curves. A young German physicist, Max Planck, approached the problem by attempting to guess

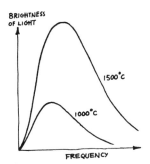

Fig. 26.4 Radiation curves —the brightness and frequencies of light emitted from an incandescent solid increase as the temperature rises.

the solution by a process of trial and error. In a brilliant speculative analysis, guided by the partial successes and failures of others who tried, he found a successful formula. At the time he could give no physical basis for his formula. Two months later Planck offered justification for his formula, but the arguments he used contradicted the ideas of classical physics.

Classical physics maintains that a vibrating body can have any amount of energy within certain limits. The lower limit is zero and the upper limit is the amount of energy that would interrupt the regularity of the vibrating system. For example, a pendulum undergoing simple harmonic motion can have any amount of energy as long as it does not swing higher than some angle that will alter its period of motion. The potential energy possessed by a simple pendulum can be measured by the angle it makes with its equilibrium position. According to classical physics, this angle is in no way restricted to discrete values. The angle may be 5 degrees or 5.00001 degrees, or any value between these two.

Planck could justify his formula only if he assumed that the vibrating electrons emitted the radiation in discrete bunches of energy, which he called *quanta*.

The term *quantum* designates the discreteness of any system. It means that some aspect or characteristic property of a system occurs only in certain sizes. For example, when we place a ball on a stairway we must place it on one of the stairs—it cannot be successfully placed between two stairs. The gravitational potential energy of the ball is then quantized. It can have only discrete

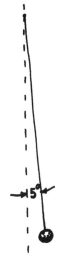

Fig. 26.5 The potential energy of the pendulum bob may be any value between a minimum and maximum value. The energy is nonquantized.

Fig. 26.6 The potential energy of the ball resting on the stairs takes on only discrete values, and therefore is quantized.

values, for energy values corresponding to elevations between two stairs are not permitted since the ball must be on one stair or the other. If the ball bounces down the stairs its potential energy will decrease in discrete jumps, maybe one or two stairs at a time, but always by some whole-number multiple of the energy difference between two stairs.

Matter is quantized; the mass of a brick of gold, for example, is equal to some whole-number multiple of the mass of a single gold atom. Electricity is quantized, as all electric charge is some whole-number multiple of the charge of a single electron. In a similar sense, Planck postulated that the energy states of electrons in an atom are quantized; that is, electrons could vibrate only with certain discrete amounts of energy. He further postulated that radiation would occur only when an electron made a transition from a higher-energy state to a lower-energy state, and the energy of the resulting quantum of radiation would be equal to the difference in the energy states of the atom. The frequency of the emitted radiation is proportional to this energy difference, thus the energy of each quantum of radiation is proportional to its radiation frequency:

$$E \sim f$$

A quantum of infrared radiation then has a tiny energy, a quantum of green light a small energy, and a quantum of ultraviolet radiation a larger energy. The greater the radiation frequency of a quantum, the greater its energy.

When the energy of a quantum of radiation is divided by its frequency, the single number that results is the proportionality constant, called *Planck's constant, h.** We shall see that Planck's constant is a fundamental constant of nature which serves to set a lower limit on the smallness of things. It ranks with the velocity of light as one of the two basic constants of nature, and appears again and again in quantum physics. We can insert this constant in the above proportion and express it as an exact equation,

$$E = hf$$

This equation gives the smallest amount of energy that can be converted to light. The radiation of light is not emitted continuously as sound is from a vibrating string, but is emitted in units of hf.†

---

*h has the numerical value 6.6×10^{-34} joule-second.

†The energy in a beam of light containing n quanta is $E = nhf$.

Physicists were reluctant to adopt Planck's quantum explanation of the formula describing the radiation curve. Before it could be taken seriously the quantum idea would have to be verified by some means independent of the radiation of an incandescent source. The verification was supplied less than five years later by Albert Einstein in his explanation of the photoelectric effect.

The Photoelectric Effect

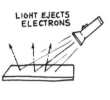

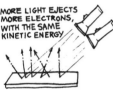

Fig. 26.7 The photoelectric effect.

Several investigators had noticed in the latter part of the nineteenth century that light was capable of ejecting electrons from various metal surfaces. This is the *photoelectric effect*, now put to use in electric eyes, in the photographer's light meter, and with the sound track of motion pictures. This effect was not particularly surprising to the early investigators. The ejection of electrons could be accounted for by classical mechanics which would picture the incident light waves building an electron's vibration up to greater and greater amplitudes until it finally broke loose from the metal surface. Accordingly, a dim light after some delay would build up enough vibration for ejection, whereas a very bright light would immediately eject electrons with greater energies. But this didn't happen. Some facts about this phenomenon had no obvious explanation:

1. The effect was easy to do with violet or ultraviolet light, but not with red light.
2. The rate at which electrons were ejected was proportional to the brightness of the light.
3. The energies of the ejected electrons were independent of the brightness of the light, but there were indications that the energy did depend on the frequency of the light.

An arrangement for observing the photoelectric effect is shown in Figure 26.8. Light shining on the negatively charged photo-

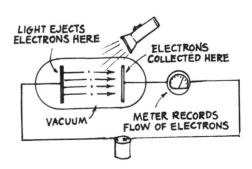

Fig. 26.8 Apparatus used for measuring the photoelectric effect.

sensitive metal surface liberates electrons, which are attracted to the positive plate, producing a measurable current. By instead charging this plate negatively, so that it repels electrons, the current can be stopped. From the easily measured potential difference between the plates, the energies of the electrons are calculated.

The fact that the brightness of light in no way affects the energies of ejected electrons was perplexing. Light was known to be electromagnetic radiation and the stronger electric fields of bright light were thought surely to interact with the electrons causing them to eject at greater speeds. Yet this was not the case. More electrons were ejected, but not at greater speeds. No increase in electron kinetic energies was detected. A weak beam of ultraviolet light, on the other hand, produced a fewer number of ejected electrons, but at much higher kinetic energies. This was most puzzling.

Einstein produced the answer in 1905, the same year he explained Brownian motion and set forth his theory of special relativity. His clue was Planck's quantum theory of radiation. Planck had assumed that the emission of light in quanta was due to limitations on the vibrating electrons that produced the light, which he considered to be discrete pulses of the electromagnetic waves described by Maxwell. Einstein, on the other hand, attributed the quantum properties to light itself, and viewed radiation as a hail of particles. To emphasize this particle aspect, we speak of *photons* (analogous to electrons, protons, neutrons, etc.) whenever we are thinking of the particle nature of light. One photon is completely absorbed by each electron ejected from the metal. The electron absorbs all of the energy in the photon. Since the energy of the photon is directly proportional to its frequency, the photoelectric effect would not occur for red light, however bright. The small energies of low-frequency photons of red light were insufficient to dislodge electrons from the metal surface. This also explained how a feeble beam of high-frequency ultraviolet light ejected electrons at greater energies than a beam of whatever intensity lower-frequency light. An electron could absorb at most a single photon, and the energy of ejection depended on the energy of the single absorbed photon, not on how many photons were striking other parts of the surface. Brighter light ejected more electrons, but not faster ones.

The first experimental verification of Einstein's explanation of the photoelectric effect was made eleven years later by the

American physicist Robert Millikan. Every aspect of Einstein's interpretation of the photoelectric effect was confirmed. Millikan found the numerical value of Planck's constant to be the same as that which Planck had earlier found by a completely independent method. Thus the same quantization appeared when light was emitted and when it was absorbed, which supported Einstein's view that the quantization was a property of light itself. Just as the mass of a pure substance is some whole-number multiple of the mass of a molecule, and electricity is some whole-number multiple of the charge of an electron, the energy of a single-frequency light beam is some whole-number multiple of hf.

The photoelectric effect cannot be explained by a wave theory of light. A wave has a broad front. It is difficult to understand how all the energy of a wave can be concentrated to eject a single electron from a metal surface. This is as improbable as an ocean wave hitting a beach and knocking a single seashell far inland—and with an energy equal to the energy of the whole wave. Instead of conceiving of light as a continuous train of waves, the photoelectric effect suggests we conceive it as a succession of corpuscular wavepackets, or photons.

The photoelectric effect proves conclusively that light has particle properties. We cannot conceive of the photoelectric effect on the basis of waves. On the other hand, as we will see in more detail in Chapter 29, the phenomena of interference prove conclusively that light has wave properties. We cannot conceive of interference in terms of particles. This appears to be and *is* contradictory. Some phenomena can be explained by the particle theory alone. Other phenomena can be explained by the wave theory alone. Still other phenomena can be explained by either theory. Perhaps we should think of light, not as a particle or wave, but as a "wavicle."

The Bohr Model of the Atom

A few years after Einstein announced the photoelectric effect, the British physicist Ernest Rutherford performed his now famous gold-foil experiment. He directed a beam of particles from a radioactive source through a very thin gold leaf and measured their scattering angle as they emerged. His results showed that the atom was mostly empty space with nearly all its mass concentrated at the center. Rutherford had discovered the atomic nucleus.

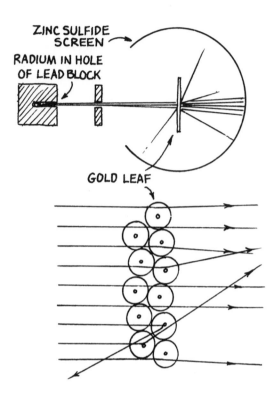

Fig. 26.9 The occasional large-angle scattering of alpha particles from the gold atoms led Rutherford to the discovery of the small very massive nucleus at their centers.

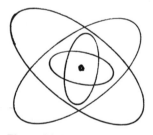

Fig. 26.10 The Bohr model of the atom—although this model is very oversimplified, it is still useful in understanding light emission.

Shortly thereafter a young Danish physicist, Neils Bohr, applied the quantum theory of Planck and Einstein to the nuclear atom of Rutherford and formulated the well-known planetary model of the atom that we discussed in Chapter 9. Bohr reasoned that Planck's quantized electron energy states would correspond to electron orbits of different radii. Electrons orbiting in the farthermost orbits would be at a higher energy state than those in the orbits closer to the nucleus. Bohr reasoned that light is emitted when electrons make a transition from a higher to lower orbit, and that the frequency of emitted radiation is given by the quantum relationship $E = hf$, where E is the difference in energy between the orbits.

The Bohr model of the atom, very oversimplified in comparison with today's models, is useful in understanding the process of light emission. We shall discuss the emission of light from atoms in the following chapter, and return to atomic models and the quantum theory in Chapter 32.

Summary of Terms

Quantum theory. The theory that energy is radiated in definite units called quanta, or photons: just as matter is composed of atoms, radiant energy is composed of quanta. The theory further states that all material particles have wave properties.

Planck's constant. A fundamental constant h which relates the energy and the frequency of light quanta: $h = 6.6 \times 10^{-34}$ joule-second.

Photoelectric effect. The ejection of electrons from a substance by the incidence of light or ultraviolet radiation upon it.

Suggested Reading

Holton, Gerald, and D. H. D. Roller, *Foundations of Modern Physical Science*, Reading, Mass., Addison-Wesley, 1958.

Jaffe, Bernard, *Michelson and the Speed of Light* (Science Study Series), Garden City, N.Y., Doubleday (Anchor), 1960.

Questions

1. Members of the Florentine Academy tried to measure the speed of light between two distant mountain tops. How far apart would the mountains have had to have been for the light to take one second in traveling from one mountain to the other?

2. A candle has a certain brightness. By how much does this brightness decrease when we stand twice as far from it?

3. If the rotating mirror used by Michelson and Morley had only four sides rather than eight sides, would it be necessary to rotate it faster or slower in order to measure the speed of light? How much faster or slower?

4. The first World's Fair took place in Chicago in 1893. The second World's Fair took place in Chicago forty years later, in 1933. The fair was officially opened by light from the star Arcturus, which was focused on an "electric eye" by the telescope at Yeakes Observatory. Why do you suppose the star Arcturus was selected?

5. Which photon has the greatest energy—an infrared, a visible, or an ultraviolet?

6. A beam of red light and a beam of blue light have exactly the same energy. Which beam contains the greatest number of photons?

7. Why is the radiation curve (Figure 26.4) for a material heated to 1500°C higher than the radiation curve for a material heated to 1000°C?

8. Silver bromide (AgBr) is a light-sensitive substance used in some types of photographic film. To cause exposure to the film

it must be illuminated with light having sufficient energy to dissociate the molecules. Why do you suppose this film may be handled without exposure in a darkroom illuminated with red light? How about blue light? How about very bright red light as compared to very dim blue light?

9. Compare the relative current readings in the ammeter in Figure 26.8 for illumination of the photosensitive plate by light of various colors. For various intensities.

10. Explain briefly how the photoelectric effect is utilized in the operation of at least two of the following: an electric eye, a photographer's light meter, the sound track of a motion picture.

27

Light Emission and Color

If energy is pumped into a metallic antenna in such a way as to cause free electrons to vibrate up and down a few thousand times per second, a radio wave is emitted. If free electrons could be made to vibrate up and down a few million-billion times per second, a visible light wave would be emitted. Light is not produced from metallic antennae, nor is it produced by electrons jiggling up and down in atomic antennae. Light is emitted by electrons moving from higher to lower atomic energy states, as briefly discussed in the previous chapter. We shall now investigate this emission process in more detail.

Excitation

An electron farther from the nucleus has a greater electric potential energy with respect to the nucleus than an electron nearer to the nucleus. We say that the farthermost electron is at a higher *energy level*. In a sense, this is similar to the energy of a spring door or a pile driver—the wider the door is pulled open, the greater its spring potential energy, or the higher the ram of a pile driver is raised, the greater its gravitational potential energy.

When an electron is in any way raised to a higher energy level, the atom is said to be *excited*. The electron's higher level is only momentary, for like the spring door pushed open, it soon returns to its stable state. The electron loses its temporarily acquired energy in returning to a lower level and this energy is released as a photon. The atom has undergone the process of *excitation* and *de-excitation*.

As each element has its own number of electrons, each element also has its own characteristic set of energy levels. Electrons dropping from higher to lower energy levels in an excited atom

Fig. 27.1 The different orbits in an atom are like steps. When an electron is raised to a higher orbit, the atom is excited. When the electron falls to its original step, it releases energy in the form of light.

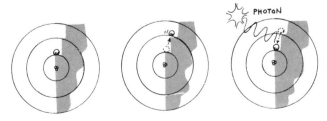

PHOTON

361

emit a photon with each jump. Many frequencies characteristic of the atom are emitted, corresponding to the many paths the electron may take in jumping from level to level. These frequencies combine to give the light from each excited element its own characteristic color.

The light emitted by a neon advertising sign is a familiar example of excitation. The different colors in the sign correspond to the excitation of different gases, although it is common to refer to any of these as "neon." Only the red light is that of neon. At the ends of the glass tube that contains the neon gas are electrodes. Electrons are boiled off these electrodes and are jostled back and forth at high speeds by a high-ac voltage. Millions of high-speed electrons vibrate back and forth inside the glass tube and smash into millions of target atoms; each smash drives orbital electrons into higher energy levels by an amount of energy equal to the decrease in kinetic energy of the bombarding electron—and this energy is radiated as the characteristic red light of neon when the electrons fall back to their stable orbits. The process occurs and recurs many times, as neon atoms are continually undergoing a cycle of excitation and de-excitation. The overall result of this process is the transformation of electrical energy into radiant energy.

Another example is the newer type street lamps. Many streets are now illuminated with light emitted by the excitation of mercury vapor. Not only is the light brighter, but it is less expensive. Whereas most of the energy in an incandescent lamp is converted to heat, most of the energy put into a mercury vapor lamp is converted to light. The light from these lamps is rich in the blues and violets and therefore is a different "white" than the light from an incandescent lamp. You will notice that the coloring of various objects is altered under the illumination of a mercury-vapor lamp.

The colors of various flames are due to excitation. Different atoms in the flame emit colors characteristic of their energy-level spacings. Common table salt placed in a flame, for example, produces the characteristic yellow of sodium. Every element, excited in a flame or otherwise, emits its own characteristic color—a composite of the many colors that make up its characteristic spectrum.

The excitation/de-excitation process can be accurately described only by quantum mechanics. An attempt to view the process in terms of classical physics runs into contradictions. Classically, electromagnetic radiation is induced by an accelerating electric charge. Interestingly enough, an electron does accelerate in a transition from a higher to lower energy level, for just as the innermost planets of the solar system have greater orbital speeds than those in the outermost orbits, the electrons in the innermost orbits of the atom have greater speeds. An electron gains speed in dropping to lower energy levels. Fine— the accelerating electron radiates a photon! But not-so-fine— the electron is continually undergoing acceleration (centripetal acceleration) in any orbit, whether or not it changes energy levels. Classically, it should continually radiate energy. But it doesn't. All attempts to accurately explain the emission of light by an excited atom in terms of a classical model have been unsuccessful. We have no simple model for conceptualizing this process. We shall simply say that light is emitted when electrons in an atom make a transition from a higher to a lower energy level, and that the energy and frequency of the emitted photon is described by the quantum relationship $E = hf$.

The next time you see evidence of atomic excitation, perhaps the green flame produced when a piece of copper is placed in a fire, squint your eyes and see if you can imagine electrons jumping from one energy level to another in a pattern characteristic of the atom being excited—a pattern that gives off a resulting color unique for that atom. Because that too is what's happening, Mr. Jones.

Incandescence   Light emitted from a neon gas tube is red. This is because the average difference in neon energy levels is proportional to the frequency of red light. Light emitted by a common incandescent lamp, however, is white. All the frequencies of visible radiation are emitted. Does this mean the tungsten atoms making up the lamp filament are characterized by an infinite number of energy levels? The answer is no—if the filament were vaporized and then excited, the tungsten gas would emit a finite number of frequencies producing an overall bluish color. The frequency of light emitted by atoms depends not only on the energy-level spacings within the atoms, but also on the spacings between neighboring atoms themselves. In a gas the atoms are far apart. Electrons undergo transitions between energy levels within the atom quite unaffected by the presence of neighboring atoms. But when the atoms are close-packed, as in a solid, electrons of the outer orbits make transitions not only within the energy levels of their "parent atoms," but also between the levels of neighboring atoms. Such transitions occur continually in metals, where the atoms are actually ions anchored amidst a sea of swarming "free" electrons. These are the electrons that constitute the flow of electricity under electric pressure, contribute to the conductivity of heat, and, as we shall see, give rise to the heat radiation discussed in Chapter 15.

Whereas the energy levels for the innermost electrons in atoms are relatively far apart and well defined, the energy levels of the outermost electrons are closer together. In a solid these energy levels are no longer well defined, but are altered by interactions between neighboring atoms. As a result the excitation and de-excitation in solids takes place between an infinite variety of energy-level differences, giving rise to an infinite number of radiation frequencies. A plot of radiated energy over a wide range of frequencies for two different temperatures is shown in the pair of radiation curves in Figure 27.2. (These are the same radiation curves we discussed in Chapter 26.) As the solid is heated further, wider energy-level transitions take place and higher frequencies of radiation are emitted. The most predominant frequency of emitted radiation, the peak frequency, is directly proportional to the absolute temperature of the emitter:

$$\bar{f} \sim T$$

We use the bar above the f to indicate *peak* frequency, for many frequencies of radiation are emitted from incandescent sources. If the temperature of an object (in Kelvin degrees) is doubled, the peak frequency of emitted radiation is doubled. The electromagnetic waves of violet light have twice the frequency of red light waves. A violet-hot star therefore has twice the temperature of a red-hot star. The temperature of incandescent bodies, whether they be stars or blast-furnace interiors, can be determined by measuring the peak frequency (or color) of radiation they emit.

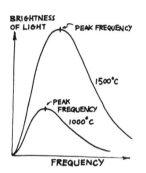

Fig. 27.2 Radiation curves for an incandescent solid.

Fluorescence

Thermal agitation or a bombarding particle such as a high-speed electron is not the only means of imparting excitation energy to an atom. An atom may be excited by absorbing a photon of light. From the relationship $E = hf$, we see that high-frequency light, such as ultraviolet, delivers much more energy per photon than lower frequency light. Many substances undergo excitation when illuminated with ultraviolet light.

Some materials that are excited by ultraviolet light emit visible light upon de-excitation. The action of these materials is called *fluorescence*. What happens in some of these materials is that a photon of ultraviolet light collides with an atom of the material and gives up its energy in two parts. Part of the energy goes into heat, increasing the kinetic energy of the entire atom. The other part of the energy goes into excitation, boosting an electron to a higher orbit. Upon de-excitation, this part of the energy is released as a photon of light. Since some of the energy of the ultraviolet photon is converted to heat, the photon emitted has less energy, and therefore lower frequency, than the ultraviolet photon.

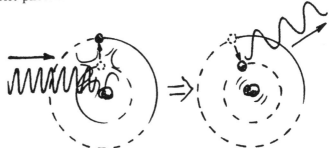

Fig. 27.3 In fluorescence, some of the absorbed energy of an ultraviolet photon goes into excitation and the remainder goes into heat. The photon then emitted is less energetic and therefore of a lower frequency than the ultraviolet photon.

In some other materials, an electron raised to a higher-energy level by a photon of ultraviolet light returns to its stable orbit in several steps. The photon energy released at each step is less than the amount of energy that was originally in the ultraviolet photon. So at each step the energy is released as a photon of lower frequency light. Hence ultraviolet light shining on such a material may cause it to glow red, yellow, or some color characteristic of the material. Fluorescent dyes are used in paints and fabrics to make them glow when bombarded with ultraviolet photons in sunlight. These are the so-called "day-glo" colors, which are spectacular when illuminated with an ultraviolet lamp.

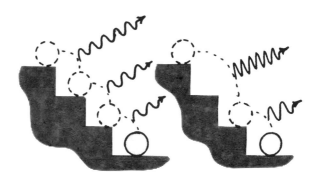

Fig. 27.4 An excited atom may de-excite in several combinations of jumps.

Detergents that make the claim of cleaning your clothes "whiter than white" utilize the principle of fluorescence. Such detergents contain a fluorescent dye that converts the ultraviolet light in sunlight into blue visible light, so clothes dyed in this way reflect more blue light than they otherwise would. This makes the clothes appear whiter.

The next time you visit a natural-science museum, go to the geology section and take in the exhibit of minerals illuminated with ultraviolet light. You'll note that different minerals radiate different colors. This is to be expected because different minerals are composed of different elements, which in turn have different sets of electron energy levels. Seeing the radiating minerals is a beautiful visual experience which is even more fascinating when integrated with a mind trip on nature's submicroscopic happenings: high-energy ultraviolet photons impinging on the surface of the minerals, causing the excitation of atoms in the mineral structure; and then the radiation of light frequencies corresponding exactly to the tiny energy-level spacings—and every excited atom emitting its characteristic frequency, with no two different minerals giving off exactly the same color light. Beauty is in both the eye and the mind of the beholder.

Fluorescent Lamp

Light emitted by a fluorescent lamp is produced by a primary and secondary excitation process. The primary process is excitation of gas by electron bombardment, and the secondary process is excitation by ultraviolet photons—fluorescence. The common fluorescent lamp consists of a cylindrical glass tube with electrodes at each end. Like the neon-sign tube, electrons are boiled from the electrodes and forced to vibrate back and forth at high speeds within the tube by the ac voltage. The tube is filled with very low-pressure mercury vapor which is excited by the impact of the high-speed electrons. As the energy levels in mercury are relatively far apart, the resulting emission of light is of high frequency, mainly in the ultraviolet region. This is the primary excitation process. The secondary process occurs when the ultraviolet light impinges upon a thin coating of powdery material made up of *phosphors* on the inner surface of the tube. The phosphors are excited by the absorption of the ultraviolet photons and give off a multitude of lower frequencies that combine to produce white light. Different phosphors can be used to produce different colors of light.

Phosphorescence

When excited, some materials remain in a state of excitement for a prolonged period of time. Their electrons are boosted into higher orbits and become "stuck." As a result there is a time delay between the process of excitation and de-excitation. Materials that exhibit this peculiar property are said to be *phosphorescent*. The element phosphorus is a good example. Such materials are used in luminous clock dials and in other objects that are made to glow in the dark. Atoms in these objects are excited by incident visible light. Rather than de-exciting immediately as fluorescent materials do, many of the atoms remain in a state of excitement, sometimes for as much as several hours—although most undergo de-excitation rather quickly. If the source of excitation is removed—for example, if the lights are put out—the phosphorescent object will glow for some time while millions of atoms spontaneously undergo gradual de-excitation.

The Laser

The phenomena of excitation, fluorescence, and phosphorescence underlie the operation of a most intriguing instrument, the *laser* (*l*ight *a*mplification by *s*timulated *e*mission of *r*adiation). To understand how a laser operates, we must first discuss coherent light.

Fig. 27.5 Incoherent white light contains waves of many frequencies and wavelengths which are out of phase with each other.

Light emitted by a common lamp is incoherent. That is, photons of many frequencies and many phases of vibration are emitted. The light is as incoherent as the footsteps on an auditorium floor when a mob of people are chaotically rushing about. Incoherent light is chaotic. A beam of incoherent light spreads out after a short distance, becoming wider and wider and less intense with increased distance.

Fig. 27.6 Light of a single frequency and wavelength is still out of phase.

Even if the beam is filtered so that it is a single frequency (monochromatic), it would still be incoherent, for the waves would be out of phase with one another. The slightest differences in their directions would result in a spreading with increased distance.

Fig. 27.7 Coherent light —all the waves are identical and are in phase.

A beam of photons having the same frequency, phase, and direction—that is, a beam of photons that travel exactly alike—is said to be coherent. Only a beam of coherent light will not spread and diffuse.

A laser is an instrument that produces a beam of coherent light. One model, the earliest, consists of a ruby crystal rod about two inches long which has been "doped" with impurity atoms of chromium. The ruby rod is surrounded by a photo flash tube that sends high-intensity green light into the ruby, Figure 27.8. Excitation of the chromium atoms occurs as the outer electrons are boosted to higher energy levels. The electrons fall back to an intermediate level and then, more slowly, to their lowest level. At this last stage they emit a photon of red light: the ruby fluoresces.

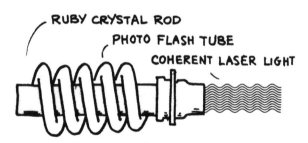

RUBY CRYSTAL ROD

PHOTO FLASH TUBE

COHERENT LASER LIGHT

Fig. 27.8   A ruby crystal laser.

The photon of red light within the crystal will trigger the de-excitation of a neighboring excited atom. The photon stimulated into radiation will be identical in both frequency and phase with the incident photon. The pair of photons then may further stimulate the radiation of other excited atoms, thereby producing a beam of coherent light. Most of this light escapes through the sides of the crystal in random directions. Light traveling along the crystal axis, however, is reflected from semitransparent reflective coatings on each end of the crystal. The distance between the mirrored ends is an integral multiple of one-half the wavelength of laser light in the ruby. The reflected waves are then able to reinforce each other after each round-trip reflection between the mirrors. This sets up a resonant condition in which the light builds up to an appreciable intensity. The light then escapes through the more transparent mirrored end and we have a laser beam, Figure 27.9.

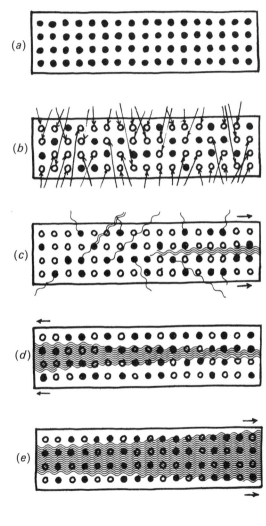

Fig. 27.9 A ruby crystal is "doped" with atoms of chromium. When green light is shone through it, the chromium atoms are excited. Upon de-excitation the electrons become momentarily "stuck" at an intermediate level; when de-exciting from this level they emit a photon of red light. The ruby crystal shown here is fully silvered on the right end and semisilvered on the left end.

(*a*) Chromium atoms (solid circles) are in their ground states.

(*b*) Green light is flashed through the crystal, raising most of the atoms to the excited state (open circles).

(*c*) Chromium atoms undergo the last stage of de-excitation and emit red photons.

(*d*) Photons in irregular directions pass out of the crystal, but those parallel to the axis of the crystal reflect from the mirrors and strike other atoms and stimulate their electrons to fall, thereby producing more photons of the same frequency, and in the same direction.

(*e*) The photons flash to and fro between the silvered ends, causing an avalanche of red light to build up. When the intensity is great enough, a burst issues forth through the semisilvered end.

The whole process takes less than a millionth of a second and is repeated every few millionths of a second.

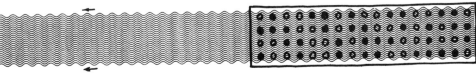

The laser is not a source of *energy*. It is simply a converter of energy, taking advantage of the process of stimulating emission to concentrate a certain fraction of its energy (about 1 percent) into radiation of a single frequency moving in a single direction. Like all devices, a laser can put out no more energy than is put in.

The list of practical applications of the laser is growing rapidly. The straightness of the laser beam is useful in surveying. Lasers were used to line up the dredging equipment for the underwater tunnel in San Francisco Bay, and inside the tunnel to ensure its straightness.

Laser beams have been bounced off the moon and returned, little altered from the way they started. Laser reflectors were placed on the moon by astronauts for experiments measuring the exact distance between the earth and moon.

Lasers are so intense (and concentrated) that eye surgeons use them to "weld" detached retinas back into place without making an incision. The light is simply brought to focus in the region where the welding is to take place.

Unlike radio waves, measured in hundreds of yards, and television waves, measured in feet, laser wavelengths are measured in tens of millionths of an inch. These supershort wavelengths are capable of carrying a great volume of messages on a very narrow band of frequencies.

Laser light can be used for transmitting power. Electrical power is translated to laser light, and at the end of the distant beam the reverse process takes place. On earth, where fog or rain would interfere with transmission, lasers must be beamed through evacuated pipelines to prevent power loss. Such pipelines must be perfectly straight to accommodate the arrowlike laser beam; direction changes require mirrors to send the beams around corners.

One of the latest uses for the laser is in the field of computers. A laser gun "burns" tiny, microscopic holes in the surface of a computer tape—each hole representing a bit of information. The holes are later "read" by a second laser. In this way a trillion bits of data can be stored on a single standard-length reel of computer tape. This is equivalent to twenty pages of information on every man, woman, and child in the United States.

The future for laser applications seems unlimited. The inventors of the laser, Charles H. Townes of the University of California at Berkeley and Arthur L. Schawlow of Stanford

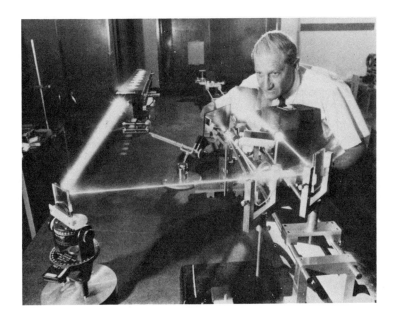

Fig. 27.10 A high-intensity laser beam at work. Stanford research engineer Matt Lehmann is shown with the materials used to make the first three-dimensional movie without a lens. (Photo by Associated Press.)

University, predict wall-size, three-dimensional television pictures. Smaller three-dimensional pictures, called *holograms*, can presently be seen. A hologram is simply a photographic plate exposed with laser light. It is a recording of visual information in terms of the phase and amplitude of light waves rather than intensity, as in the ordinary photographic image. Laser light is split into two parts, one of which illuminates the scene to be photographed. This light is scattered from the objects of the scene, and recombines with the other half of the beam to form an interference pattern on the photographic plate. The interference pattern records the shifts of phase produced as the light travels paths of different lengths. By illuminating the hologram with laser light, a reconstruction of the original scene can be seen. The image is so realistic that you can actually look around the corners of the objects and see the sides.

Color   Light from a sodium-vapor lamp is yellow; light from the mineral carnotite is green when illuminated with ultraviolet radiation; light from a ruby laser is red. These are the colors of light from emitting substances. The colors themselves are physiological, and depend on the frequency of the emitted light. Different frequencies of light are perceived as different colors, the lowest frequency being red and the highest violet. In between are orange, yellow, green, blue, and the infinite number of different hues. The frequency of emitted light in turn depends on the electron transitions between the atomic energy levels of the source. But what of the colors of nonemitters? Most of the objects around us do not emit light, yet they are colored. Why is this so?

A rose, for example, doesn't emit light—it reflects light. If we pass sunlight through a prism and then place a deep-red rose in various parts of the spectrum, the rose will appear brown or black in all parts of the spectrum except in the red. In the red part of the spectrum the rose will appear red but the green stem and leaves will appear black. This shows that the red rose has the ability to reflect red light, but it cannot reflect other kinds of light; the green leaves have the ability to reflect green light, and likewise cannot reflect other kinds of light. When the rose is held in white light, the rose appears red and the leaves green, because the rose reflects the red part of the white light and the leaves reflect the green part of the white light. To understand why objects reflect different colors of light, we can make use of the following model.

Consider the electrons of an atom (or molecule) as hooked to the nucleus by invisible springs, so the atom is a tiny oscillator. When the atom is disturbed its electrons can be set into oscillation at a frequency characteristic of the atom. The electrons of some atoms can be set into oscillation over a certain narrow range of frequencies while the electrons of other atoms

Fig. 27.11 This square reflects all the colors illuminating it. In sunlight it is white. When illuminated with red light it is red.

This square absorbs all the colors illuminating it. It reflects no colors and therefore is black.

oscillate over different ranges. An electron set into vibration will radiate light quanta at a frequency equal to its oscillation frequency. Incoming light of a frequency that is within the range of the atom's oscillation frequency will be absorbed, thereby setting an electron into vibration. The vibrating electron then emits radiant energy which is in effect a reradiation of the incident energy. If the frequency of the incoming light does not match the oscillation frequency of the atom, it will be absorbed and its energy transformed into heat. If an object reradiates (reflects) all the light incident upon it, its color will be that of the illuminating light. If an object absorbs all the light incident upon it, it reflects none and is no color—it is black. Hence, when the rose is illuminated with red light, the leaves become warmer than the petals; when it is illuminated with green light, the petals become warmer than the leaves.

This absorption and reradiation of selected frequencies is similar to the absorption and reradiation of sound waves we studied in Chapter 18. Atoms as well as tuning forks resonate.

An important factor in the appearance of a colored body is the kind of light used. A candle flame gives off light that is deficient in blue; it gives off a yellowish light. An incandescent lamp gives off light that is richer toward the lower frequencies, enhancing the reds; while a fluorescent lamp is richer in the higher frequencies, thus enhancing the blues. With this kind of illumination it is difficult to tell the true color of objects. Colors appear differently in the daylight than when illuminated with either of these lamps.

When all the colors of the spectrum are mixed together white light is obtained. But white light can also be obtained by superimposing a beam of yellow light on a beam of a certain hue of blue light; or a mixture of magenta and green lights produces white. Any two colored lights that, when mixed, produce white light are called *complementary* colors.*

The three colors—red, green, and blue—when mixed in a certain proportion will give white light; but it is possible to produce any color whatever by mixing selected proportions of these three colors. For this reason they are called the three *primary colors*. A close examination of the picture on a color television tube will reveal that the picture is composed of an assemblage of tiny dots, each less than a millimeter across. When the screen is lit, some of the dots are red, some green, some blue—

*This complementarity is a biological property of the eye.

the mixtures of these primary colors at a distance will provide a complete range of colors, plus white, Figure 27.12.

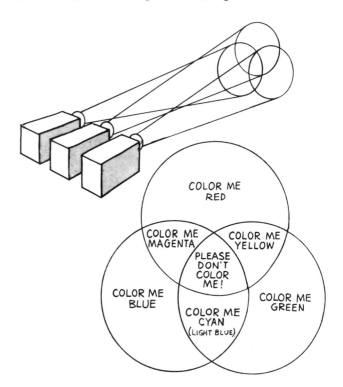

Fig. 27.12 Color addition by the mixing of colored lights. When three projectors shine red, blue, and green light on a white screen, the overlapping parts produce different colors. The *addition* of the three primary colors produces white light.

Every artist knows that if you mix red, green, and blue paint, the result will not be white, but brown. Or if blue and yellow are mixed, the resulting color is green. But the mixing of pigments is an entirely different process than that of mixing colored lights. Yellow pigment reflects yellow. In addition, it reflects, to a lesser degree, the colors on either side of yellow—some red and some green. It absorbs blue and violet. Blue pigment reflects blue. Likewise, it reflects, to some extent, the colors on either side of blue—some green and some violet. When yellow and blue pigments are mixed, the result is that the only reflected light is green; all the other colors are absorbed. The effect of mixing pigments therefore is greatly different from that of mixing lights. When two light beams reflect off a white screen, the light seen is an *additive mixture* because the two lights are added together before the observer sees them. When colored pigments are mixed, colors are *subtracted*—the observer sees the light left over after absorption has taken place. This is shown in Figure 27.13.

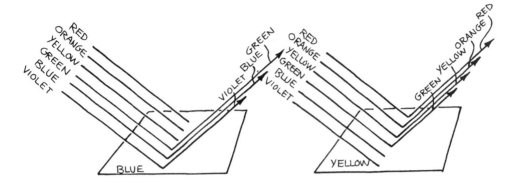

Fig. 27.13 Color subtraction by the mixing of colored pigments. Blue pigment reflects not only blue, but also colors to either side of blue, namely green and violet. It absorbs red, orange, and yellow.

Yellow pigment reflects not only yellow, but also red, orange, and green. It absorbs blue and violet.

When blue and yellow pigments are mixed, the only common color reflected is green. The other colors have been *subtracted* from the incident white light.

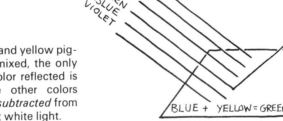

BLUE + YELLOW = GREEN

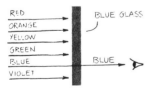

Fig. 27.14 Only energy having the frequency of blue light is transmitted—energy of the other frequencies is absorbed and heats the glass.

The color of a transparent object depends upon the color of the light it transmits. A red piece of glass appears red because it absorbs all the colors that compose white light, except red, which it transmits. Similarly, a blue piece of glass appears blue because it transmits only blue and absorbs all the other colors composing white light. From an atomic view, electrons in the pigment molecules are set into oscillation by the frequencies of blue light, and they reradiate this energy from molecule to molecule in the glass. The other frequencies are absorbed by the molecules as a whole and are not reradiated. The kinetic energy of the molecules is increased and the glass is warmed by the absorbed frequencies. An ordinary window pane is colorless, that is, it transmits all the colors of white light equally well. Atomically, the electron oscillators vibrate at all the visible frequencies. We will discuss the transmission of light through transparent materials in more detail in the next chapter.

Summary of Terms

Excitation. The process of boosting one or more electrons in an atom or molecule from a lower to a higher energy level. An atom in an excited state will usually decay (de-excite) rapidly to a lower state by the emission of radiation. The frequency and energy of emitted radiation are related by:

$$E = hf$$

Incandescence. The state of glowing while at a high temperature. This is caused by electrons in vibrating atoms and molecules which are shaken in and out of their stable energy levels, emitting radiation in the process. Radiation of many frequencies is emitted; the peak frequency is proportional to the peak kinetic energy of the vibrating atoms and molecules— therefore the peak frequency of radiation is proportional to the absolute temperature of the heated substance:

$$\bar{f} \sim T$$

Fluorescence. The property of absorbing radiation of one frequency and re-emitting radiation of a lower frequency. Part of the absorbed radiation goes into heat, and the other part into excitation; hence the emitted radiation has a lower energy, and therefore lower frequency, than the absorbed radiation.

Phosphorescence. A type of light emission that is the same as fluorescence except for a delay between excitation and de-excitation, which provides an afterglow. The delay is caused by atoms being excited to energy levels that do not decay rapidly. The afterglow may last from fractions of a second to hours, or even days, depending on the type of material, temperature, and other factors.

Complementary colors. Any two colors that, when added, produce white light.

Primary colors. The three colors—red, blue, and green—which when added in certain proportions will produce any color in the spectrum.

Suggested Reading   *Scientific American*, September, 1968. This issue of the magazine deals exclusively with light; it has an excellent article on lasers and their applications.

Wright, W. D., *The Rays Are Not Coloured: Essays on the Science of Vision and Colour*, London, Hilger, 1967.

Questions   1. Have you ever watched a fire and noticed that the burning of different materials often produces flames of different colors? Why is this so?

2. Most of the radiation emitted by a red-hot star is in the infrared. Most of the radiation emitted by a violet-hot star is in the ultraviolet. Why is it that there are no green-hot stars? (*Hint*: If there were green-hot stars, what would this tell you about the relative rates of individual molecular vibrations in the star? What would its radiation curve look like? Is this likely?).

3. Why are fluorescent colors so bright?

4. Can an atom be excited by the absorption of infrared radiation and in turn emit visible radiation? Explain.

5. Why would the element phosphorus be an unsuitable coating on the inner face of a television picture tube?

6. What is common to the phenomenon of phosphorescence and the laser?

7. Are the better lasers capable of putting out a greater amount of energy than is put into them? How about power? Explain.

8. Why will the leaves of a rose be heated more than the petals when illuminated with red light? Why do people in the hot desert wear white clothing?

9. If the sunlight were green instead of white, what color garment would be most advisable on an uncomfortably hot day? On a very cold day?

10. Suppose two flashlight beams are shone on a white screen, one beam through a pane of blue glass and the other through a pane of yellow glass. What color appears on the screen where the two beams overlap? Suppose instead that the two panes of glass are placed in the beam of a single flashlight. What then?

Photo by Jerry Hosken.

28

The Behavior of Light:
Reflection and Refraction

**Some Important
Facts and Terms**

Thus far we have studied the nature of light and how it is produced. Our concern now is the behavior of light after it has left its source. Several well-known facts regarding light and some commonly used terms should be understood.

Objects can be seen only when a *source* of light is present. There is a difference between *luminous* bodies, such as incandescent and fluorescent lamps, and *illuminated* bodies, which give light by *reflection*, such as this page. Most visible objects are illuminated by a luminous source and are seen by the light which they *reflect* to the eye.

Some objects, like window glass, allow the passage of light in straight lines. Such objects are said to be *transparent*. Other objects, like thin paper, are *translucent*—that is, they allow the passage of light, but in diffused directions so that one cannot see objects through them. The majority of objects are *opaque*; that is, they do not allow the passage of light, except when very thin layers of them are used. A line along which light travels is called a *ray* of light. When the path of light is narrow, like the path of light projected across the sky by a searchlight, it is said to be a *beam* of light. A beam and a ray are along the same direction.

A boy shooting a B-B gun aims the muzzle in the direction in which he sees the target. In doing so, he is making use of the fact that *light travels in straight lines*. There are, however, cases in which light is bent. We will discuss two of these cases in this chapter.

Fig. 28.1 A pinhole camera. Because light travels in straight lines, it forms an inverted image when passing through a very small hole.

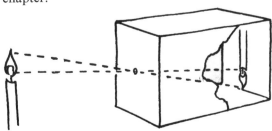

Photo by John Hedgecoe

Reflection   *Law of Reflection*

When light is incident upon a surface, part of the light is reflected. On a metallic surface almost 100 percent of incident light is reflected, while on the surface of clear glass only a small percentage is reflected. The law of reflection is illustrated in Figure 28.2. The law simply states that *the angle of incidence is equal to the angle of reflection.* Instead of measuring incident and reflected rays from the reflecting surface, it is customary to measure both from a line perpendicular to the plane of the reflecting surface. This line is called the *normal.* The incident ray, the normal, and the reflected ray all lie in the same plane.

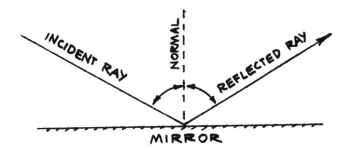

Fig. 28.2 Reflection.

Diffuse Reflection

When light is incident on a rough surface it is reflected in many directions. This is called *diffuse reflection*. If the surface is so smooth that the distances between successive elevations on the surface are less than about one-quarter the wavelength of the light, there is very little diffuse reflection and the surface is said to be *polished*. A surface therefore may be polished for radiation

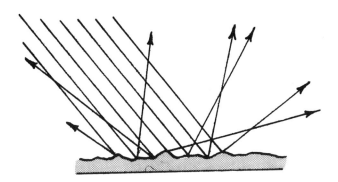

Fig. 28.3 Diffuse reflection.

of long wavelength, but not polished for light of short wavelength. The wire-mesh "dish" shown in Figure 28.4 is a "polished" reflector of radio waves, but hardly for light waves.

Light reflecting from this page is diffuse. It may be smooth to a long radio wave, but to a fine light wave it is rough. Rays of light incident upon this page encounter millions of tiny flat surfaces facing in all directions. The incident light therefore is reflected in all directions. This is a desirable circumstance. It enables us to see objects from any direction or position. Most of our environment is seen by diffuse reflection.

Fig. 28.4 The open-meshed parabolic dish is a diffuse reflector for short-wavelength light, but polished for long-wavelength radio waves. (Photo by George Hall, Photophile, S.F.)

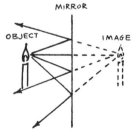

Fig. 28.5 A virtual image is formed behind the mirror and is located at the position where the extended reflected rays (broken lines) converge.

The Plane Mirror

Suppose a candle flame is placed in front of a plane mirror. Rays of light are sent from the flame in all directions. Figure 28.5 shows only four of the infinite number of rays leaving the candle flame. When these rays encounter the mirror they are reflected at angles equal to their angles of incidence. The rays diverge from the flame, and upon reflection diverge from the mirror. These divergent rays *appear* to emanate from behind the mirror, at a point located where the rays converge (broken lines). An observer sees an image of the candle flame at this point. The light rays do not actually come from this point, so the image is called a *virtual image*. The image is as far behind the mirror as the object is in front of the mirror, and image and object have the same size.

| Question | What is the minimum-sized plane mirror required for a six-foot person to see his full-length image? (Sketch a ray diagram of a person standing in front of a mirror, similar to the diagram shown in Figure 28.5.) |

The Velocity of Light in a Transparent Medium

The speed of light is a constant in nature. That is, its speed in a vacuum is a constant 186,000 miles per second. We shall call the speed of light c. Light has a lesser speed in a transparent medium. In water, for example, light travels at 75 percent of its speed in a vacuum or $0.75c$; in glass, about $0.67c$ depending upon the type of glass; in diamond, only $0.41c$. When light emerges from these media it again travels at its original speed, c. From what we have learned about energy, this seems like strange behavior. For example, if a bullet is fired through a board, the bullet slows down in passing through the board and emerges at a speed less than its incident speed. It loses some of its kinetic energy while interacting with the fibers and splinters of wood making up the board material. We would certainly be surprised if, after slowing down in the board, the bullet emerged with a speed equal to its original speed! Yet this is apparently what happens in the case of light. A beam of light is incident upon glass at speed c, slows down in the glass, and emerges at speed c!

To understand this behavior we must consider the individual photons of light that make up the beam. We must also consider the interaction between the photons and the molecules they encounter. Incident photons interact with the electrons of these molecules. We can think of the orbital electrons in atoms and molecules as tiny oscillators, where electrons are attached to invisible springs that will resonate at certain frequencies, and which are easily forced to vibrate over a range of frequencies. This range varies for different molecules. In clear glass, for example, this range extends over the entire visible region. When a photon is incident upon a transparent medium such as glass, it is absorbed by a molecule at the surface. An electron in the absorbing molecule is set into vibration at a frequency equal to that of the incident photon. This vibration then causes the emission of a second photon of identical frequency. It is a different, but indistinguishable, photon. This second photon travels at speed c until it is very quickly absorbed by another molecule in the glass, whereupon an electron is set into vibration, re-emitting a different but indistinguishable photon of its own. This absorption-re-emission process is not an instantaneous event —some time is required for the process and as a result the *average* speed of light through the material is less than *c*. So although the *instantaneous speed* of a single photon is *c*, the average speed of a beam of photons being *absorbed* and *re-emitted* in a medium is less than *c*.* We must make a distinction between the *instantaneous speed* of light in traveling between individual molecules in a material and the *average speed* of light in traversing through a succession of millions of molecules in a transparent material. This average speed is implied when we speak of light slowing down when it passes through a transparent substance. Unlike the bullet passing through the board, photons do not "burrow" through glass. A photon emerging from a glass surface is not the same photon that entered the glass. The view you see when looking out a window is composed of photons ejected from the inner surface of the glass.

The Greenhouse Effect

A transparent substance is composed of atoms and molecules whose electrons will oscillate throughout the range of visible frequencies. The electron oscillators in clear glass, for example, will resonate at frequencies throughout the visible region of the spectrum, but will not resonate or pass radiation in the infrared and ultraviolet regions of the spectrum. Energy in visible light will be transmitted through the glass in a greenhouse, for example, and be absorbed by the plants within. The plants reradiate some of this energy, but at frequencies proportional to their temperature (considerably lower than the temperature of the sun). These frequencies are in the infrared part of the spectrum. Glass is opaque to these low frequencies and the energy is trapped inside the greenhouse. The glass acts as a one-way valve—allowing

---

*Just how much the average speed of light differs from its speed in a vacuum is given by the index of refraction, *n*, of the material; *n* is the ratio of the speed of light in a vacuum to the speed of light in the material:

$$n = \frac{\text{speed of light in vacuum}}{\text{speed of light in material}}$$

For example, the speed of light in a diamond is $(1/2.4)c$; so $n = 2.4$. For a vacuum $n = 1$.

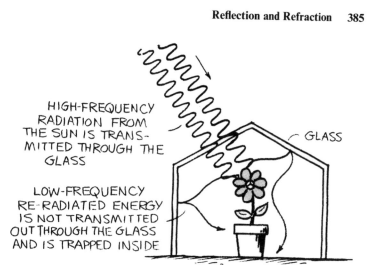

Fig. 28.6 Glass is transparent to high-frequency radiation but opaque to low-frequency radiation. Radiation from the sun has a high frequency because the sun has a high temperature. Reradiated energy from the plant has low frequency because the plant has a relatively low temperature.

HIGH-FREQUENCY RADIATION FROM THE SUN IS TRANSMITTED THROUGH THE GLASS

GLASS

LOW-FREQUENCY RE-RADIATED ENERGY IS NOT TRANSMITTED OUT THROUGH THE GLASS AND IS TRAPPED INSIDE

high-frequency radiation in, and preventing low-frequency radiation from going out.

It is common knowledge that we can't get a sunburn when a sheet of glass is between our skin and the sun. It is the ultraviolet light in sunlight that produces a sunburn or tan. This part of the spectrum finds the glass opaque. The glass filters both ultraviolet and infrared and transmits the visible radiation.

Refraction

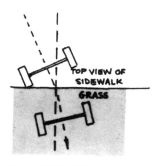

TOP VIEW OF SIDEWALK

GRASS

Fig. 28.7 The direction of the rolling wheels changes when one part slows down before the other part.

Light bends when it passes obliquely from one medium to another. This is called *refraction*. It is the slowing down of light upon entering a transparent medium that causes refraction. To understand why this is so, consider the action of a pair of toy cart wheels connected to an axle as the wheels roll from a smooth sidewalk onto a grass lawn. If the wheels meet the grass at some angle, Figure 28.7, they will be deflected from their straight-line course. The direction of the rolling wheels is shown by the dotted line in the figure. Note that upon meeting the lawn, where the wheels roll slower owing to interaction with the grass, the left wheel is slowed down first. This is because it meets the grass while the right wheel is still on the smooth sidewalk. The faster-moving right wheel tends to pivot about the slower-moving left wheel. It travels farther during the same time the left wheel travels a lesser distance in the grass. This action bends the direction of the rolling wheels toward the "normal," the dashed line perpendicular to the grass-sidewalk border.

A similar situation with a light wave is shown in Figure 28.8. If the wave is incident upon a transparent surface at an angle, the left portion of the wave slows down before the part of the

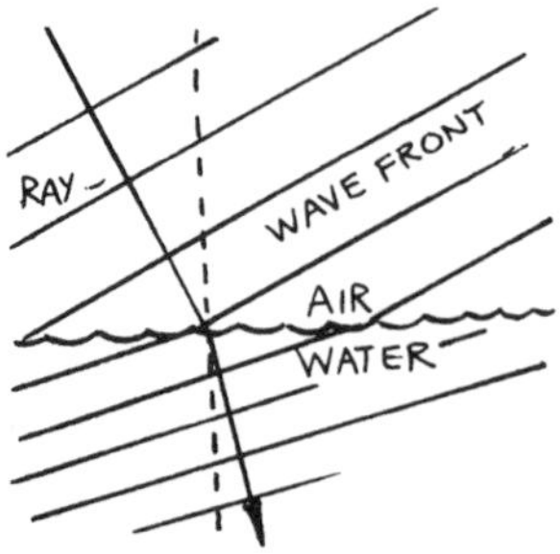

Fig. 28.8 The direction of the light waves changes when one part of the wave slows down before the other part.

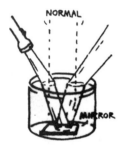

Fig. 28.9 A beam bends toward the normal when entering a denser medium and away from the normal when leaving.

wave still in the air. The ray or beam of light is perpendicular to the wavefront, and bends just as the direction of the wheels bend. When the speed of light decreases in going from one medium to another, the light bends toward the normal. When the speed of light increases in traveling from one medium to another, the light ray bends away from the normal. This situation is shown in Figure 28.9.

The refraction of light is responsible for many illusions. Figure 28.10 shows how the refraction of light causes the apparent bending of a measuring stick partly immersed in water.

Fig. 28.10 Because of refraction, the measuring stick appears to be bent when part of it is immersed in water. (Helen Ansel, Photophile, S.F.)

Another illusion is shown in Figure 28.11. The full glass mug appears to hold more root beer than it actually does. The reason for this illusion is that the thickness of the glass walls is greater than the light refraction makes it appear. The eye, accustomed to perceiving light traveling along straight lines, perceives the root beer to be at the outer edge of the glass, along the broken lines.

Fig. 28.11 Because of refraction the mug appears to hold more root beer than it actually does.

When we stand on a bank and view a fish in the water, the fish appears to be nearer to the surface than it actually is. It will also seem closer, Figure 28.12. Because of refraction, submerged objects appear to be magnified. If we look straight down into water, an object submerged four feet beneath the surface will appear to be three feet deep.

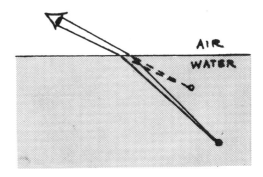

Fig. 28.12 Because of refraction a submerged object appears to be nearer to the surface and closer than it actually is.

Consider the world above the water surface as viewed by a fish. Figure 28.13 shows various lines of sight for a fish making observations above the water surface. Light coming from directly above is not bent, but light coming from other regions appears

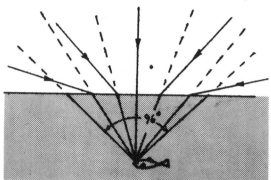

Fig.   28.13   Refracted light rays.

to be higher in the sky (broken lines) than to an observer above water. A ray of light parallel to the surface of the water is refracted so as to form an angle of approximately 48 degrees with the normal to the surface. In fact, all the light coming from above to a submerged eye looking upward lies within a cone of 96 degrees. The submerged eye has the same impression it would have if it were looking through a hole in the ceiling, and all that it would ordinarily see in a full 180-degree horizon-to-horizon view would be crowded into this peephole. Figure 28.14 is a view

Fig.   28.14   A fish-eye view of people standing around a small pond.

from beneath the water showing what a fish would see if it stared straight up from a small pool surrounded by people.

Atmospheric Refraction

Although the velocity of light in air is only 0.03 percent less than the velocity of light in a vacuum, there are situations in which atmospheric refraction is far from negligible. One of the most interesting occurs in the *mirage*. On hot days there may be a layer of very hot air in contact with the ground. Since the air molecules in hot air are farther apart (less dense), the light travels faster through it than through the cooler air above. The speeding up of the part of the wave nearest the ground causes a gradual bending of the light rays. An observer, Figure 28.15, sees the tree upside down (as well as right side up), just as if it

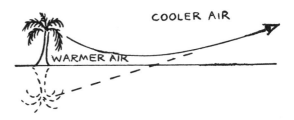

Fig. 28.15 The refraction of light in air produces a mirage.

were reflected from a surface of water. But the light is not reflected; it is refracted.

Figure 28.16 shows in more detail how faster light waves traveling through the hot air get ahead of the positions (broken lines) they would occupy if the entire wavefront traveled at one speed. The lower part of the wavefront moves faster and bends the light ray (which is always 90 degrees to the wavefront) upward as shown.

Fig. 28.16 Waves of light travel faster in the hot air near the ground, thereby bending the rays of light upward.

A motorist is familiar with this phenomenon which makes a hot highway appear wet in the distance. The sky appears to be reflected from a wet surface but, in fact, light from the sky is being refracted through a layer of hot air. A mirage is not, as many people mistakenly believe, a "trick of the mind." A mirage is formed by real light and is perfectly capable of being photographed, as is shown in Figure 28.17.

Fig. 28.17   A mirage on the Mojave Desert. (Photo by Richard Brooks.)

When the air next to the ground is substantially cooler than air above, rays of light are deviated downward, Figure 28.18. In this way an image of a ship may appear above the ship itself. This phenomenon is called *looming*. It is a rather common observation over a snow field or body of water which has a substantially colder layer of air near its surface than the warmer air above. When conditions are right a lighthouse can be seen from a distance of as much as 40 miles where ordinarily the curvature of the earth would completely cut off a view of the lighthouse.

Fig. 28.18   Looming.

When we look at an object over a hot stove or over a hot pavement we see a wavy, shimmering effect. This is due to the bending of light as it passes through varying temperatures and therefore varying densities of air. The twinkling of stars is due in part to similar phenomena in the sky, where light passes through unstable layers in the atmosphere.

Whenever we watch a sunset, we see the sun for several minutes after it has really sunk below the horizon. This is because light is refracted by the earth's atmosphere, Figure 28.19. Since

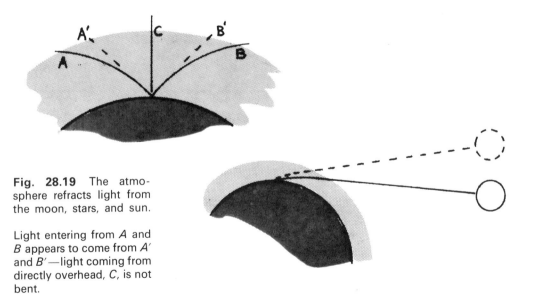

Fig. 28.19 The atmosphere refracts light from the moon, stars, and sun.

Light entering from *A* and *B* appears to come from *A'* and *B'* —light coming from directly overhead, *C*, is not bent.

the density of atmosphere changes gradually, the refracted rays bend gradually, producing a curving path. When the sun (or moon) is near the horizon, the rays from the lower edge are bent more than the rays from the upper edge. This produces a shortening of the vertical diameter, causing the sun to appear elliptical, Figure 28.20.

Fig. 28.20 Atmospheric refraction produces an apparent shortening of the sun's vertical diameter when it is near the horizon. (Photo by Ted Mahieu, Photophile, S.F.)

Total Internal Reflection

In Figure 28.13 we saw that a fish in water looking upward sees a 180-degree, horizon-to-horizon view in a cone of 96 degrees. That is, if the fish looks upward 48 degrees from a normal to the surface, the fish sees the horizon. What does the fish see at angles greater than 48 degrees? At greater angles the light is not refracted, but reflected. So at these angles a fish sees light from the bottom or sides of the pond beneath the surface which is reflected from the water surface, Figure 28.21. For water, 48 degrees is called the *critical angle*. For angles less than the critical angle, light is refracted in passing from one medium to another. Beyond the critical angle, light reaches the eye of the fish by *total internal reflection*. This light obeys the law of reflection, where the angle of incidence is equal to angle of reflection. Total internal reflection can occur whenever light is incident on a surface where the average speed of light outside the surface is greater than within the surface.

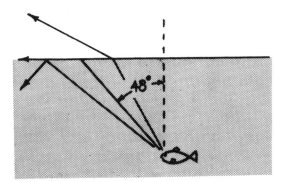

Fig. 28.21 The angle for which light is neither transmitted nor totally internally reflected is called the *critical angle.*

The critical angle for glass is about 43 degrees, depending on the type of glass. This means that within glass, light which is incident at angles greater than the critical angle will be totally internally reflected. No light will escape the glass which is incident upon a surface at an angle greater than 43 degrees. Instead, all of it is reflected back into the glass. Whereas a mirror absorbs some light on reflection, the glass prism shown in Figure 28.22 is more efficient. Light is incident upon the slanted face at 45 degrees and is totally reflected. Moreover, all the light incident upon the slanted face is reflected and is not marred by any dirt or dust on the outside surface.

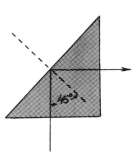

Fig. 28.22 Total internal reflection.

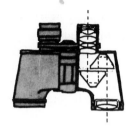

Fig. 28.23 Prism binoculars.

Fig. 28.24 "Piped" light.

A pair of prisms reflecting light through 180 degrees is shown in Figure 28.23. Pairs of prisms are used in binoculars to lengthen the light path between lenses without inconveniently lengthening the barrels of the binoculars. This makes it possible for a compact pair of binoculars to be as effective as a much longer telescope. Another advantage of prisms is that whereas the image of a straight telescope is upside down, reflection by the prisms in binoculars reinverts the image, so that we see things right side up.

Another interesting use of total internal reflection is in light pipes, Figure 28.24. A light pipe "pipes" light from one point to another by a series of total internal reflections. Light pipes are used in decorative table lamps. Dentists use curved plastic rods at the ends of their flashlights in order to get light where they want it. Bundles of tiny glass fibers are used to see what is going on in inaccessible places, such as a patient's stomach or the interior of motors. Light shines down some of the fibers to illuminate the scene and is reflected back along others.

Refraction in a Prism

Earlier in the chapter we discussed how the average speed of light is less than c in a transparent medium—how much less depends upon the nature of the medium and upon the frequency of the light. The closer the frequency of light is to the natural frequency of the electron oscillators in the molecules making up the transparent medium, the greater the interaction between light and matter. Since there is some time lag associated with these interactions, a slowing down of the average speed results. So the speed of light in a transparent medium is frequency dependent. Since the natural frequency of most transparent materials is in the ultraviolet range of frequencies, the higher frequencies of visible light interact in the absorption/re-emission sequence more often than the lower frequencies. This results in a lower average speed for higher frequencies of light. Hence violet travels the slowest through glass while red travels the fastest. The other colors between red and violet travel at intermediate speeds.

The degree to which light bends as it travels from one medium to another depends on the change in the speed of the light. The greater the change in speed, then the greater is the deviation of light from its original path. Since different frequencies of light travel at different speeds in transparent materials, it follows that

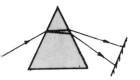

Fig. 28.25 Dispersion through a prism.

different frequencies of light will be bent by different amounts. When light is bent twice, as in a prism, the separation of the different colors of light is quite noticeable. This separation of light into colors arranged according to their frequency is called *dispersion*, Figure 28.25.

The Rainbow

A most spectacular illustration of dispersion is the rainbow. The conditions for seeing a rainbow are that the sun be shining in one part of the sky and rain be falling in the opposite part of the sky. Turning one's back to the sun, a spectrum of colors is seen in a circular arc. From an airplane, the bow may form a complete circle. The colors are dispersed from the sunlight by thousands of tiny drops which act like prisms.

To understand how light is dispersed by the spherical raindrops, consider an individual raindrop as shown in Figure 28.26. A ray of sunlight is shown entering the drop near its top surface. At this point some of the light is reflected (not shown), and the remainder is refracted into the water. At this first refraction the light is dispersed into its spectrum colors, violet being deviated the most and red the least. Reaching the opposite side of the drop, each color is partly refracted out into the air (not shown) and partly reflected back into the water. Arriving at the lower surface of the drop, each color is again reflected (not shown) and refracted into the air. This second refraction is similar to that of a prism, where refraction at the second surface increases the dispersion already produced at the first surface.

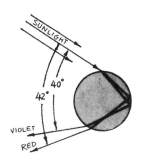

Fig. 28.26 Dispersion of sunlight by a single raindrop.

Although each drop disperses a full spectrum of colors, an observer sees only a single color from any one drop, Figure 28.27. If violet light from a single drop is incident upon the eye of an observer, red light from the same drop is incident elsewhere toward his feet. To see red light he must look to a drop higher in the sky. He will see the color red when the angle between a

Fig. 28.27 Sunlight is incident on two sample raindrops as shown and emerges from them as dispersed light. The observer sees the red light from the upper drop and the violet light from the lower drop. With millions of drops, the spectrum of all the colors is seen.

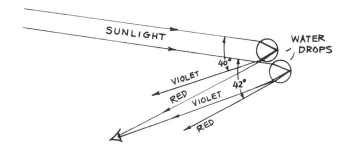

beam of sunlight and the dispersed light is 42 degrees. The color violet is seen when the angle between the sunbeams and dispersed light is 40 degrees.

Why does the light dispersed by the raindrops form a bow? The answer to this involves a little geometrical reasoning. For simplicity we will consider only the dispersion of red light. Every drop of water in the sky disperses red light at an angle of 42 degrees to the rays of illuminating sunlight. Because each drop is a sphere, this dispersed red light is spread into three dimensions, forming the surface of a cone. At the apex (tip) of each cone is the drop, and the axis (straight line down the middle from the apex) of the cone is along the illuminating sunray. All rays of dispersed red light forming this cone make an angle of 42 degrees with respect to this axis.

A single observer, in turn, sees red dispersion from only those drops in a view 42 degrees from the extended sunray that the back of his head intercepts. Why this is so is shown in Figure 28.28. He sees red dispersion in all directions that make an angle of 42 degrees with respect to the extended sunray. This

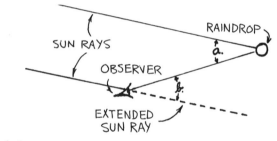

Fig. 28.28 A well-known theorem in geometry states that when a pair of parallel straight lines are intersected by a straight line, the alternate interior angles are equal. Hence, angle *a* = angle *b*.

extended ray makes up the axis of his "cone of vision," Figure 28.29. The apex of this cone is at the eye of the observer and the rim of the cone is the rainbow.

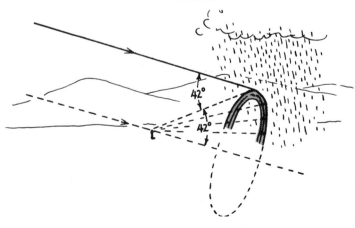

Fig. 28.29 The observer sees a bow-shaped spectrum because each color is dispersed at the same angle to his reference sunbeam (dashed line).

To get a better conceptualization of this, consider an observer looking along the axis of a hollow cone, Figure 28.30. He sees all points along the rim of the cone at the same angle from the axis. Imagine that rays of sunlight are parallel to this axis and that there are water drops along the rim of the cone which disperse light at conical angles equal to that of the cone. Can

Fig. 28.30 The angle of the cone's surface with respect to its axis is constant all the way around the axis (and therefore to rays of light parallel to its axis).

you see that a ring of light would be seen by the observer? And can you see that the same color light dispersed from water drops elsewhere, away from the rim or surface of the cone, would not be directed to the observer's eye? Do you see why a rainbow is bow-shaped?

Often a larger secondary bow with colors reversed can be seen at greater angles about the primary bow. We won't treat this secondary bow except to say that it is formed by similar reasoning and is a result of double reflection within the raindrops, Figure 28.31. Because of this extra reflection (and extra refraction loss) the secondary bow is much dimmer.

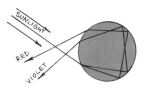

Fig. 28.31 Double reflection in a drop produces a secondary bow.

Summary of Terms

Reflection. The return of light rays from a surface in such a way that the angle at which a given ray is returned is equal to the angle at which it strikes the surface. When the reflecting surface is irregular, light is returned in irregular directions; this is *diffuse reflection.*

Refraction. The bending of an oblique ray of light when it passes from one transparent medium to another. This is caused by a difference in the speed of light in the transparent media. When the change in medium is abrupt (say from air to water), the bending is abrupt; when the change in medium is gradual (say from cool air to warm air), the bending is gradual, accounting for *mirages* and *looming.*

Greenhouse effect. Glass enclosures, such as florist's greenhouses, transmit radiant energy in the visible region of the electromagnetic spectrum, but are opaque to lower frequency infrared radiation. Consequently, energy in the form of light passes into such an enclosure, is absorbed by matter within, and much of it is reradiated—but not as visible light. It is emitted as infrared radiation, for the frequency of emitted radiation is proportional to the temperature of the emitter (which is hardly the temperature of the sun that produced the visible frequencies). Infrared cannot go through the glass, so energy is trapped within the enclosure.

Questions

1. What must be the minimum length of a plane mirror in order that you can see a full view of yourself?

2. What effect does your distance from a plane mirror have on the size of your image, compared to the size of the mirror? (Try it and see!)

3. Why do different colors of light travel at the same speed in a vacuum, but travel at different speeds in transparent materials?

4. A beam of white light is shone through a thick piece of glass. What is the first color to emerge? Why is this not seen by the human eye? And if it could be, then how would motion pictures and television pictures appear to such an eye?

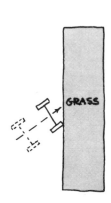

5. A pair of toy cart wheels is rolled obliquely from a smooth surface onto two plots of grass—a rectangular plot as shown on the left, and a triangular plot as shown on the right. The ground is on a slight incline so that after slowing down in the grass, the wheels will speed up again when emerging to the smooth surface. Finish each sketch by showing some positions of the wheels inside the plots and on the other sides, thereby indicating the direction of travel.

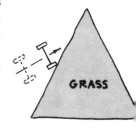

6. Why do blue light waves bend more than red light waves when passing obliquely from air to water?

7. The large refraction of light in a cut diamond and the total internal reflection within result in the dispersion of every color when it is illuminated with white light. What would happen if it were illuminated with red light?

8. Does atmospheric refraction tend to lengthen or shorten the day?

9. What does a fish see when looking upward at an angle of 45 degrees?

10. Sometimes a window will be "blown out" of a car with tightly closed windows when exposed to the sun on a hot day. Why does this happen?

11. Two observers standing apart from one another do not see the "same" rainbow. Explain.

12. How is a rainbow similar to the halo sometimes seen around the moon on a night when ice crystals are in the upper atmosphere?

A Girard grid for analyzing light. (See *Scientific American*, September 1968, p. 72.)

29

The Behavior of Light:
Scattering, Diffraction, Interference, and Polarization

Scattering   Beams of light from the sun are seen coming through the trees in Figure 29.1. A searchlight beam sweeps across the nighttime sky. We see such beams by light scattered from their paths by particles in the atmosphere—usually dust or tiny droplets of water.

Fig. 29.1 Sunbeams through redwood trees. (Photo by W. P. Finney.)

The phenomenon of scattering is similar to the phenomenon of resonance that we discussed in the chapter on sound. Recall that a tuning fork of a certain frequency could be set into vibration when sound of the same frequency was incident upon it. If a "beam" of sound of a certain frequency is incident upon a tuning fork of like frequency, the tuning fork will be set into vibration and scatter sound of the same frequency in all directions. We could think of a tuning fork in the path of a "beam" of sound as a scatterer of sound. In a similar fashion, atoms in the atmosphere scatter light. And because the atmosphere scatters light, the sky is blue.

Why the Sky Is Blue

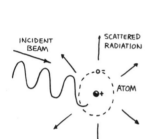

Fig. 29.2 A beam of light falls on an atom and causes the electrons in the atom to vibrate. The vibrating electrons in turn radiate in various directions.

About 80 percent of the atmosphere is nitrogen, and most of the remainder is oxygen. The electrons in these molecules may be thought of as tiny oscillators. The natural (resonant) frequencies of these oscillators match the frequencies of ultraviolet light. Ultraviolet light from the sun is scattered by atmospheric nitrogen and oxygen molecules (although most ultraviolet light is absorbed by a layer of ozone gas in the upper atmosphere). Visible violet light is too low in frequency for molecular resonance, but its frequency is close enough to the resonant frequency to result in considerable forced vibration, resulting in a considerable scattering of violet light. Some blue and even less green is scattered in the same way. Lower frequencies of light which further depart from the resonant frequency of the nitrogen and oxygen are scattered even less. Red light, for example, is scattered only about one-tenth as much as violet light. Thus, when sunlight enters the earth's atmosphere, violet and blue light are scattered the most, followed by green, yellow, orange, and red, in the order named. For every ten violet photons scattered from a beam, only one red photon is scattered. The overall effect is that the average frequency of scattered light is that of blue. Hence we see a blue sky!

A fly in the midst of a searchlight beam, even on a dark night, would see light in all directions. Of course, he would see the most intense light if he looked right into the light source, but even if he looked at right angles to it he would still see light scattered from dust and other particles in the air. In the same way, we see an illuminated sky. Only the sky is blue, being a composite of the colors scattered most effectively by the air molecules, Figure 29.3.

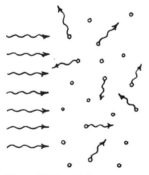

Fig. 29.3 Light waves are scattered in all directions.

Why Sunsets Are Red

The lower frequencies of light are scattered the least. Therefore red, orange, and yellow light are transmitted more readily than the blue. Red, which is scattered the least, traverses more atmosphere relatively unhindered than any other color. Thus, in passing through a thick atmosphere, the higher frequencies are scattered while the lower frequencies are transmitted. This is why the white sun appears reddish at sunset. At noon it appears yellowish, as the path through the atmosphere is at a minimum, and a smaller amount of blue is scattered from the white light. As the day progresses, and the sun is lower in the sky, Figure 29.4, the path through the atmosphere is longer, and more blue is scattered from the sunlight. The sun becomes progressively redder, going from a yellow to an orange, and finally to a deep red-orange at sunset.

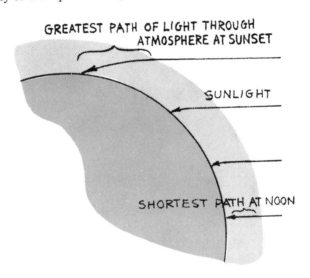

Fig. 29.4 More light is scattered from a sunbeam at sunset than at noontime.

Why Clouds Are Bright and White

The theory of scattering also tells us why clouds are bright and why they are white. The reasoning involves only classical physics but is a bit more complicated—let's give it a try.

The energy of a photon depends on the vibrating frequency of the electron that emits the photon. This energy also depends on the square of the amplitude of the vibrating electron. That is, if an electron vibrates twice as far in its oscillatory back-and-forth motion, it radiates *four* times as much energy. When two atoms are very close together, the electrons in each atom are driven by the electromagnetic field incident upon them, and they vibrate together. We say they vibrate *in phase*. Now, two electrons vibrating in phase is equivalent to one electron vibrating at twice the amplitude, and, consequently, the pair of electrons emits four times as much energy. A clump of atoms vibrating together will scatter a greater amount of energy than the same number of atoms distant from one another and vibrating out of phase. Therefore, although water vapor in the atmosphere scatters light, water vapor condensed into tiny droplets scatters a tremendous amount of light. Hence, clouds are bright!

The reason clouds are white has to do with the size of these droplets. Two atoms together will radiate in phase. The size of two atoms is very much smaller than the wavelength of the driving light incident upon them. As more and more atoms are clumped together, the distance between atoms on the farthest edges of the clump increases. When this distance is about the size of the wavelength of light, then atoms at one end of the drop are radiating slightly out of phase with atoms on the other end of the drop. The intensity of radiation begins to diminish with the increasing size of the drop, especially for the short wavelengths. Short-wavelength blue light may be very much out of phase while longer-wavelength red light will be only slightly out of phase. In a single atom blue is scattered ten times as much as red, but as the size of the drop increases, this ratio begins to reverse itself. Red becomes more predominant. With a greater number of long waves being scattered along with the short waves, the overall effect is a composite of all the visible frequencies—white light. This is why clouds are white!

If the size of the droplets continues to increase, more and more radiation is out of phase and the intensity diminishes. The clouds become darker. Further increase in the size of the drops causes them to fall to earth, and we have a shower.

Diffraction

We think of light as traveling in straight lines, and by and large it does. Because of this, an object in the path of light casts shadows. The straighter the line that light travels, the sharper the shadow. Upon close examination, however, even the sharpest

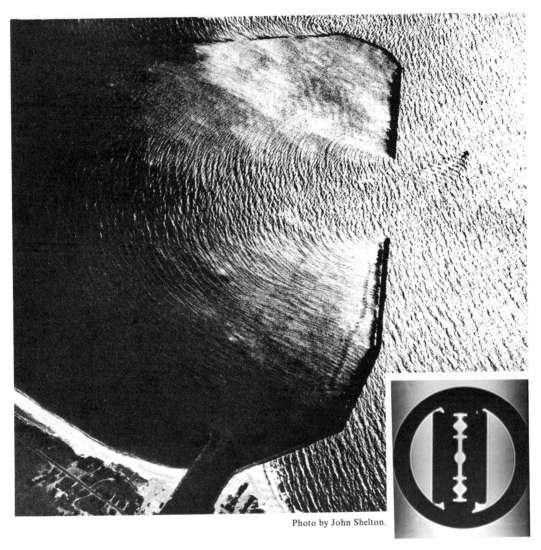

Photo by John Shelton.

Fig. 29.5 Examples of Diffraction.

shadow is blurred slightly at the edges. This is because there is a slight bending of light around the edges of the object. This bending of light (or any wave motion) around corners is called *diffraction*.

When a wave passes a point in a medium, the resulting disturbance of the medium at that point is itself a source of a new wave motion of the same frequency (Huygens' Principle). Consider waves of water incident from the left upon a barrier with a narrow opening, Figure 29.6. In (*a*) the opening is small compared to the wavelength of the wave. As the waves are incident upon the opening, the water sloshing up and down in the opening

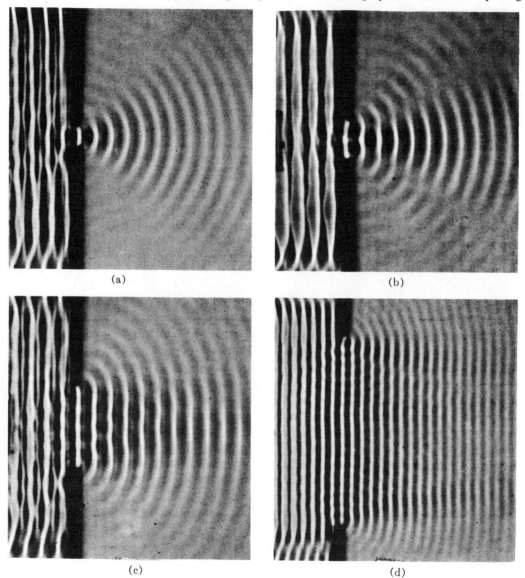

(a)

(b)

(c)

(d)

Fig. 29.6 Straight waves passing through openings of various sizes. Note that the smaller the opening, the greater the bending of the waves at the edges. (From PSSC *Physics*, Boston, Heath, 1965.)

Fig. 29.7   Diffraction of light through a keyhole.

acts as a "point" source of new waves. As a result, concentric-shaped waves are produced on the other side of the barrier. As the opening is widened, (b), the waves produced on the other side no longer emanate from a pointlike source, and the resulting waves are less circular in shape. When the opening is very wide compared to the wavelength of the waves, (c) and (d), the waves from the left side simply pass through unobstructed, with only slight diffraction at the edges. In the case of light waves, this slight diffraction blurs the edges of a shadow. If the source of light causing the shadow of an object is very small (preferably a point), fringes of brightness and darkness can be seen, Figure 29.7. The explanation for the fringes has to do with a related phenomenon called *interference*, which will be discussed in the next section.

The amount of diffraction depends on the wavelength of the wave. Radio waves are very long, ranging from 600 to 20,000 feet for the standard AM broadcast band. As a result, radio waves readily bend around objects that might otherwise obstruct them. The radio waves of the FM band range from 9 to 12 feet, and don't bend as much as AM waves. This is one of the reasons that FM reception is often poor in localities where AM comes in loud and clear. Diffraction, therefore, aids radio reception.

A negative consequence of diffraction is the limitation it imposes on microscopy. The shadows of small objects become less and less well defined as the size of the object approaches the wavelength of light illuminating it. If the object is smaller than a single wavelength, no structure—if anything—can be seen. No amount of magnification or perfection of microscope design can defeat this fundamental diffraction limit. To circumvent this problem, microscopists illuminate tiny objects with electron beams, rather than light. They use electron microscopes. All matter has wave properties, and a beam of electrons has a wavelength smaller than visible light. Their diffraction limit is much less than that of visible light. Electric and magnetic fields, rather than optical lenses, are used to focus and magnify images.

Interference

We have all noticed the beautiful colors reflected from gasoline on a wet street; or the spectrum of colors reflected from a soap bubble; or the colors reflected from some types of bird feathers which seem to change in hue as the bird moves. These colors are produced by the *interference* of light waves.

Waves of any kind superimposed on one another produce a resulting wave that is different than either wave alone. The superposition of waves and the resulting interference was discussed in Chapter 18. Recall that longitudinal sound waves interfere to produce beats. In a similar way, we will see that the interference of transverse light waves produces colors. Constructive and destructive interference, as discussed on page 254, is reviewed in Figures 29.8 and 29.9.

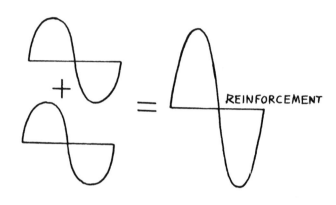

Fig. 29.8 Constructive interference.

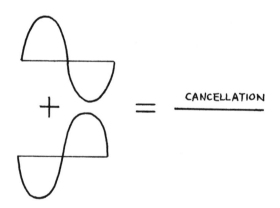

Fig. 29.9 Destructive interference.

The interference of water waves is a common sight, Figure 29.10. In some places crests overlap crests, while in other places crests overlap troughs of other waves.

Under more carefully controlled conditions, interesting patterns are produced when two sources of waves are placed side

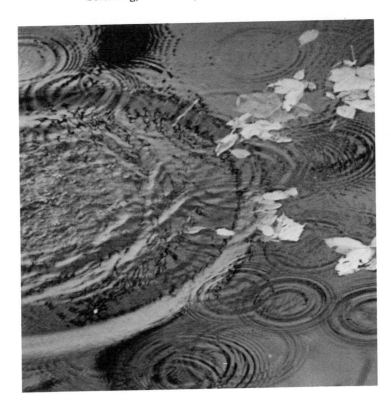

Fig. 29.10   Interference of water waves. (Photo by Charles Phillips.)

by side, Figure 29.11. Drops of water are allowed to fall at a controlled frequency into ripple tanks while their patterns are photographed from above. Note that areas of constructive and

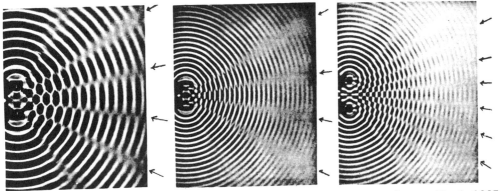

Fig. 29.11   Interference of two sets of identical waves. (From PSSC *Physics*, Boston, Heath, 1965.)

destructive interference are incident on the right side of the ripple tanks, and that the number or spacing of these regions depends on the distance between the wave sources. It also depends on the wavelength (or frequency) of the waves.

If a single wave source is incident upon two narrow openings in a barrier, the disturbances in the openings act as new wave sources. These waves then interfere with each other and produce interference patterns on the right side of the ripple tank, as illustrated in Figure 29.12. Note that the shorter the wavelength (or higher the frequency), the greater is the number of null regions (nodes).

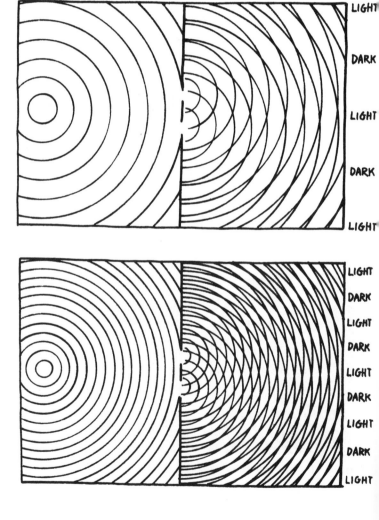

Fig. 29.12 Interference of waves through a double slit.

The wavelength of light is measured by a similar technique. Monochromatic light (light of a single frequency, one color) is incident upon two or more fine, closely spaced slits, Figure 29.13. As a result of interference, fringes of lightness and darkness are produced on a screen. A fringe of light is produced by the waves arriving in phase (constructive interference), and a dark fringe is produced by waves arriving out of phase (destructive interference). Measurement of the distance between entrance slits and the distance between interference fringes permits a calculation for the wavelength of light.

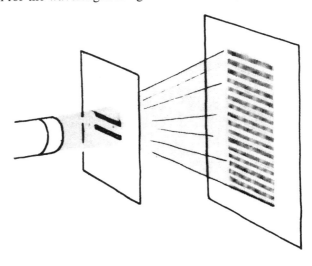

Fig. 29.13 Interference fringes.

Another way interference fringes can be produced is by the reflection of light from the top and bottom surfaces of a thin film. A simple demonstration can be set up with a mono-

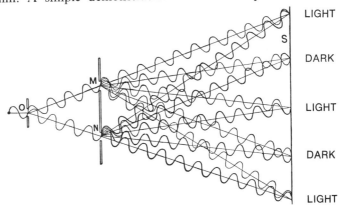

Fig. 29.14 Light from O passes through slits M and N and produces an interference pattern on the screen S.

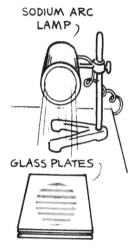

SODIUM ARC
LAMP

GLASS PLATES

Fig. 29.15 Interference fringes.

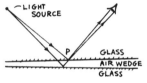

Fig. 29.16 Reflection from the upper and lower surfaces of a "thin film of air."

chromatic light source and a couple of pieces of glass. A sodium-vapor lamp provides a good source of monochromatic light. (Or a piece of asbestos paper soaked in a solution of common salt and wrapped about the upper end of a Bunsen burner so the salt solution touches the flame will do. The burning salt provides a monochromatic yellow light.) The two pieces of glass are placed one atop the other, as shown in Figure 29.15. A very thin piece of paper is placed between the plates at one edge. This leaves a very thin, wedge-shaped film of air between the plates. If the eye is placed so as to see the reflected image of the lamp, the image will not be a continuous one, but will be made up of dark and bright bands.

The cause of these bands is the interference between the waves reflected from the glass surface of the upper side of the air film and the waves reflected from the glass surface on the lower side of the air film. The thickness of the film is greatly exaggerated in Figure 29.16. Since the film is slightly wedge-shaped, the light coming from point *P* on the surface of the film comes from the source to the eye by two different paths. In one of these paths the light is reflected from the top of the air film, in the other path it is reflected from the lower side. If the eye is focused on point *P*, the rays shown on the figure will reach the same point on the retina of the eye. Because these rays have traveled different distances, they may not meet in step, or in phase. They may interfere with each other. For example, if one of the reflected rays is an *odd* number of half-wavelengths behind the other reflected ray, there will be destructive interference, and that part of the film will appear dark. But at another place, the film may be thinner or thicker, and one ray may reach the eye an *even* number of half-wavelengths behind the other. In that case, the two rays will reinforce each other, and that part of the film will appear bright. When we look over the surface of the whole film, we see alternate dark and bright regions, the dark portions being where the thickness is just right to produce interference of the two rays, and the bright portions where the film is just the proper amount thinner or thicker to result in the reinforcement of the rays. The dark and bright bands are caused by the interference of light waves reflected from the two sides of the thin film.

If the surfaces of the glass plates used are perfectly flat, the bands are regular in shape and uniformly spaced. But if the surfaces are not flat, the bands are distorted. The interference

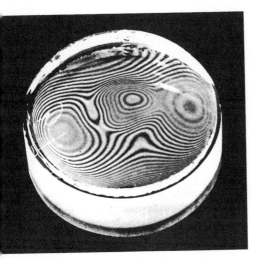

Fig. 29.17   An optical flat used for testing the flatness of surfaces.

of light waves provides an extremely sensitive method for testing the flatness of surfaces. Surfaces producing equispaced fringes are said to be *optically flat*, that is, flat compared with the wavelength of optical radiation (visible light).

When a plano-convex lens is placed on an optically flat plate of glass and illuminated from above with monochromatic light, a series of light and dark rings is produced. This pattern is known as *Newton's rings*, Figure 29.18. These light and dark rings are analogous to the light and dark fringes observed with plane surfaces. This technique is used in grinding precision lenses.

Fig. 29.18 Newton's rings. (Photo from PSSC *Physics,* Boston, Heath, 1965.)

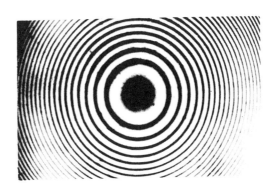

Interference Colors by Reflection

The spectrum of colors observed in thin films results from the interference of light reflected from the two surfaces of the film. Interference depends not only on the thickness of the film, but also on the wavelength of light used. Short waves may reinforce each other at a place where long waves would cancel each other. When a thin film is illuminated by *white* light, at one place the film may be of the right thickness to cause interference of red light. When red light is subtracted from white light, the mixture left will be the complementary color of red, which is green. At another place, where the film is thinner, a different color may be canceled by interference and the light seen will be its complementary color. A thin film of gasoline on a smooth surface of water is a familiar example, Figure 29.19. If the incident beam is monochromatic red, as the figure suggests, then the gasoline surface appears dark to the eye. If the incident beam is white, then the gasoline surface appears green to the eye. This is because the red is subtracted from the white, leaving the complementary color, green. The different colors, then, correspond to different thicknesses of the thin film, providing a vivid "contour map" of microscopic differences in surface "elevations."

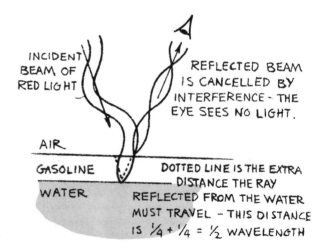

Fig. 29.19 Red light reflected from the gasoline is canceled by red light reflected from the water because the film thickness is one-quarter the wavelength of red light.

Over a wider field of view, different colors can be seen even if the thickness of the gasoline film is uniform. This is because light reaching the eye from different parts of the surface is incident and reflected at different angles. The "apparent thickness" of the film differs for different angles of incidence. If the light is incident at a *grazing* angle, for example, the ray transmitted to the gasoline's lower surface travels a longer distance. Longer waves are canceled in this case and different colors appear.

Dishes washed in soapy water and poorly rinsed have a thin film of soap on them. Hold such a dish up to a light source so that interference colors can be seen. Then turn the dish to a new position, keeping your eye on the same part of the dish, and the color will change. Light reflecting from the bottom surface of the transparent soap film is canceling light reflecting from the top surface of the soap film. Different wavelengths of light are canceled for different angles.

The principle of interference provides a means of measuring extremely small distances with great accuracy. The wavelength of light and other regions of the electromagnetic spectrum are measured with interference techniques. Instruments, such as the Michelson interferometer, that utilize the principle of interference are the most accurate instruments known to man for measuring small distances.

Polarization

Interference and diffraction provide the best evidence that light is wavelike in nature. The two types of wave motion are longitudinal and transverse. Sound in air travels in longitudinal waves, where the vibratory motion is *along* the direction of wave propagation. When we shake a taut rope, the vibratory motion that propagates along the rope is perpendicular, or *transverse*, to the rope. Both longitudinal and transverse waves exhibit interference and diffraction effects. Are light waves, then, longitudinal or transverse? The fact that light waves can be polarized demonstrates that they are transverse.

If we shake a taut rope up and down as in Figure 29.20, a transverse wave travels along the rope in a plane. We say that such a wave is *plane-polarized*.* If the rope is shaken up and down vertically, the wave is vertically plane-polarized. That is, the waves traveling along the rope are confined to a vertical plane. If we shake the rope from side to side, we produce a horizontally plane-polarized wave.

A vibrating electron emits an electromagnetic wave that is also plane polarized. If it vibrates up and down vertically, the electromagnetic wave it emits is as shown diagrammatically in

Fig. 29.20 A vertically polarized plane wave and a horizontally polarized plane wave.

---

*Light may also be circularly or elliptically polarized, which also are transverse polarizations—we will not consider these cases.

Figure 29.21. The wave doesn't *look* like the diagram—nobody knows what an electromagnetic wave *looks* like—it doesn't have an "appearance." The diagram merely shows a representation of the orientations of the electric and magnetic fields induced by the accelerating electron. Note that the electric and magnetic fields are perpendicular to each other. It is the electric part of the wave that interacts with the eye and various optical instruments, so we will ignore the magnetic part of the wave in the following discussion.

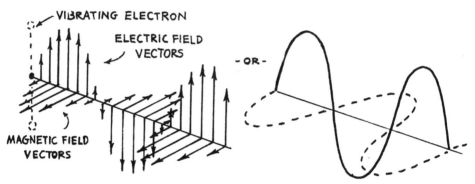

Fig. 29.21   Graphic representations of electromagnetic waves.

We shall also speak of plane-polarized waves as simply polarized waves. The plane of polarization will be along the direction of the vibrating charge. A vertically accelerating electron, then, emits light that is vertically polarized.

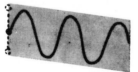

Fig. 29.22   Vertically polarized plane wave from a charge vibrating vertically.

Horizontally polarized plane wave from a charge vibrating horizontally.

A common light source, such as an incandescent or fluorescent lamp, a candle flame, or an arc lamp, emits light that is nonpolarized. This is because there is no preferred vibrational direction for the accelerating charges producing the light. Although any single photon would be polarized about some plane, a great number of photons would vibrate about randomly directed planes. The number of planes of vibration might be as numerous as the accelerating charges producing them. A few planes are represented in Figure 29.23a. We can represent all these planes by radial lines, Figure 29.23b, or more simply by vectors in two mutually perpendicular directions, Figure 29.23c, as if we had resolved all the vectors of Figure 29.23b into horizontal and vertical components. This simpler schematic representation is a useful shorthand. In this case, the diagram represents non-polarized light, for there is no single preferred direction of vibration since the horizontal and vertical components of all vibrations are equal.

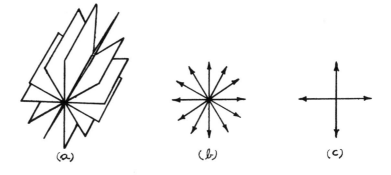

Fig. 29.23 Graphic representations of planes of plane-polarized waves. (Adapted from Albert V. Baez, *The New College Physics: A Spiral Approach*, San Francisco, Freeman, 1967.)

(a)   (b)   (c)

All transparent crystals of a noncubic natural shape have the property of transmitting light through two mutually perpendicular planes. These are called the *optic axes* of the crystals. Certain crystals* not only produce two internal beams polarized at right angles to each other, but also strongly absorb one beam while transmitting the other. Tourmaline is one such common crystal, but unfortunately the transmitted light is colored. Herapathite, however, does the job without discoloration. Microscopic crystals of herapathite are embedded between cellulose sheets in uniform alignment and are used in making Polaroid filters.

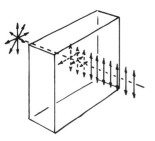

Fig. 29.24 One component of the incident, nonpolarized light is absorbed, resulting in emerging polarized light.

Some Polaroid sheets consist of certain aligned molecules rather than tiny crystals.† The sheets have a polarization axis and will transmit components of light vibrating in this axis. Components at right angles to this axis are absorbed. An ideal Polaroid will transmit 50 percent of incident nonpolarized light.

---

*Called *dichroic*.

†The molecules are polymeric iodine in a sheet of polyvinyl alcohol (H sheet) or polyvinylene (K sheet).

That 50 percent is, of course, polarized. When two Polaroids are arranged so that their polarization axes are aligned, light will be transmitted through both, Figure 29.25. If their axes are at right angles to each other, no light will get through the pair. Actually, some of the shorter wavelengths do get through, but not to any significant degree. When Polaroids are used in pairs like this, the first one is called the *polarizer*, and the second one the *analyzer*.

Much of the light reflected from nonmetallic surfaces is polarized. The glare from glass or water is a good example. Except for normal incidence, the reflected ray contains more vibrations parallel to the reflecting surface, while the transmitted beam contains more vibrations at right angles to these, Figure 29.26. An analogy is skipping flat rocks off the surface of a pond. When the rocks are incident parallel to the surface,

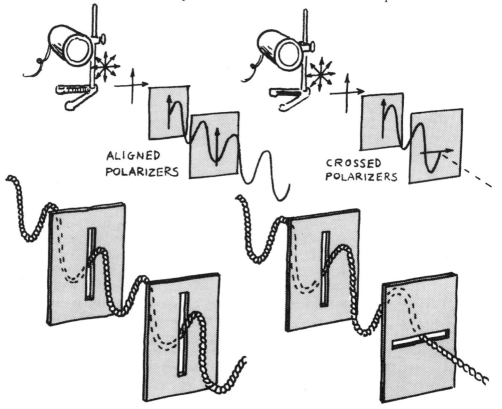

ALIGNED POLARIZERS

CROSSED POLARIZERS

Fig. 29.25 A rope analogy illustrates the effect of crossed polarizers. (Adapted from Albert V. Baez, *The New College Physics: A Spiral Approach*, San Francisco, Freeman, 1967.)

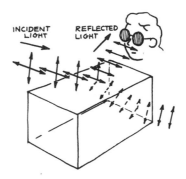

Fig. 29.26 Polarization by reflection.

they easily reflect, but if they are incident with their faces at right angles to the surface, they "refract" into the water. The glare from reflecting surfaces can be appreciably diminished with the use of Polaroid sunglasses. The polarization axes of the lenses are vertical, as most glare reflects from horizontal surfaces. Properly aligned Polaroid eyeglasses enable us to see the projection of stereoscopic movies or slides upon a flat screen in three dimensions.

Three-Dimensional Viewing

Vision in three dimensions is based primarily on the fact that both eyes give their impressions simultaneously, each eye viewing the scene from a slightly different angle. Figure 29.27 illustrates

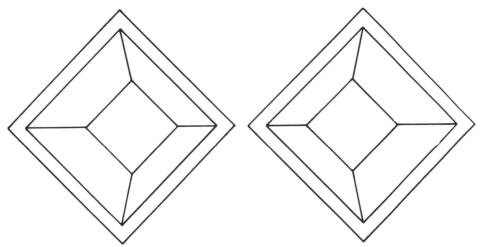

Fig. 29.27 If these figures are observed with the eyes focused for distant viewing, each figure will be seen double. By adjusting the eyes, the two inside images can be superimposed and will then appear in relief like a solid standing up from the page. This effect is more easily realized by holding a card or piece of paper between the eyes and between the two figures so that the left eye can see only the left figure and the right eye only the right figure.

Fig. 29.28 A stereo
viewer.

two such views of a truncated pyramid. The familiar hand-held
stereoscope viewers, Figure 29.28, simulate the effect of depth. In
this device there are two photographic transparencies (or slides)
taken from slightly different positions. When they are viewed at
the same time, the arrangement is such that the left eye sees the
scene as photographed from the left, and the right eye sees it from
the right. As a result the objects in the scene "stand out" in correct
perspective, giving so-called depth to the picture. The viewer
is constructed so that each eye sees only the proper view.
There is no chance for one eye to see both views. If the slides
are removed from the hand viewer and each view projected
upon a screen by slide projectors (so that the views are superimposed), a blurry picture results. This is because each eye sees
both views simultaneously, and this is where Polaroid filters
come in. If Polaroids are placed in front of the projectors, say
one horizontal and the other vertical, and the polarized image
viewed with polarized glasses of the same orientation, each eye
sees the proper view as with the stereo viewer, Figure 29.29.
We then see an image in three dimensions.

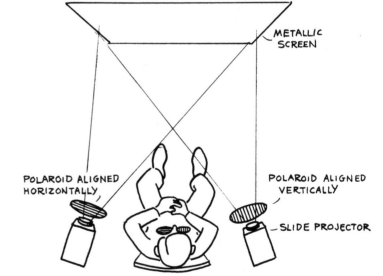

Fig. 29.29 A three-
dimensional slide show
using Polaroids. The left
eye sees only light from the
left projector and the right
eye sees only light from the
right projector.

METALLIC
SCREEN

POLAROID ALIGNED
HORIZONTALLY

POLAROID ALIGNED
VERTICALLY

SLIDE PROJECTOR

Interference Colors by Transmission

The colors produced when light is passed through a crystal
placed between crossed Polaroids are a spectacular sight. Since
cellophane is composed of chain molecules that behave optically

like microscopic noncubic crystals, a crumpled sheet of cellophane between crossed Polaroids produces an array of colors, different colors corresponding to the different apparent thicknesses of the cellophane. The more crumpled the better, as a greater variety of path lengths through the cellophane provides a greater variety of colors—and quite vivid colors. The effect has to be seen to be appreciated. It is an instant psychedelic light show!

The explanation of this effect is not simple. A fairly good understanding of vectors is required. The following paragraph may require several rereadings and referral to Figure 29.30.

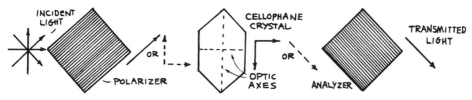

Fig. 29.30 The cellophane should be sandwiched between the crossed Polaroids but is here spread out for convenience. Follow the transformations of the light vector from incidence, left, to transmission, right. (Fig. 29.31 shows how the vertical component changes direction in the cellophane.)

We will consider a single wavelength of light traversing a system comprised of a polarizer, a piece of cellophane, and an analyzer. The Polaroids are crossed, that is, at right angles to each other. The optic axes of the cellophane are at 45 degrees with respect to either of the Polaroid axes. Incoming light passes through the polarizer and is polarized at 45 degrees with respect to the horizontal and vertical axes of the cellophane. The 45-degree vector has a horizontal and vertical component, as shown by the broken lines, which will be transmitted along the axes of the cellophane. These components will travel through the cellophane at different speeds. As a result, one wave component gets ahead of the other. In the figure we suppose that the thickness of the cellophane is such that the vertical component gains one-half wavelength over the horizontal component. The emerging vertical component in this case points down instead of up. The resultant of the vectors is effectively rotated through 90 degrees from the vector passed by the polarizer. It is then in a direction corresponding to the axis of the analyzer and passes through at maximum transmission. Only for this particular wavelength, and this particular cellophane thickness, will a 90-degree rotation of the incident vector occur. A wave diagram illustrating this case is shown in Figure 29.31. If the analyzer is rotated to a different position, some other rotated wavelength will correspond to the alignment with the axis of the analyzer. As the analyzer is turned, then, different colors are transmitted by the system.

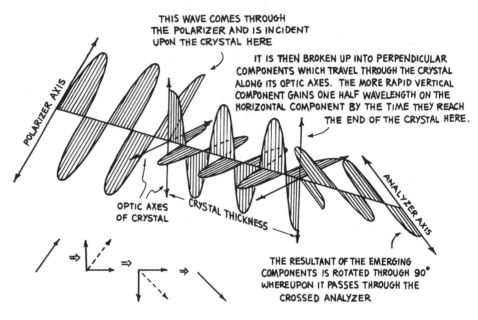

THIS WAVE COMES THROUGH
THE POLARIZER AND IS INCIDENT
UPON THE CRYSTAL HERE

IT IS THEN BROKEN UP INTO PERPENDICULAR
COMPONENTS WHICH TRAVEL THROUGH THE CRYSTAL
ALONG ITS OPTIC AXES. THE MORE RAPID VERTICAL
COMPONENT GAINS ONE HALF WAVELENGTH ON THE
HORIZONTAL COMPONENT BY THE TIME THEY REACH
THE END OF THE CRYSTAL HERE.

POLARIZER AXIS

OPTIC AXES
OF CRYSTAL

CRYSTAL THICKNESS

ANALYZER AXIS

THE RESULTANT OF THE EMERGING
COMPONENTS IS ROTATED THROUGH 90°
WHEREUPON IT PASSES THROUGH THE
CROSSED ANALYZER

Fig. 29.31   A wave diagram of polarized light undergoing rotation through a crystal.

Summary of Terms   *Scattering.* When light falls on a medium, electrons in the medium are set into oscillation by the time-varying electric vector of the incident light. The electrons in turn emit light in random directions, scattering the incident beam from its straight-line path.

Diffraction. The bending of light around an obstacle or through a narrow slit in such a way that parallel fringes of light and dark or colored bands are produced.

Interference. The superposition of waves producing regions of reinforcement and regions of cancellation. Constructive interference refers to regions of reinforcement; destructive interference refers to regions of cancellation. The interference of selected wavelengths produces colors, known as interference colors.

Polarization. The alignment of the electric vectors comprising electromagnetic radiation. Such waves of aligned vibrations are said to be polarized.

Suggested Reading

Battan, Louis J., *Cloud Physics and Cloud Seeding* (Science Study Series), Garden City, N. Y., Doubleday (Anchor), 1962.
Baumeister, Philip, and Gerald Pincus, "Optical Interference Coatings," *Scientific American*, December, 1970.

Questions

1. If the sky were ordinarily orange instead of blue, what color would sunsets be?

2. What color is the sky on the moon?

3. The atmosphere of Jupiter is over a thousand miles thick. From the surface of this planet, would you expect to see a white sun?

4. What are some of the assets and liabilities of diffraction?

5. Why does a microscopist use blue light to illuminate the objects he views?

6. How can darkness be made with light?

7. When dishes are not properly rinsed after washing, different colors are reflected from their surfaces. Explain.

8. How would the spacings between Newton's rings, Figure 29.18, differ for illumination by red light and by blue light?

9. How could you determine whether sunglasses are polarizing material or tinted glass?

10. What is the advantage of sunglasses made with polarizing materials over those that simply absorb or reflect some of the incident light?

11. How could you determine the polarization axis for a single sheet of Polaroid?

12. How can a single sheet of Polaroid film be used to show that the sky is partially polarized?

13. If you had duplicates made of ordinary photographic slides, and viewed pairs of identical slides in a stereo viewer, Figure 29.28, would you see three dimensions?

14. If the left and right views of the pyramid in Figure 29.27 are exchanged, how will the combined image appear? (Draw your own, and see for yourself!)

15. What effect do you suppose would occur if the Polaroids in front of the projectors in Figure 29.29 were rotated 90 degrees?

30

Lenses

Converging and Diverging Lenses

A very practical case of refraction occurs in *lenses*. In nearly all optical instruments that produce images, lenses are used. Although most lenses are made of common glass, a few special lenses are made of other transparent materials like quartz and fluorite.

There are two classes of lenses. When a beam of parallel light rays travels into a lens having convex surfaces, the beam is converged, Figure 30.1a. This type of lens is called a *converging* or *positive* lens. But when a beam of light passes into a lens having concave faces, the beam diverges as it leaves the lens. This type is called a *diverging* or *negative* lens, Figure 30.1b.

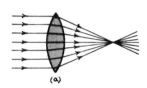

Fig. 30.1 Converging and diverging lenses.

We can explain the action of a lens if we assume it consists of a set of several matched prisms and blocks of glass arranged in the order shown in Figure 30.2a. The prisms and blocks of glass are arranged to refract incoming parallel light rays that converge to a focus at a single point. In the case of the diverging lens, Figure 30.2b, the prisms diverge the incident rays in such a way as to make the rays appear to come from a single point in front of the lens. In both lenses the greatest deviation of rays occurs at the outermost prisms, for they have the greatest angle between the two refracting surfaces. No deviation occurs for the central rays, for in that region the glass faces are parallel to each

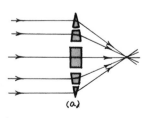
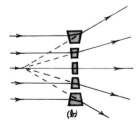

Fig. 30.2 A lens may be thought of as a set of prisms.

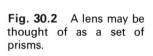

424

Real lenses are not made of prisms, of course, as indicated in Figure 30.2, but of a solid piece of glass with surfaces ground to a usually circular curve.

We can also understand the action of lenses by considering the *waves* of light traveling through them and remembering that light travels more slowly in glass than it does in air. The convex lens of Figure 30.3 is thicker at the center than it is at the edge. Since light travels more slowly in glass than in air, the part of the wave that travels through the central portion of the lens is retarded more than the wave near the edge. The part of the wave emerging near the edge is speeded up while the part still in the glass near the middle lags behind. This results in a bending of the light as shown in the figure. Since light or any wave motion travels in a direction perpendicular to the waves, light converges toward the center of the curvature of these waves. Light therefore is converged because the central part of the waves is retarded in the thicker central portion of the lens.

In a lens that is thinner at the center than at its edge, the central part of the wave does not travel through as much glass as the part that travels through the edges. Therefore the central part is not retarded but speeds up upon emerging, while the rest of the wave in the glass lags behind. The waves are then bent as shown in Figure 30.4, appearing as if they originated from a point source in front of the lens. Light therefore diverges in passing through a lens that is thinner at the center.

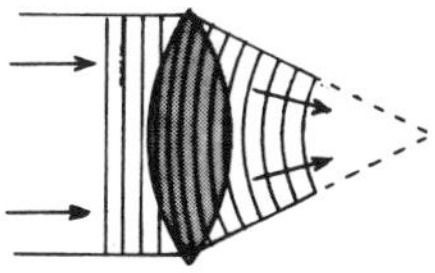

Fig. 30.3 Wave convergence.

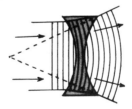

Fig. 30.4 Wave divergence.

Cross sections of several standard lenses are shown in Figure 30.5. The first three lenses, which are thicker in the middle, are converging lenses and the last three are diverging

Fig. 30.5 Converging lenses; diverging lenses.

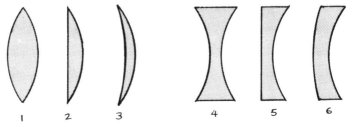

1   2   3   4   5   6

lenses. Special names for each are (1) double convex, (2) plano-convex, (3) convex meniscus, (4) double concave, (5) plano-concave, and (6) concave miniscus.

Most lenses are made with spherical surfaces. In Figure 30.6, the two positions of the centers of curvature of the spherical portions that form the surfaces of the converging lens are shown. The line drawn through the two centers is called the *principal axis*. The *focal point* is the point at which a beam of light, parallel to the principal axis, converges. Incident parallel beams that are not parallel to the principal axis focus at points above or below the focal point. All such possible points make up a *focal plane*. Since a lens has two surfaces it has two focal points and two focal planes. When the lens of a camera is set for distant objects, the film is in the focal plane behind the lens in the camera.

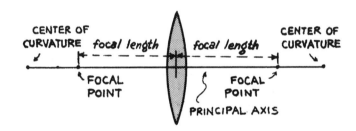

Fig. 30.6   Illustration of terms.

In the case of a diverging lens, an incident beam of light parallel to the principal axis is not converged to a point, but is diverged, so that the light appears to come from a point in front of the lens, Figure 30.1*b*. The *focal length* of a lens, whether converging or diverging, is the distance between the center of the lens and its focal point, Figure 30.6.

Image Formation by Lenses

If a converging lens is held near an object, so that the object is *inside* the focal point, a magnified image will be seen. Any converging lens serves as a magnifying glass when it is held near the object to be magnified. A simple magnifying glass is a converging lens. In Figure 30.7 an object (arrow) lies between a converging lens and its focal point. Note that the two sample rays of light shown appear to the eye as if they originated from the tip of the broken-line arrow. This represents the image. It

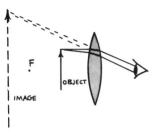

Fig. 30.7 A magnifying glass.

is most important to note that the image is observed through a wider angle with the use of the lens than it is without the lens. It is therefore magnified. We see objects magnified when we can observe objects through a wider viewing angle. An object far away is seen through a relatively small angle of view, while the same object when closer is seen through a larger angle of view, enabling the perception of more detail, Figure 30.8. A lens simply increases the angle of view, thereby making objects appear to be closer or larger than they really are.

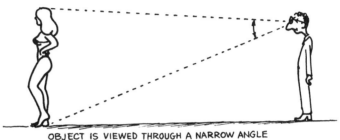

OBJECT IS VIEWED THROUGH A NARROW ANGLE

Fig. 30.8

OBJECT IS VIEWED THROUGH A WIDE ANGLE

A converging lens will magnify only when the object is inside the focal point of the lens. Then the image will be farther from the lens than the object, will be right side up and magnified. No physical image is really formed at the image distance in this case; that is, if a screen were placed at the image distance, no image would appear on the screen. To the eye, the image only appears to exist and therefore is called a *virtual image*.

When the object is outside the focal point of a converging lens, instead of a virtual image a *real image* is obtained.

Figure 30.9 shows a case in which a converging lens forms an image of a candle on a screen. In this case the light is converged on a screen and forms a *real*, inverted image. A similar arrangement is used for projecting transparent slides and motion pictures on a screen. A converging lens is used in cameras for projecting a real image on the photographic film. Real images will always be inverted.

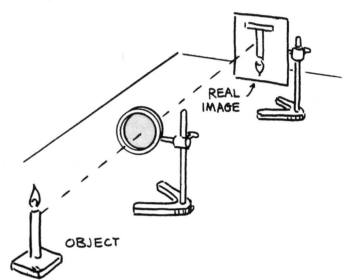

REAL IMAGE

OBJECT

Fig. 30.9 A converging lens forming a real image.

A diverging lens, when used alone, produces only diminished *virtual* images. Figure 30.10 shows the virtual image produced by a diverging lens. When a diverging lens is used alone, it makes no difference how far away the object is: the image is always virtual, erect, and diminished. A diverging lens is sometimes mounted as a "finder" on a camera. On looking at the object to be photographed through such a lens, we see a virtual image of approximately the same proportions as the photograph.

Graphical Construction of Images

It is not difficult to learn to use a graphical method for locating the position of images formed by a thin lens.* To find the position of the image of any point of an object, we only have to know the

---

*The mathematical relationship between object distance o, image distance i, and focal length f is given by $1/o + 1/i = 1/f$. This is called the thin-lens equation.

Fig. 30.10 A virtual image produced by a diverging lens. (Photo by Richard Stacks.)

paths of two rays from that point. One path is known from the definition of the focal point. For example, in Figure 30.11 a ray from the tip of the arrow, parallel to the principal axis, will be refracted by the lens toward the focal point as shown. Another path is known: through the center of the lens where the faces are parallel to each other. A ray of light will pass through the center with no appreciable deviation. Therefore a ray of light from the tip of the arrow through the center of the lens is directed as shown. The two rays from the tip of the arrow diverge as they leave the lens and appear to come from a point in front (same side of the lens as the object) of the lens. This locates the image of the arrowhead. In a similar manner the image of any other point of the object may be located. (You should make the construction for the other end of the arrow. Go ahead, make your construction with pencil on Figure 30.11. Or be brave and use ink!) The example just given is for a magnifying glass. In this case the object was inside the focal point on the left side.

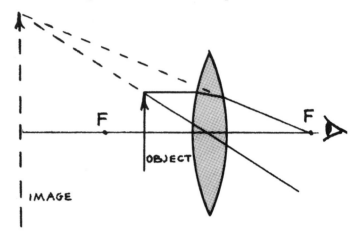

Fig. 30.11   Ray diagram.

When the object is outside the focal point of a converging lens, we can find the location of the inverted *real* image that is formed, Figure 30.12. A ray from the tip of the object arrow, parallel to the principal axis, is bent down through the focal point. A ray from the tip of the arrow through the center of the lens passes through with no bending. The intersection of these two rays locates the position of the image. Note that the image is inverted, which indicates that it is a real image. (You should make the construction for the image of the lower end of the arrow.) Again, an inverted but real image is formed with a converging lens only when the object is outside the focal point.

In the case of the real images formed by converging lenses, it is always possible to interchange the position of the object and

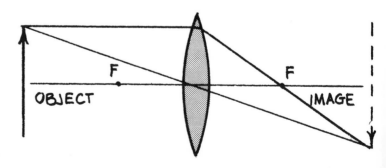

Fig. 30.12   Ray diagram.

image. For example, if in Figure 30.12 the object is put where the image is, the image will be found where the object is.

The method of graphical construction applies also to diverging lenses, Figure 30.13. A ray parallel to the principal axis from a point on the object, say the tip of the arrow, will be bent by the lens in the same direction as if it had come from the focal point, *F*. A ray from the tip of the arrow through the center of the lens goes straight through. On emerging from the lens, the two rays seem to come from a point that defines the position of the image. The image is nearer the lens than the object. It is virtual and diminished in size but is right side up. It can be shown by this method that, regardless of the object position, the image formed by a diverging lens is always virtual, diminished, and erect.

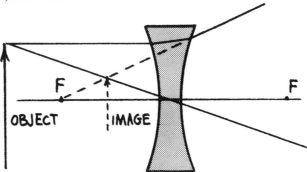

Fig. 30.13   Ray diagram.

Summary of Image Formation by Lenses

When the object is inside the focal point, a converging lens is a simple magnifying glass, producing an image that is virtual, magnified, and erect.

When the object is outside the focal point, a converging lens produces a real, inverted image. The location of the image depends on how close the object is to the focal point—if it is close (but still outside), the image is far away (as with a slide or movie projector); if the object is far from the focal point, the image is nearer (as with a camera). In all cases where a real image is formed, the object and the image are on opposite sides of the lens.

When the object is viewed with a diverging lens, the image is virtual, diminished, and erect. This is true for all locations of the object. In all cases where a virtual image is formed, the object and the image are on the same side of the lens.

Some Defects of Lenses

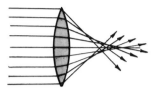

Fig. 30.14 Spherical aberration.

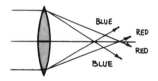

Fig. 30.15 Chromatic aberration.

No lens gives a perfect image. The distortions in an image are called *aberrations.* By combining an appropriate system of lenses in certain ways, aberrations can be minimized. For this reason, most optical instruments use compound lenses, each consisting of several simple lenses, instead of a single lens.

Spherical aberration occurs because light going through the edge of a lens does not focus at the same place as the light going through the center of the lens, Figure 30.14. This can be circumvented by covering the edges of the lens. This is one of the reasons that diaphragms or stops are used in camera lenses. In most cases spherical aberration is corrected by a combination of lenses.

Chromatic aberration occurs because red light, blue light, and the other frequencies of light refract at different angles and therefore do not come to focus at the same place. The focal length of a simple lens for red light is somewhat longer than that of blue light; hence an image formed by red light is not in exactly the same place as one formed by blue light. *Achromatic lenses,* a combination of simple lenses of different kinds of glass, correct this defect.

Summary of Terms

Converging lens. A lens that is thicker in the middle than at the edges, which refracts parallel rays passing through it to a focus.

Diverging lens. A lens that is thinner in the middle than at the edges, causing parallel rays passing through it to diverge.

Focal length. The distance between the center of a converging lens and the point at which parallel rays of incident light converge; or the distance between the center of a diverging lens and the point from which parallel rays of light appear to diverge.

Real image. An image formed by the actual convergence of light rays upon a screen.

Virtual image. An illusionary image that is seen by an observer through a lens but cannot be projected on a screen.

Aberration. A distortion in an image resulting from defects in the lens producing the image.

Questions

1. What kind of lens is used for a simple magnifying glass? How does the image differ for an object viewed within and beyond the focal point of the lens?

2. Why do you suppose that a magnifying glass is also often called a *burning glass*?

3. Why is the greater part of the photograph in Figure 30.10 "out of focus"?

4. Why is a diverging lens rather than a converging lens used as a "finder" on a photographic camera?

5. What is responsible for the rainbow colored fringe commonly seen at the edges of a spot of white light from the beam of a lantern or slide projector?

31

Optical Instruments

We have discussed the nature of light, how it is emitted, and how it behaves when it interacts with different media. We will now concern ourselves with light as it is directed to our eyes. We will consider some common optical instruments that serve to extend our sense of sight to the very large as well as the very small. Much knowledge of the micro and macro worlds unseen by the naked eye is revealed with these extensions of vision. Who, for example, would have thought a century and a half ago that mankind would know the chemical constitution of the stars? Today we know as much if not more about the chemical composition of the stars as we do about the earth. We know this from the light the stars emit, which is analyzed by one of the most fascinating instruments of modern science—the spectroscope.

The Spectroscope

A prism will separate light into its component colors. When we combine a prism with a set of lenses and a piece of opaque material with a thin slit in it, we have a *spectroscope*, Figure 31.1.

A spectroscope is used to analyze light and study the specific frequencies or colors it contains. The essential part of the instrument is a prism.* The lenses focus the light to be analyzed through the prism and onto a viewing screen or appropriate detector. To avoid overlapping of the neighboring colors, the light is best analyzed if it originates from a narrow slit. The narrower the slit, the better we can distinguish between neigh-

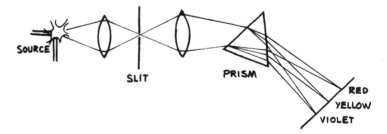

Fig. 31.1 A simple spectroscope.

*Diffraction gratings consisting of thousands of thin slits are also used to separate colors. An LP phonograph record acts as a diffraction grating when it separates a grazing beam of white light into its component colors.

boring frequencies—we say a narrower slit provides better resolution. There is a happy medium, for if the slit is too narrow the smaller amount of light admitted might not be detected. Each component color is focused at a definite position on the screen or film according to its frequency, forming an image of the source, which in this case is the slit. The various images of the slit are the so-called "lines" of the spectrum, Figure 31.2.

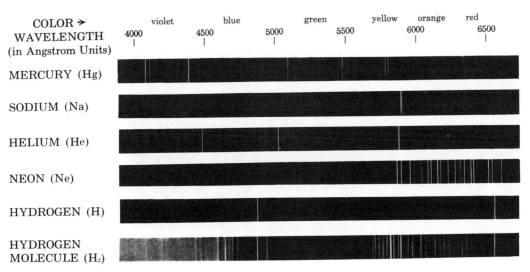

Fig. 31.2   Some typical spectral patterns.

Emission Spectra

When a solid or liquid is heated to glowing, the emitted light produces a continuous rainbowlike spectrum. Light from a flame or a gas, however, produces line spectra. If the light given off by a sodium-vapor lamp is analyzed in a spectroscope, a single yellow line is produced—a single image of the slit. If we narrow the width of the slit we find that this line is really composed of two very close lines. These lines correspond to the two predominant frequencies of light emitted by excited sodium atoms. The rest of the spectrum is dark.* The light emitted by sodium gas appears to be restricted to two frequencies—quite a different situation from the light emitted from an incandescent solid which gives off an infinite number of frequencies.

---

*The sodium spectrum contains many other lines that are too dim to be seen by the naked eye.

The situation is not unique to sodium. On examining the light from a mercury-vapor lamp, now widely used in street lighting, we find two strong yellow lines close together (but in different positions from those of sodium), a very intense green line, and several blue and violet lines. We get a similar but more complicated pattern of lines from the light emitted by a neon tube. We find that the light emitted by every element in the vapor state produces its own characteristic pattern of lines. These lines correspond to the electron transitions between atomic energy levels and are as characteristic of each element as are the fingerprints of people. The spectroscope therefore is widely used in chemical analysis.

Absorption Spectra

Atoms absorb light as well as emit light. An atom will most strongly absorb light having the frequencies to which it is tuned— the same frequencies it emits. When a beam of white light passes through a gas, the atoms of the gas absorb selected frequencies from the beam. This absorbed light is reradiated, but in *all* directions instead of only in the direction of the incident beam. When the light remaining in the beam is spread out into a spectrum, the frequencies that were absorbed show up as dark lines in the otherwise continuous spectrum. The positions of these dark lines correspond exactly to the positions of lines in an emission spectrum of the same gas.

Although the sun is an incandescent source, the spectrum it produces, upon close examination, is not continuous. There are many dark lines distributed through it. These are called *Fraunhofer lines* in honor of the Bavarian optician who first observed and mapped them accurately. Similar lines are found in the spectra produced by the stars. These lines indicate that the sun and stars are each surrounded by an atmosphere of cooler gases that absorb some of the frequencies of light coming from the main body. Analysis of these lines reveals the chemical composition of the atmospheres of such sources. We find from

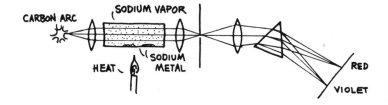

Fig. 31.3 Experimental arrangement for demonstrating the absorption spectra of a gas.

such studies that the stellar elements are the same elements that exist on earth. An interesting sidelight is that when spectroscopic measurements were made of the sun, spectral lines different from those measured in the laboratories were found. These lines identified a new element which was named helium, after Helios, the sun. Helium was discovered in the sun before it was discovered on earth.

From a study of the spectra emitted by the stars we can determine their speeds. Just as a moving sound source produces a Doppler shift in its pitch, Chapter 20, a moving light source produces a Doppler shift in its light frequency. The frequency (not the speed!) of light emitted by an approaching source is increased, while the frequency of light from a receding source is decreased. The corresponding spectral lines are displaced toward the violet end of the spectrum for approaching sources and toward the red end of the spectrum for receding sources. Since the universe is expanding, the galaxies show a red shift in their spectra.

We shall see in the next chapter how the spectra of elements enable us to determine atomic structure.

The Telescope

The astronomical telescope consists of a simple arrangement of two converging lenses, the objective lens and the eyepiece lens. The paths of a few of the rays that travel through the lenses of an astronomical telescope are shown in Figure 31.4. The *objective* lens has a rather long focal length. Since the object viewed is at a great distance, the image is formed at or just

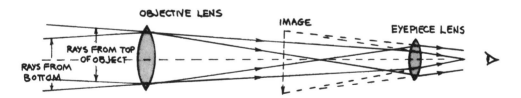

Fig. 31.4   Astronomical telescope.

beyond the focal point of the objective lens. This image is real and inverted, and is viewed with a simple magnifying glass, the *eyepiece* lens. In focusing the telescope, the distance between the lenses is changed until the objective image lies inside the focal point of the eyepiece, and at a place where the eye can see the final image distinctly.

The magnifying power of a telescope is defined as the ratio of the angle subtended at the eye by the final image and the angle that would be subtended in viewing the object with the unaided eye. In other words, it is the number of times larger an object appears to be when viewed with the telescope. By applying plane geometry to a simple light-ray diagram of a telescope, it can be seen that the magnifying power is equal to the ratio of the focal lengths of the two lenses. That is,

$$\text{Magnifying power} = \frac{\text{focal length of objective}}{\text{focal length of eyepiece}}$$

As an illustration, consider a small telescope with an objective lens having a focal length of 40 inches, and suppose that it is used with an eyepiece having a focal length of 1 inch. The magnifying power would be 40/1 or 40. Distant objects viewed through this telescope would appear to be forty times as tall and forty times as wide as when viewed with the unaided eye. The longer the focal length of the objective, the greater is the magnification. This is why high-powered telescopes are so long. Magnification can also be increased by using a short-focal-length eyepiece.

The image seen by an astronomical telescope is inverted. There are several ways to turn the image right side up. In *prism binoculars* the inversion is accomplished by totally reflecting prisms. Prism binoculars are simply a pair of twin telescopes mounted side by side. The reflecting prisms invert the rays to give erect images. The doubling back of the light rays has the advantage of enabling long-focus objective lenses to be used in short tubes. The length of the optical path is nearly three times the length of the binocular tubes.

In the *terrestrial* telescope, an extra lens is used to invert the image. This is shown by the middle lens in Figure 31.6. It forms a second real image which is viewed by the magnifying lens or eyepiece. This is the common drawtube spyglass, the telescope used on surveyors' transits and on gun sights.

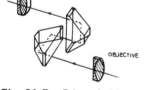

Fig. 31.5   Prisms in binoculars.

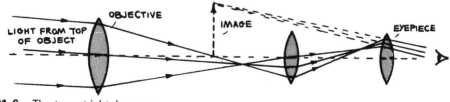

Fig. 31.6   The terrestrial telescope.

The simplest method for inverting the image is employed in the type of telescope called the *opera glass*. The paths of a few rays that travel through the lenses of an opera glass are shown in Figure 31.7. The objective lens acting alone would form a real image beyond the length of the telescope tube. But a *diverging* eyepiece lens is interposed in the path of light so as to form a virtual image. This provides a compact design which is not very satisfactory except for small magnifications. An ordinary opera glass magnifies a distant object only three or four times. A further disadvantage is its small field of view.

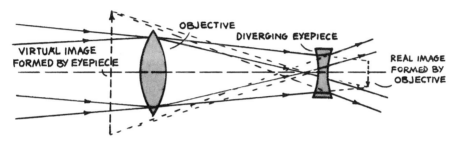

Fig. 31.7   The opera glass.

The Compound Microscope

Whereas a single converging lens used to view an object positioned inside the focal point is a magnifier, greater magnifications can be obtained with a pair of converging lenses. The objective lens of a microscope is a lens of very short focal length; hence it may be placed quite near the object and yet form a real image. This real image is viewed through a magnifying eyepiece lens, and the final virtual image is seen. Because the objective image is much farther from the objective lens than the object, it is considerably magnified. This image in turn is magnified by the eyepiece. The shorter the focal length of the objective, the nearer the object must be to the objective, and hence the

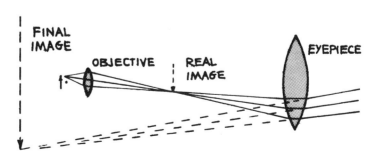

Fig. 31.8   The compound microscope.

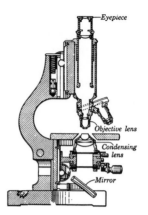

Fig. 31.9 Cross-section view of the compound microscope.

larger is its image. The compound microscope is the same in principle as the astronomical telescope, where objective and eyepiece play reversed roles. Look through a telescope the wrong way and you have a microscope.

The Eye

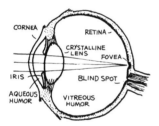

Fig. 31.10 The human eye.

The optical instruments considered thus far are all extensions of the most remarkable optical instrument, the eye. Light enters the eye through the *cornea*. It then passes through the crystalline lens and is focused on a layer at the back of the eye called the *retina*, so that different parts of the retina receive light from different parts of the visual field outside. The retina is not uniform. There is a spot in the center of our field of view at which we have the greatest acuity of vision; it is called the *fovea*, or region of most distinct vision. Much greater detail can be seen here than at the side parts of the eye. There is also a spot in the retina where the nerves carrying all the information run out; this is the *blind spot*. The existence of the blind spot can be demonstrated by closing the left eye and holding the book at arm's length, looking continuously at the center of the circle of Figure 31.11 with the right eye. Both the circle and the X will be seen at this distance. If the book is now moved slowly toward the eye, with the eye still fixed upon the circle, a position (about 8 to 10 inches from the eye) will be reached at which the X disappears. A similar experiment with the left eye focused on

Fig. 31.11 Blind-spot experiment.

the X will make the circle disappear. When both eyes are opened, no position will be found where either the X or circle disappears because one eye sees the part of the object to which the other eye is blind. Aren't you glad you have two eyes?

The retina is composed of tiny antennae that resonate to the incoming electromagnetic radiation we call light. There are basically two kinds of antennae, the *rods* and the *cones*. As the names imply, some of the antennae are rod-shaped and some cone-shaped. The rods and cones in the retina of the eye are not connected directly to the optic nerve. Interestingly enough, they are connected to many other cells, which are connected to each other. There are several kinds of cells; some carry information toward the optic nerve while others are mainly interconnected. Through these interconnections a certain amount of information is combined from several visual receptors and digested in the retina. In this way the light signal is "thought about" before it goes to the optic nerve and then to the main body of the brain. It is important to understand that some brain functioning occurs in the eye itself. The eye does some of our "thinking."

The rods predominate closer to the periphery of the retina while the cones are denser toward the fovea. The cones are very dense in the fovea itself, being packed in so tightly that the cones are much finer or narrower than elsewhere in the retina. Color vision is possible because of the cones. Hence color is seen most acutely by focusing an image on the fovea. There are no rods in the fovea. Primates and a species of ground squirrel are the only mammals that have cones and experience color vision. The retinas of other mammals consist only of rods, which are sensitive only to lightness or darkness, like a black-and-white photograph or motion picture. In the human eye the number of cones decreases as we move away from the fovea. It's interesting that the color of an object disappears if viewed on the periphery of vision. This can be tested by having a friend enter your periphery of vision with some brightly colored objects. You will find that you can see the objects before you can see what color they are.

Another interesting fact is that the periphery of the retina is very sensitive to motion. Although our vision is poor from the corner of our eye, we are sensitive to anything moving there. We are "wired" to look for something jiggling to the side of our visual field, a feature that must have been important in our evolutionary development.

Another distinguishing feature of the rods and cones is the intensity of light to which they respond. The cones require more energy before they will "fire" an impulse through the nervous system. If the intensity of light is very low, the things we see have no color. We see low intensities with our rods. Dark-adapted vision is almost entirely due to the rods, while vision in bright light is due to the cones. Stars, for example, look white to us. Yet most stars are actually brightly colored. A time exposure of the stars with a camera will reveal reds and oranges for the "cooler" stars, and blues and violets for the "hotter" stars. The starlight is too weak, however, to fire the color-perceiving cones in the retina. So we see the stars with our rods, and perceive them as white, or at best, only very faintly colored. Females have a slightly lower threshold of firing for the cones, however, and can see a bit more color than males. So if she says she sees colored stars and he says she doesn't, she is probably right!

The sensitivity of the rods decreases in bright light. It turns out that rods see better toward the blue than cones do. The cones can see a deep red where the rods see no light at all. Red light is black as far as the rods are concerned. Thus, two colored objects, say blue and red, though the red might be much brighter than the blue in good light, will appear completely reversed in dim light. It is a very striking effect. Try this: In a dark room, find a magazine or something that has colors and, before you know for sure what the colors are, judge the lighter and darker areas. Then carry the magazine into the light. You should see a remarkable shift between the brightest and dimmest colors.*

Focusing on the retina is accomplished primarily by the cornea and the crystalline lens. As with the photographic camera, it is necessary to focus the eye differently for near and distant objects. In the camera this is done by changing the distance between the lens and the film, but in the eye it is done by the muscles of the eye, which change the shape and the focal length of the lens system. This ability to alter the focal length is called *accommodation*. While reading a book, if you look at a distant object and then back to the book, you may find that some time is required for the eye to accommodate itself. As you get older, the time required will be longer.

---

*This phenomenon is called the *Purkinje effect*.

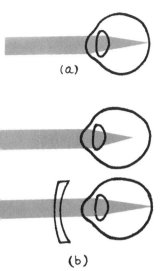

(a)

(b)

Fig. 31.12 (a) Normal eye; (b) nearsighted eye.

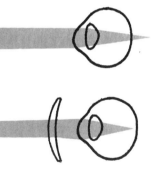

Fig. 31.13 Farsighted eye.

The *iris*, the colored part of the eye, expands or contracts, thus enlarging or diminishing the size of the *pupil* to admit more or less light as the intensity of the light changes. It so happens that the relative size of this enlargement or contraction is also related to our emotions. If we see, smell, taste, or hear something that is pleasing to us, our pupils automatically increase in size. If we see, smell, taste, or hear something repugnant to us, our pupils automatically contract. Many a card player has betrayed the value of his hand of cards by the size of his pupils!*

A *nearsighted* person does not see distant objects clearly because they are focused too near the lens, and in front of the retina. Images of nearer objects will be formed farther back in the eye and may fall on the retina. Although distant objects cannot be seen distinctly, nearby objects can. The remedy is to wear *diverging* eyeglasses, Figure 31.12. These will neutralize part of the converging effect of the eye lens, and the image will be formed farther away from the lens and upon the retina.

The eyes of a *farsighted* person form images behind the retina. The remedy is to increase the converging effect of the eye. This is done by wearing *converging* eyeglasses, Figure 31.13. These will move the real image closer to the eye lens and upon the retina.

Astigmatism of the eye is a defect due to the fact that the cornea of the eye may be curved more in one direction than another, somewhat like the side of a barrel. Because of this defect, the eye does not form sharp, clear images. The remedy for this is to wear cylindrical glasses, or glasses that have more curvature in one direction than in another.

Summary of Terms

Spectroscope. An optical instrument that separates light into its constituent frequencies in the form of spectral lines.

Emission spectra. A continuous or partial spectrum of colors resulting from the dispersion of light from a luminous source.

Absorption spectra. A continuous spectrum, like that of white light, interrupted by dark lines or bands that result from the absorption of certain frequencies of light by a substance through which the radiation passes.

---

*The study of the size of the pupil as a function of attitudes is called *pupilometrics*. An interesting article about it can be found in *Scientific American*, April, 1965, issue.

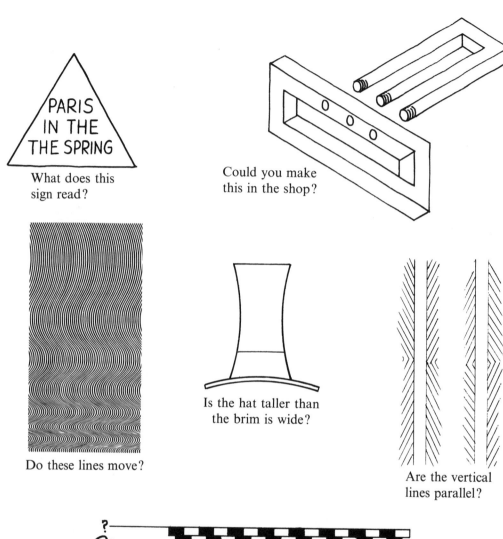

PARIS
IN THE
THE SPRING

What does this
sign read?

Could you make
this in the shop?

Do these lines move?

Is the hat taller than
the brim is wide?

Are the vertical
lines parallel?

Are the tiles really crooked?

Fig. 31.14 Some visual illusions.

Suggested Reading
The Way Things Work—An Illustrated Encyclopedia of Technology; this very interesting book has much information about various kinds of cameras, projectors, microscopes, telescopes, and many optical instruments. New York, Simon & Schuster, 1967.

An excellent treatment on the mechanics of vision is given in Chapters 35 and 36 of Richard Feynman's *Lectures on Physics*, Vol. I, Reading, Mass., Addison-Wesley, 1962.

Land, Edwin H., "Experiments in Color Vision," *Scientific American*, May, 1959.

Wald, George, "Life and Light," *Scientific American*, October, 1959.

Wald, George, "Eye and Camera," *Scientific American*, August, 1950.

Questions
1. If light were passed through a round hole instead of a thin slit in a spectroscope, how would the spectral "lines" appear? Why would a hole be disadvantageous compared to a slit?

2. A lamp filament is made of tungsten. Why do we get a continuous spectrum rather than a tungsten line spectrum when light from an incandescent lamp is viewed with a spectroscope?

3. What might be the basis for a claim that iron exists in the cool gas surrounding the sun?

4. How might the Fraunhofer lines in the spectrum of sunlight that are due to absorption in the sun's atmosphere be distinguished from absorption by gases in the earth's atmosphere?

5. Why are high-powered telescopes long, while high-powered binoculars are relatively short?

6. What is the principal difference between an astronomical telescope and a terrestrial telescope?

7. Maps of the moon are actually upside down. Why is this so?

8. Why do we not see color at the periphery of our vision?

9. Some of the stars are white, but most of them are actually colored. Why, then, do they appear white?

10. When she holds you and looks at you with her contracting eye pupils and says, "I love you," what inference can you draw?

32

The Atom
and the Quantum

We discussed the atom as a building block of matter in Chapter 9. Then in Chapters 26 and 27 we discussed the atom as an emitter of light. In this chapter we will again discuss the atom. We will outline some of the developments that led to our present understanding of atomic structure, and trace the start of these developments from a physics of particles and certainties to a physics of waves and probabilities—quantum mechanics. We will see how our quest for knowledge about the atom has given us a new view of the physical world. We start with the clues that enabled Niels Bohr to construct his planetary model of the atom. He found these clues in the atomic "fingerprints" we discussed in the previous chapter—atomic spectra.

**Atomic Spectra—
The Clue to
Atomic Structure**

At about the turn of the century when chemists were making much use of the spectroscope for chemical analysis, physicists were busy trying to find order in the confusing arrays of spectral lines. It had been long noted that the lightest element, hydrogen, had a far more orderly spectrum than the other elements. The sequence of lines in the hydrogen spectrum runs from a single line in the red region of the spectrum to one in the green, and then to one in the blue, then several in the violet, and finally to a great many in the ultraviolet. From the first line in the

Fig. 32.1 A portion of the hydrogen spectrum.

red to the last in the ultraviolet, the distance between adjacent lines becomes less and less, until the lines become so close they seem to merge. A Swiss school teacher by the name of J. J. Balmer was the first to express the positions of these lines in a single mathematical formula. Balmer could give no reason why his formula worked, but work it did. From his formula lines were located that had not yet been measured. This success spurred the discovery of other formulas which placed the line positions of other elements.

Another regularity in atomic spectra was found by J. Rydberg. He noticed that the sum of the frequencies of two lines in the spectrum of hydrogen equals the frequency of a third line. This relationship was later advanced as a general principle by W. Ritz, and is called the *Ritz combination principle*. It states that the spectral lines of any element have frequencies that are either the sum or difference of the frequencies of two other lines. Like Balmer, Ritz was unable to offer an explanation for this regularity.

These regularities in atomic spectra were the clues used by Bohr to understand the structure of the atom itself.

The Explanation of Spectra and the Bohr Atom

Recall from Chapter 26 the formulation of the quantum theory by Max Planck and Albert Einstein. Planck had showed that energy changes in the atom are quantized. Both Planck and Einstein showed that the energy and frequency of radiation are inseparably linked by the constant h. And now Balmer had produced a formula giving the frequencies of radiation emitted by the hydrogen atom. From these facts Bohr was able to calculate the energy states in the hydrogen atom and show they were quantized circular orbits. From the Balmer formula he was able to calculate the angular momentum of an electron in each allowed orbit. Bohr showed that the angular momentum is a whole-number multiple of $h/2\pi$—Planck's constant again.

Bohr's planetary model of the atom faced a major difficulty. Accelerating electrons radiate energy—an electron accelerating around a nucleus should radiate energy continuously. This radiating away of energy should cause the electron to lose orbital speed and spiral into the nucleus. Bohr boldly broke with classical physics by stating that the electron doesn't radiate light while it accelerates around the nucleus in a single orbit, but that radiation of light takes place only when the electron jumps orbits from a higher energy level to a lower energy level. The farthermost orbits are at higher energy levels than the orbits closer to the nucleus. The energy of the emitted photon is equal to the *difference* in the two energy levels, obeying the quantum relationship, $E = hf$.

Bohr's views, as outlandish as they seemed in 1913, accounted for the heretofore unexplained regularities found in atomic spectra. Bohr's explanation of the Ritz combination principle

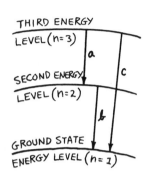

THIRD ENERGY
LEVEL (n=3)

a

SECOND ENERGY   *c*
LEVEL (n=2)

b

GROUND STATE
ENERGY LEVEL (n=1)

Fig. 32.2 Three of the many energy levels in an atom. The energy jumps *a* + *b* equal the energy jump *c*. The frequencies of light emitted from jump *a* + jump *b* therefore equals the frequency of light emitted from jump *c*.

is shown in Figure 32.2. If an electron is raised to the third energy level, it can return to its initial level by a single jump from the third to the first level—or by a double jump, first to the second level and then to the first level. These two return paths will produce three spectral lines. Note that the energy jump along path *a* plus *b* is equal to the energy jump *c*. Since frequency is proportional to energy, the frequencies of light emitted along path *a* and path *b* when summed equal the frequency of light emitted when the transition is along path *c*. So we see why the sum of two frequencies in the spectrum is equal to a third frequency in the spectrum.

Bohr was also able to account for X-rays, and show that they were emitted when electrons jumped from outermost to innermost orbits. He predicted X-ray frequencies that were later experimentally confirmed. Bohr was also able to calculate the "ionization energy" of a hydrogen atom, the energy needed to knock the electron out of the atom completely. This also was verified by experiment.

Using measured X-ray and visible frequencies, Bohr mapped energy levels of all the atomic elements. His model had electrons orbiting in neat circles (or ellipses) arranged in groups or shells. This model of the atom accounted for the general chemical properties of the elements, and predicted properties of a missing element which led to its discovery (hafnium).

Relative Sizes of the Atoms

The diameters of the electron orbits in the Bohr model of the atom are determined by the amount of electrical charge in the nucleus. For example, the single positively charged proton in the hydrogen atom holds one negatively charged electron in an orbit at a specific radius. If we double the positive charge in the nucleus, the orbiting electron will be pulled into an orbit with half its former radius, because the electrical attraction is doubled. This doesn't quite happen, however, because the double charge in the nucleus holds a second orbital electron, which diminishes the effect of the positive nucleus. This added electron also makes the atom electrically neutral. The atom is no longer hydrogen, but is helium. The two orbital electrons assume an orbit characteristic of helium. An additional proton in the nucleus pulls the electrons into a tighter orbit and, furthermore, holds a third electron in a second orbit. This is the lithium atom, atomic number 3. We can continue with this process, increasing the positive charge of the nucleus and adding successively more electrons and more orbits all the way up to atomic numbers above 100, to the man-made radioactive elements.*

It is important to note that as the nuclear charge increases and additional electrons are added in outer orbits, the inner orbits shrink in size because of the stronger nuclear attraction. This means the heavier elements are not much larger in diameter than the lighter elements. The diameter of the uranium atom, for example, is only about three hydrogen diameters even though it is 238 times more massive. The schematic diagrams in Figure 32.3 are drawn approximately to the same scale.

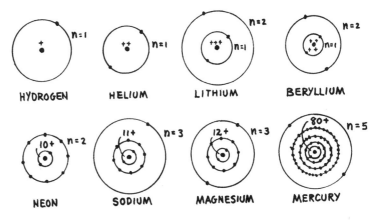

Fig. 32.3 Orbital models for some light and heavy atoms drawn to approximate scale. Note that the heavier atoms are not appreciably larger than the lighter atoms.

HYDROGEN   HELIUM   LITHIUM   BERYLLIUM

NEON   SODIUM   MAGNESIUM   MERCURY

We find that each element has an arrangement of electron orbits unique to that element. For example, the radii of the set of orbits for, say, the sodium atom are the same for all sodium atoms, but different than the set of orbits for other kinds of atoms. When we consider the 92 naturally occurring elements, we find there are 92 distinct patterns of orbits, a different pattern for each element.

Bohr solved the mystery of atomic spectra while at the same time providing an extremely useful model of the atom. He was quick to point out that his model was to be interpreted as a crude beginning, and the picture of electrons whirling like

---

*Each orbit will hold only so many electrons. A rule of quantum mechanics states that an orbit is filled when it contains a number of electrons given by $2n^2$; where n is 1 for the first orbit, 2 for the second orbit, 3 for the third orbit, and so on. For example, for $n = 1$ there are 2 electrons; for $n = 2$ there are $2(2^2)$ or 8 electrons; for $n = 3$ there are a maximum of $2(3^2)$ or 18 electrons, etc. n is called the *principal quantum number*.

planets about the sun was not to be taken literally (to which popularizers of science paid no heed). His discrete orbits were conceptual representations of an atom whose truer description would have to await quantum mechanics. Nevertheless, his planetary model of the atom with electrons occupying discrete energy levels underlies the more complex models of the atom today.

The Explanation of Quantized Energy Levels— Electron Waves

So photons are emitted when electrons make a transition from a high to a lower energy level, and the frequency of the photon is equal to the energy-level difference divided by Planck's constant h. If an electron jumps through a large energy-level difference the emitted photon is of high frequency, perhaps ultraviolet. If an electron jumps through a lesser energy difference, the emitted photon is lower in frequency, perhaps a brief burst of red light. Each element has its own characteristic energy levels, thus transitions of electrons between these levels result in each element emitting its own characteristic colors. Each of the elements emits its own pattern of spectral lines.

The idea that electrons may occupy only certain levels was very perplexing to early investigators and to Bohr himself. It was perplexing because the electron was considered to be a particle, a tiny B-B whirling around the nucleus like a planet whirling around the sun. Just as a satellite can orbit at any distance from the sun, it would seem that an electron should be able to orbit about the nucleus at any radial distance, depending, of course, like the satellite, on its speed. But it doesn't. It can't. Why the electron occupies only discrete levels is understood by considering the electron to be not a particle, but a *wave*.

If light can be a particle, why can't an electron be a wave? This question was posed by the French physicist de Broglie in 1924. He went on to show that the values of angular momentum in Bohr's orbits were a natural consequence of standing electron waves. A Bohr orbit exists where an electron wave closes in on itself in phase. In this way it reinforces itself constructively in each cycle, just as the wave on a music string is constructively reinforced by its successive reflections. In this view the electron is not thought of as a particle located at some point in the atom, but as though its mass and charge were spread out into a standing wave surrounding the atomic nucleus—the wavelength of which must fit evenly into the circumference of the orbits,

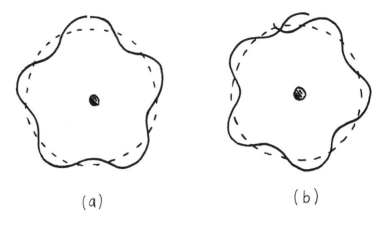

Fig. 32.4 Orbital electrons form standing waves only when the circumference of the orbit is equal to an integral number of wavelengths, (*a*). In (*b*) the wave does not close in on itself in phase and therefore undergoes destructive interference.

(a)   (b)

Figure 32.4. The circumference of the innermost orbit is equal to one wavelength of the electron wave. The second orbit has a circumference of two electron wavelengths, the third three, and so forth, Figure 32.5. This is similar to a "chain necklace" made of paper clips. No matter what size necklace is made, its circumference is equal to some multiple of the length of a single

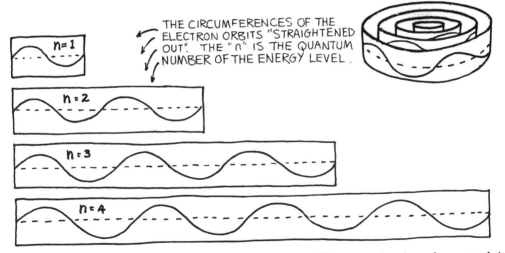

THE CIRCUMFERENCES OF THE ELECTRON ORBITS "STRAIGHTENED OUT". THE "n" IS THE QUANTUM NUMBER OF THE ENERGY LEVEL.

n=1

n=2

n=3

n=4

Fig. 32.5   The electron orbits in an atom have discrete radii because the circumferences of the orbits are integral multiples of the electron wavelengths. The wavelengths differ for different elements (and also different orbits within the elements), resulting in discrete orbital radii, or energy levels, which are characteristic of each element. The figure is greatly oversimplified as the standing waves make up spherical and ellipsoidal shells rather than flat circular ones.

paper clip.* Since the circumferences of electron orbits are discrete, it follows that the radii of these orbits, and hence the energy levels, are also discrete.

This view explains why electrons don't spiral closer and closer to the nucleus, resulting in atoms shrinking in on themselves. If each electron orbit is described by a standing wave, the circumference of the smallest orbit can be no smaller than one wavelength—no fraction of a wavelength is possible in a circular (or elliptical) standing wave.

Experimental verification for de Broglie's wave nature of the electron was provided in 1926 by the American physicists Davisson and Germer, who scattered low-energy electrons off the surface of a metal crystal. The scattered electrons formed diffraction patterns characteristic of the patterns produced by diffracted light. A comparison of light and electron diffraction is shown in Figure 32.6.

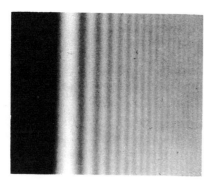 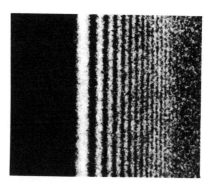

Fig. 32.6 Fringes produced by the diffraction of light (left), and for an electron beam (right). (J. Valasek, *Introduction to Theoretical and Experimental Optics*, New York, Wiley, 1949.) (H. Raether, "Elektroninterferenzen," *Handbuch der Physik*, XXXII, Berlin, Springer, 1957.)

Wave Mechanics   The mid-twenties saw many changes in physics. Not only did light have particle properties, but particles were found to have wave properties. According to de Broglie, every particle of matter is endowed with a wave to guide it as it travels. Under the proper conditions, then, every particle will produce an interference or diffraction pattern. All bodies—electrons, pro-

---

*Electron wavelengths are successively larger for orbits of increasing radii; so to make our analogy accurate we would have to use not only more paper clips to make increasingly larger necklaces, but use increasingly larger paper clips for each larger necklace as well.

tons, atoms, mice, men, planets, suns—have a wavelength that is related to their momentum by

$$\text{Wavelength} = \frac{h}{\text{momentum}}$$

where h is Planck's constant. A body of large mass and ordinary speed has such a small wavelength that interference and diffraction are negligible—rifle bullets fly straight and do not pepper their targets far and wide with interference patches. As Figure 32.6 shows, small particles such as electrons exhibit appreciable wave effects.

Starting with de Broglie's matter waves, the Austrian-German physicist Erwin Schrödinger formulated a wave equation that plays the same role in quantum mechanics that Newton's equation (force = mass × acceleration) plays in classical physics.* Schrödinger's equation provides us with a purely mathematical rather than a visual model of the atom. In this view the de Broglie waves are not regarded as waves of moving matter or waves of changing fields, but as "probability" waves. They don't tell the physicist where an electron *is* at any given moment, but merely where it is *likely to be*. An individual measurement of the position of an electron in, say, the first Bohr energy state, can be as precise as the method used to measure it will allow. If the measurement is repeated many hundreds of times and the results plotted in the form of dots, the resulting pattern of dots will resemble a wave pattern, a sort of electron cloud. An individual electron may at various times be anywhere in this

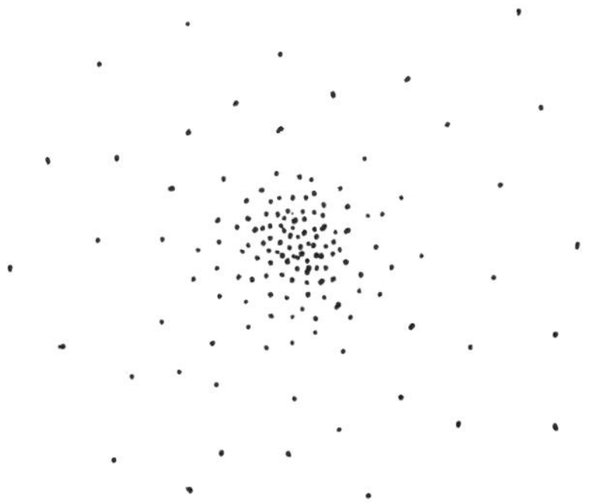

Fig. 32.7 Result of repeated measurements of an electron's position in the first Bohr orbit.

*$\left(-\dfrac{h^2}{2m}\nabla^2 + V\right)\psi = ih\dfrac{\partial\psi}{\partial t}$. Believe it or not, this equation does not lend itself to a visual interpretation.

probability cloud; it even has an extremely small but finite probability of momentarily existing inside the nucleus. It spends most of its time, however, at an average distance from the nucleus which fits the orbital radii described by Bohr. The Schrödinger wave equation may be applied to the nucleus, where radioactivity is interpreted in terms of particle waves seeping through a nuclear barrier.

The Correspondence Principle

If a new theory is valid, it must account for the verified results of the old theory. This is the principle of correspondence, first enunciated by Bohr. New theory and old must overlap and agree in the region where the difference between their assumptions does not matter.*

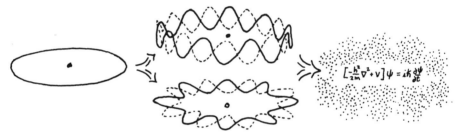

Fig. 32.8   From the Bohr model of the atom to the modified model with de Broglie waves to the mathematical model of Schrödinger.

Schrödinger's wave equation satisfies this principle. It not only agrees with the results of the Bohr model of the atom, but far outdoes it in successful predictions. Whereas Bohr ran into trouble predicting the characteristics of atoms more complex than hydrogen, the Schrödinger interpretation predicts finer details not only for hydrogen, but for complex atoms as well. For larger systems, such as the motion of planets where classical physics is successful, the Schrödinger equation leads to results that differ by infinitesimal amounts from classical theory. In atomic systems, where classical physics is useless, the Schrödinger equation leads to results that are in excellent agreement with experiment.

---

*This is a general rule not only for good science, but for all good theory—even in areas as far removed from science as government, religion, and ethics.

**The Uncertainty
Principle**

Before the advent of quantum mechanics, it was believed that we could obtain better and better accuracy in measurement if we simply improved our measuring instruments. This is true to an extent, but *perfect* accuracy cannot be achieved no matter how fine the measuring instrument. There exists some uncertainty in every measurement we make, not only as a result of imperfect measuring instruments, but because of the unavoidable inter- action between the observer and the observed.

To observe an object requires that at least one photon bounce off it. A photon bouncing off a baseball in flight alters its motion imperceptibly, and its motion is not altered by the presence or absence of a witness. To "observe" an electron, on the other hand, is a different story. A single photon bouncing off an electron appreciably alters its motion—and in an unpredictable way. If, for example, we wish to determine the position of the electron very accurately, the wavelength of light used to detect it must be short. A short wavelength, however, corresponds to a large quantum of energy, which greatly alters the electron's state of motion. If, on the other hand, a long wavelength cor- responding to a small quantum of energy is used, the change in the electron's state of motion will be smaller, but the deter- mination of its position by the coarser wave will be less accurate. The act of observing something as tiny as an electron produces a great uncertainty in either the position or the motion being measured. Although this uncertainty is completely negligible for measurements of position and motion for everyday objects, in the atomic domain it is a predominant fact of life.

The uncertainty of measurements in the atomic domain was first stated mathematically by Werner Heisenberg of Germany, and is called the *uncertainty principle*. It is a fundamental principle in quantum mechanics. Heisenberg found that when the uncertainties in the measurement of momentum and position for a particle are multiplied together, the product is Planck's constant h. Stated mathematically, this can be written:

$$\Delta M \, \Delta x \sim h$$

The Δ symbols are used here to mean "uncertainty of": ΔM is the uncertainty of momentum, Δx is the uncertainty of position. The product of these two uncertainties is approximately equal to the size of h. Of course if the measured uncertainties of position and momentum are large, their product may be many times greater than h. The significance of the uncertainty principle is that even in the best of conditions, the lower limit of uncertainty is *h*. This means, for example, if we wish to know the momentum of an electron with great accuracy, the corresponding uncertainty in position will be large. Or if we wish to know the position with great accuracy, the corresponding uncertainty in momentum will be large. The price we pay to know one of these quantities with great accuracy is great uncertainty about the other quantity. We cannot in principle know both the position and the momentum of a particle with absolute certainty.

The uncertainty principle operates similarly with *energy* and *time*. We cannot measure a particle's kinetic energy with complete precision in an infinitely short span of time. The uncertainty in our knowledge of energy, ΔE, and the duration taken to measure the energy, Δt, are related by the expression*

$$\Delta E \, \Delta t \sim h$$

The best accuracy we can ever hope to attain is that where the product of the energy and time uncertainties are equal to *h*. The more accurately we determine the energy of a photon, electron, or particle of any kind, the more uncertain we will be of the time it had that energy.

The uncertainty principle is relevant only to quantum phenomena. The inaccuracies in measuring the position and momentum of a baseball due to the interactions of observation, for example, are completely negligible. But the inaccuracies in measuring the position and momentum of an electron are far from negligible. The inaccuracies in measuring the energy and time of fall for the ram of a piledriver are negligible, but the inaccuracies in measuring simultaneously the energy release and time of de-excitation of an atom are not negligible. This is because the uncertainties in the measurements of these subatomic quantities are comparable to the magnitudes of the quantities themselves.

---

*We can see that this follows from the uncertainty of momentum and position. Recall that momentum = force × time, and energy = force × distance. Then

$$h = \Delta \text{ momentum } \Delta \text{ distance}$$
$$= \Delta \, (\text{force} \times \text{time}) \, \Delta \text{ distance}$$
$$= \Delta \, (\text{force} \times \text{distance}) \, \Delta \text{ time}$$
$$= \Delta \text{ energy } \Delta \text{ time}$$

The Electron—Particle, Wave, or Particle-Wave?

The fundamental uncertainty of measurements impedes our efforts to pin down the exact nature of the electron. Whether it is a particle, a wave, or a particle-wave is not certain. As a particle we have a rough estimate of its "diameter," and we know its mass and charge with great accuracy. As a wave we can easily calculate its wavelength as a function of momentum from the interference fringes it produces.

We can produce an interference pattern with a beam of electrons by directing it through two narrow closely spaced slits, as was discussed in the case of light in Chapter 29. But strangely enough, electrons directed toward the slits one at a time still produce an interference pattern. This suggests that a single electron passes through two holes at the same time! On the basis of this evidence, it seems that the electron must be a wave, unless we allow that a particle can split in two just before it reaches the slits.

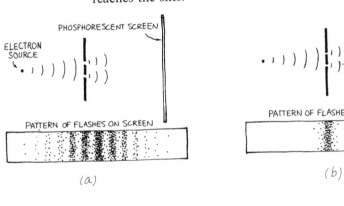

(a)

(b)

Fig. 32.9 Interference experiment with electrons.
(a) Electrons directed toward thin slit openings, one at a time, produce a wave interference pattern on the screen behind.
(b) When any attempt is made to detect which hole(s) the electron passes through (with a light source, for example), a pattern characteristic of particles is produced on the screen.
(c) The act of observing the behavior of an electron with a photon disturbs the behavior in question.

(c)

To further examine this idea, a lamp can be placed behind the slits, sending light past both openings. It is known that if a photon meets an electron it is scattered and can be observed as a tiny flash of light. Therefore, if light flashes at each slit simultaneously, it indicates that one electron has in fact passed through both holes simultaneously, thereby confirming the wave nature of the electron. When this experiment is performed, it is found that the electrons come through one slit or the other, but not both at the same time. But it is found that the pattern produced on the screen is the pattern that would be produced by *particles*. How can this be? The answer lies in the fact that we have disturbed the system we were attempting to measure. The act of observing the electron altered its momentum, thereby interrupting its synchronization with the "wave" from the other slit. The result of this experiment appears to be, if you don't "look at" the electrons they behave like waves, but if you do they behave like particles.

Many schemes designed to permit a particle to exhibit its full wave and particle characteristics at the same time have been tried. For more than forty years all such attempts have failed. The realm of the quantum is one of indeterminacy.

Determinism

The uncertainty principle has stirred much interest in a certain philosophical dilemma. With the laws of classical mechanics and a knowledge of the positions and velocities of the planets, future motions of the solar system can be accurately predicted. Before the development of quantum mechanics, scientists generally agreed that Newton's laws had a much larger application—they believed that if the exact positions and momenta of all the *particles* in the universe were known, one could evoke Newton's laws and, *in principle*, calculate the past and future course of all events. *In practice*, of course, it was realized that such calculations would not be possible because of the enormous number of particles involved—but this didn't undermine the basic idea.

Using the same broad application of Newton's laws, many philosophically inclined scientists concluded that all human actions are predetermined. Human beings, after all, are made up of tiny particles like everything else. If it was in principle possible to predict the future course of these particles, it was equally possible, in principle, to predict the course of a person composed of them. This implied that a person could not alter the future by changing his mind. Or rather, if he did change his mind, that change, along with its consequences, would be part of an inevitable predetermined chain. Our ability to choose rightly or wrongly, to decide on our actions, to control our destinies, seemed to be an illusion—mere wishful thinking. There seemed to be an inescapable division between science and free will.

The advent of quantum mechanics caused many proponents of free will to feel that science itself had come to their aid. The basic indeterminacy of quantum mechanics makes the prediction of subatomic events impossible. We know of no way, for example, to determine which electron will absorb a photon in the photoelectric effect. All we can do is calculate the probability that the photon will be absorbed by a given electron. Neither can we say exactly where a given electron will strike the screen when it produces an electron wave-interference pattern. We can only state the probability of its striking a given area. With a radioactive substance, we cannot state when an individual atom will decay, but only the probability of its decaying within a certain time. In short, here is a realm into which the relentless Newtonian compulsion cannot reach.

This indeterminacy, however, does not give us proof of free will. Large aggregates of particles lend themselves to extremely accurate prediction. We can, for example, predict with certainty the electric current produced by a beam of light on a photosensitive material, or the relative intensities of a wave-interference pattern, or the rate of the decay of a radioactive substance. In most circumstances the macroscopic domain is quite adequately described by classical physics. Human behavior involves hordes of particles, not just one or two, and since statistical averages of these hordes can be determined with great accuracy, the indeterminacy at the quantum level can be discounted.

The dilemma about free will remains unresolved.

There is a danger in applying the uncertainty principle to areas outside of quantum mechanics. Some people cite the uncertainty principle as invalidating causality and determinism, and supporting free will. Others interpret the uncertainty principle as nature's shield of its innermost secrets. Critics of science use the uncertainty principle as evidence that science itself is uncertain. Determinism, nature's secrets, and the uncertainties of science have very little to do with Heisenberg's uncertainty principle. The profoundness of the uncertainty principle has to do with the probabilistic nature of the atomic world—mainly that there is no sharp boundary between particles and waves. The world of the atom is a fuzzy place.

Summary of Terms   *Ritz combination principle.* The spectral lines of the elements have frequencies that are either the sums or the differences of the frequencies of two other lines.

de Broglie matter waves. All particles of matter have associated wave properties. The wavelength of a particle-wave is related to its momentum and Planck's constant h by the relationship

$$\text{Wavelength} = \frac{h}{\text{momentum}}$$

Quantum mechanics. The branch of quantum physics that deals with finding the probability amplitudes of matter waves, organized principally by Werner Heisenberg (1925) and Erwin Schrödinger (1926).

Schrödinger wave equation. The fundamental equation of quantum mechanics that interprets the wave nature of material particles in terms of probability wave amplitudes. It is as basic to quantum mechanics as Newton's laws of motion are to classical mechanics.

Correspondence principle. The rule that a new theory is valid only if it overlaps and agrees with the verified results of the old theory.

Uncertainty principle. The principle formulated by Heisenberg which states that the ultimate accuracy of measurement is given by the magnitude of Planck's constant h. Further, it is not possible to measure exactly both the position and the momentum of a particle at the same time, nor the energy and time of a particle simultaneously.

Suggested Reading   Baker, Adolph, *Modern Physics and Antiphysics*, Reading, Mass., Addison-Wesley, 1970.

Gamow, George, *Thirty Years That Shook Physics* (Science Study Series), Garden City, N. Y., Doubleday (Anchor), 1966.

March, Robert H., *Physics for Poets*, New York, McGraw-Hill, 1970.

Rogers, Eric, *Physics for the Inquiring Mind*, Princeton, N. J., Princeton University Press, 1960.

Weisskopf, Victor F., *Knowledge and Wonder* (Science Study Series), Garden City, N. Y., Doubleday (Anchor), 1966.

Questions   1. Uranium is 238 times more massive than hydrogen. Why, then, isn't the diameter of the uranium atom 238 times that of the hydrogen atom?

2. If all atoms of the same kind were not of the same size, what effect would this have on crystal formation?

3. Why do electrons orbiting the nucleus have discrete energy values rather than arbitrary energy values?

4. A hypothetical atom possesses four distinct energy levels. Assuming that all transitions between levels are possible, how many spectral lines will this atom exhibit? Which transitions correspond to the highest-energy light emitted? To the lowest-energy light?

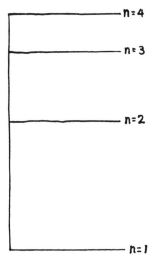

5. Comment on the statement, "If an electron is not a particle then it must be a wave." (Do you hear statements like this often?)

6. Explain how Newton's first and second laws of motion satisfy the correspondence principle.

7. When a cold thermometer is placed in a hot cup of coffee, is the resulting temperature reading the same as that which the coffee had before the measurement was made? Explain.

8. There is at least one electron on the tip of your nose. If somebody looks at it, will its motion be altered? How about if it is looked at with one eye closed? With two eyes, but crossed? Does the uncertainty principle apply here?

9. Do we alter that which we attempt to measure in a public-opinion survey? Does the uncertainty principle apply here?

10. Why does the uncertainty principle fail to resolve the dilemma between determinism and free will?

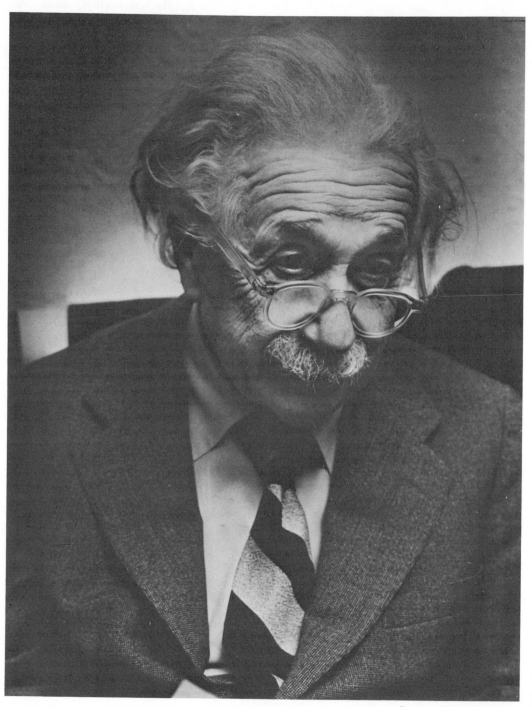

33

The Special Theory of Relativity

bert Einstein (1879–1955)

The theory of relativity is so fascinating a subject that we should at least briefly discuss its discoverer. Albert Einstein was a slow child; he learned to speak at a much later age than average and his parents feared for a while that he might be mentally retarded. One of his teachers said to him, "You will never amount to anything, Einstein," in despair at his daydreaming and his negative attitude toward formal instruction. The stimulus for his intellectual pursuits had not come from school, but from such things as a compass given to him when he was five, and a geometry book he happened upon at the age of twelve. He regarded the drill and mechanical methods at school as detrimental to intellectual growth. Fed up with school, he failed to get a high-school diploma and, with no job prospects, at the age of fifteen he loafed like a model dropout. Later he attempted to gain admission to the renowned Swiss Federal Institute of Technology in Zurich, but failed the entrance examination. After returning to high school for a year to make up deficiencies in almost everything but physics and mathematics, he tried again and passed. After gaining admittance he cut most of the lectures and succeeded in passing his examinations by cramming with the help of a friend's meticulous notes. He said later of this, "... after I had passed the final examination, I found the consideration of any scientific problem distasteful to me for an entire year." He went on to say, "It is little short of a miracle that modern methods of instruction have not already completely strangled the holy curiosity of inquiry, because what this delicate little plant needs most, apart from initial stimulation, is freedom; without that it is surely destroyed. . . . I believe that one could even deprive a healthy beast of prey of its voraciousness, if one could force it with a whip to eat continuously whether it were hungry or not. . . ."

It was not until two years after receiving his Ph.D. in physics that he got a steady job, as a patent examiner in the Swiss Patent Office at Berne. Einstein held this position for over seven years.

He found the work rather interesting and sometimes it stimulated his scientific imagination. His main interest in the job was that it freed him of financial worries, which allowed him, except for eight hours a day, free time to ponder the problems in physics that puzzled him.

With no academic connections whatsoever, and with essentially no contact with other physicists, he laid out the main lines along which twentieth-century theoretical physics has developed. In 1905 he published three papers. The first was on the quantum theory of light, including an explanation of the photoelectric effect, and the second on the statistical aspects of molecular theory and Brownian motion, a proof for the existence of atoms. His third paper was on special relativity. Although he is best known for his theory of relativity, the Nobel Prize was awarded to him for his first paper, the quantum explanation of the photoelectric effect. In 1905 his quantum theory of light was considered even more radical than his paper on special relativity. He received the Nobel Prize in 1921, five years after his quantum explanation of the photoelectric effect had been experimentally confirmed and when his theory of special relativity was still very controversial. Relativity has since been supported by every proof that could be contrived. Every attempt to find a flaw in it has only served to verify the theory. It is fundamental to modern physics.

Einstein was known not only as a scientist, but as a citizen— a citizen of the world. It is appropriate to quote here from Martin Klein.*

Einstein's active and courageous role in public affairs is widely known, and it absorbed a substantial fraction of his efforts for forty years. He stepped onto the public stage early and in characteristic style. In October 1914, two months after the outbreak of the First World War, a document was issued in Berlin bearing the grandiose title, Manifesto to the Civilized World; it carried the signatures of almost a hundred of Germany's most prominent scientists, artists, men of letters, clergymen, etc. This manifesto proclaimed its signers' full support of Germany's war effort, denounced the opponents of the fatherland, and defiantly asserted that German militarism and German culture formed an inseparable unity. Not all German intellectuals approved this chauvinistic document, but among the very few who were willing to sign a sharply worded answer, calling for an end to war and an international organization, was Albert Einstein. The highly unpopular

---

*From "Einstein and Some Civilized Discontents," by Martin J. Klein, which appeared in Physics Today, January, 1965.

stand that he took in 1914 expressed a deeply felt conviction, one on which he acted throughout his life, regardless of the consequences to himself. During the succeeding decades Einstein devoted a great deal of his energy to the causes in which he believed, lending his name to many organizations which he felt could further these causes.

The political tides moved rapidly in Germany and, in 1932, while Einstein was visiting the United States, Hitler came to power. Einstein was appalled at the racial and political policies which included the use of German scientists for building a warfare state. He resigned his position at the University in Berlin, and a price was put upon his head by Hitler. Einstein then accepted a research position at the Institute for Advanced Study in Princeton, New Jersey.

Einstein became an American citizen in 1934. In 1939, after the German scientists had succeeded in producing the fission of the uranium atom, although still a pacifist at heart, Einstein was urged by several prominent American scientists to write the famous letter to President Roosevelt pointing out the scientific possibilities of creating an atomic bomb. He was torn by this decision, and the thought of Hitler developing such a bomb prompted his action. Roosevelt followed the advice of Einstein and his associates and the first atomic bomb was detonated, ironically, after the fall of Germany. After World War II, Einstein became an intensely earnest advocate of world peace through disarmament and world government. We quote again from Martin Klein:

> Einstein was among those who have been trying to impress upon the world the very real likelihood that another war would destroy civilization and perhaps humanity as well. He was not overly optimistic about his efforts, but they had to be made. He also felt that he had to speak out, loudly and clearly, during the [Senator Joseph] McCarthy era, urging intellectuals to adopt the method of civil disobedience as practiced earlier by Gandhi (and later by Martin Luther King). As he wrote in an open letter, "Every intellectual who is called before one of the committees ought to refuse to testify; i.e., he must be prepared for jail and economic ruin, in short, for the sacrifice of his personal welfare in the interest of the cultural welfare of his country." If such a program were not adopted then, wrote Einstein, "the intellectuals of this country deserve nothing better than the slavery which is intended for them."

He prophetically feared that leading scientists working for the government and government-supported institutions would become hostages to fortune.

When he toured the world, he was shocked at the degradation

and poverty of the masses in many countries. He refused to ride in a rickshaw, unwilling to be carried about by another human being. One time when he was invited to visit the Queen of Belgium, he got off the train and walked to the palace carrying his suitcase and his violin, unrecognized in his rumpled clothes, while the limousine and reception committee waited at the station. When the Queen asked why he had not used the limousine, he replied, "It was a very pleasant walk, your Majesty."

Albert Einstein was a great scientist; but he was much more than that—he was a great human being.

Motion Is Relative

Consider two people on a railroad train. Suppose one of them is seated, while the other one is walking toward the front end of the car. Which one is moving? We might say at first that the seated person is at rest and only the walking person is moving. But if we take into account the motion of the train, we would have to say that the seated person is moving also.

There seem to be two different answers because there are really implied two different questions. If the question is, "Which person is moving *over the floor of the car*?" the answer is, "Only the person who is walking." If the question is, "Which person is moving *over the ground*?" then the answer is, "Both persons." If the walking person walks at a speed of 1 mile per hour and the train moves over the ground at a speed of 60 miles per hour, then the seated and walking persons have speeds of 0 miles per hour and 1 mile per hour respectively relative to the car, but speeds of 60 miles per hour and 61 miles per hour respectively relative to the ground.

Whenever we talk about motion, we must always specify the position from which motion is being observed and measured. We call the position from which motion is observed and measured a *frame of reference*. An object may have different speeds relative to different frames of reference.

To measure the speed of an object we first choose a frame of reference, and pretend that the frame of reference is standing still. Then we measure the speed with which the object moves relative to the frame of reference. In the foregoing example, if we pretend the train is standing still, then the speed of the walking person is 1 mile per hour. If we pretend that the ground is standing still, then the speed of the walking person is 61 miles per hour. But the ground is not really still, for the earth spins like a top about its polar axis. Depending on how near the train is to the equator, the speed of the walking person may be as much as 1000 miles per hour relative to a frame of reference at the center of the earth. And the center of the earth is moving relative to the sun. If we place our frame of reference on the sun, the speed of the person walking in the train which is on the orbiting earth is on the order of 70,000 miles per hour. And the sun is not at rest for it orbits the center of our galaxy, which moves with respect to other galaxies.

This brings up the question, "Isn't there some frame of reference that is still?" Prior to Albert Einstein, physicists thought they could answer, "Yes." They thought that *space* was standing still and that any point in space could be used as an absolute frame of reference from which all speeds could be specified. If space were really standing still, then they thought that a body would be still when its speed through space was zero, and that a body was moving when its speed through space was not zero. Using space as an absolute frame of reference, it was thought that we could measure absolute speeds.

The Michelson-Morley Experiment

The absolute speed of the earth was of special interest to physicists. They thought that precision measurements of the relative speeds of light as measured from earth would provide a means of ascertaining the absolute motion of the earth. Because light is a form of wave motion, it was assumed that something in space vibrates. This mysterious something was called "ether." Since the ether was supposed to fill all space, they thought it might serve as the frame of reference attached to space. From this the absolute motion of the earth could be measured.

In 1887 the American physicists A. A. Michelson and E. W. Morley performed an experiment that was designed to measure the motion of the earth through the ether. This was the experiment we briefly discussed in Chapter 26. The reasoning behind the experiment was the following: Light travels through the ether with the same speed in all directions, if the speed is measured with the ether as a frame of reference. But if the frame of reference is the earth moving through the ether, then the observed speed of light will not be the same in all directions. For example, from a position on the face of the earth which is traveling straight into the stationary ether, the observed speed of light would be the actual speed of light through the ether plus the speed of the earth. From a position on the opposite face of the earth traveling away from the ether, the observed speed of light would be the actual speed of light through the ether minus the speed of the earth. A measure of these relative speeds then provides the absolute speed of the earth.

The apparatus used for the experiment was an *interferometer*, set up as shown in Figure 33.1. A beam of light was directed toward a partially silvered mirror that would allow half the light incident upon it to pass through and the remaining half to be reflected. In this way the light was separated into two parts: one part passed through the mirror to a fully silvered mirror and then was reflected back; the other part was reflected at right angles. This part, like the first part, was reflected back by another mirror. The two reflected parts of the original beam were brought together and produced interference fringes like those discussed in Chapter 29.

Fig. 33.1 The interferometer. Recombination of the split beam produces an interference pattern. The slightest change in the speed of light along either of the perpendicular beams will shift the fringes of the interference pattern. When the entire apparatus is rotated 90 degrees, no change in the fringes occurs. This is because the speed of light is identical along both (or any) paths.

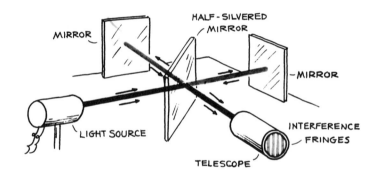

The slightest difference in the speed of either part of the light beam would produce a noticeable shift in the fringed lines of the interference pattern. The interferometer was mounted so that it could be rotated, presumably so that one part of the split light beam would first be traveling one way through the ether and then, after rotation, another way. But no matter how the instrument was rotated, no shift in the interference pattern was observed. No matter what the time of day or time of year, or what source of light was used, a rotation of the interferometer never produced a change in the interference fringes. The results were always null, indicating no motion of the earth through the ether. This was most puzzling since the earth is obviously rotating about its own axis and orbiting about the sun, and it seemed inconceivable that the ether should perform such gyrations as to remain always at rest with respect to the earth. The ether theory was abandoned —gradually.

The results of the Michelson-Morley experiment, repeated many times by many investigators, showed that measurements of the speed of light are the same from all frames of reference, no matter how the frames of reference move. This was a most puzzling fact at the turn of the century.

One interpretation of the bewildering result was suggested by the Irish physicist Fitzgerald, who proposed that the length of the experimental apparatus shrank in the direction in which it was moving by just the amount required to counteract the presumed variation in the velocity of light. Fitzgerald's hypothesis accounted for the discrepancy, but since he had no suitable theory to why this was so, it wasn't taken seriously.

Einstein's interpretation was very different. If the velocity of light does not conform to traditional or classical ideas, and velocity is simply a ratio of distance through space to a corresponding interval of time, Einstein recognized that the classical ideas of space and time were suspect. He rejected the classical idea that space and time were independent of each other and developed, with simple postulates, a profound relationship between space and time.

The Postulates of the Special Theory of Relativity

Einstein rejected the ether. Gone with the stationary ether was the notion of an absolute frame of reference. All motion is relative, not to any stationary hitching post in the universe, but to arbitrary frames of reference. A rocket ship cannot measure its speed with respect to empty space, but only with respect to other objects. If, for example, rocket ship *A* drifts past rocket ship *B* in empty space, spaceman *A* and spaceman *B* will each observe the relative motion, but each will be unable to determine which is moving and which is at rest, if either.

This is a familiar experience to a passenger on a train who looks out his window and sees the train on the next track moving by his window. He is aware only of the relative motion between his train and the other train, and cannot tell which train is moving. He may be at rest relative to the ground, and the other train may be moving, or he may be moving relative to the ground and the other train may be at rest, or they both may be moving relative to the ground. The important point here is that if you were in a train with no windows, there would be no way to determine whether the train was moving with uniform velocity or was at rest. This is Einstein's first postulate:

All laws of nature are the same in all uniformly moving frames of reference.

On a jet airplane going at 500 miles per hour, for example, coffee pours as it does when the plane is at rest; we flip a coin and catch it just as we would if the plane were at rest; we swing a pendulum and it swings as it would if the plane were on the runway. There is no physical experiment we could perform to determine our state of uniform motion. Of course, we could look out and see the earth whizzing by, or send a radar wave out or some such thing as that—we mean no experiment confined within the cabin itself can determine whether or not there is uniform motion. The laws of physics within the uniformly moving cabin are the same as those in a stationary laboratory.

Any number of experiments can be devised to detect accelerated motion, but none can be devised, according to Einstein, to detect the state of uniform motion. We can only measure uniform velocity with respect to some frame of reference.

It would be very peculiar if the laws of physics varied for observers moving at different speeds. It would mean, for example, that a billiard player would have to adjust his style of play to the season of the year, because the motion of the earth about the sun varies by 34 miles per second at six-month intervals. It is our common experience that no such adjustment is necessary, and that no experiment, however precise, has shown any difference at all. That is all the first postulate of relativity means.

One of the questions that Einstein as a youth asked his school teacher was, "What would a light beam look like if you traveled along beside it?" According to classical physics the beam would be at rest to such an observer. The more Einstein thought about this the more convinced he became of its impossibility. He finally came to the conclusion that if an observer could travel at the speed of light, he would measure the light leaving him at 186,000 miles per second. This was the second postulate in his Special Theory of Relativity. It is:

The velocity of light in free space will be found to have the same value regardless of the motion of the source or the motion of the observer; i.e., the velocity of light is invariant.

To illustrate this statement, consider a rocket ship departing from the space station shown in Figure 33.2. A flash of light is emitted from the station at 186,000 miles per second, or *c*. Regardless of the velocity of the rocket, an observer in the rocket sees the flash of light pass him at the same speed *c*. If a flash is sent to the station from the moving rocket, observers on the

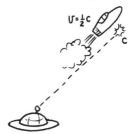

Fig. 33.2 The speed of a light flash emitted by the space station is measured to be *c* by observers on both the space station and the rocketship.

station will measure the speed of the flash at *c*. The velocity of light is measured to be the same regardless of the speed of the source or receiver. *All* observers who measure the velocity of light will find it has the same value *c*. The explanation for this has to do with the nature of space and time. As strange as it seems, the observer on the station and the observer in the rocket are measuring *different distances* and *different times*.

The measurement of space and time differs for all observers who are moving through space with respect to each other. Anyone who moves relative to you, for example, measures different distances than you do. And anyone who moves relative to you measures a time that is different than your measurements of time. Anyone who moves relative to you is in a different realm of time! The differences in the measurements of space and time are negligible at ordinary speeds, but as relative motion approaches the speed of light, the differences are appreciable. We say that objects moving with respect to one another are in different realms of "space-time."

Space-Time

We live in a three-dimensional space. We can specify the position of any point in space with three dimensions. Loosely speaking they would be how far over, how far across, and how far up or down. For example, if we are at the corner of a rectangular room and wish to specify the position of any point

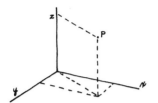

Fig. 33.3 Point *P* can be specified with three numbers—the distance along the *x*-axis, *y*-axis, and *z*-axis.

in the room, we can do this with three numbers. The first would be the number of feet the point is along a line joining the left wall and the floor; the second would be the number of feet the point is along a line joining the adjacent right wall and the floor, and the third the number of feet the point lies above the floor, or along the vertical line joining the walls at the corner. Physicists speak of these three lines as the *coordinate axes* of a reference frame, Figure 33.3. Three numbers—the distance along the *x*-axis, *y*-axis, and *z*-axis—will specify the position of a point in space.

We specify the size of objects with three dimensions. A box, for example, is described by its length, width, and height. But the three dimensions do not give a complete picture. There is a fourth dimension—time. The box was not always a box of given length, width, and height. It began as a box only at a certain point in time, on the day it was made. Nor will it always be a box. At any moment it may be crushed, burned, or destroyed. So the three dimensions of space are a valid description of the box only during a certain specified period of time. We cannot speak meaningfully about space without implying time. Each object, each person, each planet, each star, each galaxy, exists in what physicists call "the space-time continuum."

Two observers at rest relative to each other share the same space-time. Both would agree on measurements of space and time. If there is relative motion between them, however, they will not agree on measurements of space and time. At ordinary speeds differences in their measurements are imperceptible, but at speeds near the speed of light (relativistic speeds), the differences are appreciable. Each observer is in a different realm of space-time and his measurements of space and time differ from the measurements of an observer in some other realm of space-time. They differ in such a way that each observer will always measure the same ratio of space and time for light in the reference frame of the other—the greater the measured traversal in space, then the greater the measured interval of time. This constant ratio of space and time for light, *c*, is the unifying factor between different realms of space-time, and is the essence of Einstein's second postulate.

Time Dilation

Time is not an absolute, but is relative to the motion between the observer and the event being observed. Imagine, for example, that we are somehow able to observe a flash of light bouncing back and forth between a pair of parallel mirrors. If the distance

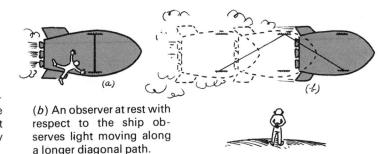

Fig. 33.4 (*a*) An observer moving with the ship observes the light beam moving vertically between the mirrors.

(*b*) An observer at rest with respect to the ship observes light moving along a longer diagonal path.

between the mirrors is fixed, then the arrangement constitutes a sort of "light clock," because the back and forth trips of the light flash take equal intervals of time. Suppose our light clock is inside a transparent high-speed space ship. If we travel along with the ship and watch the light clock, Figure 33.4*a*, we will see the flash of light reflecting straight up and down between the two mirrors, just as it would if the space ship were at rest. Our observations will show no relativistic effects because there is no relative motion between us and our light clock—we share the same space-time.

If instead we stand at some rest position and observe the space ship whizzing by us at an appreciable speed, say half the speed of light, things are quite different. We no longer share the same space-time, for in this case there is relative motion between the observer and the observed. We will not see the path of the light in simple up-and-down motion as before. Because the light flash keeps up with the fast-moving light clock, we will see the flash following a diagonal path, Figure 33.4*b*. Notice that the flash travels a *longer distance* as it moves between the mirrors in our position of space-time than in the space-time of an observer riding with the ship. Since the speed of light is the same in all space-times (Einstein's second postulate) the flash must travel for a *longer time* between the mirrors in our space-time than in the space-time of an observer on board. This follows from the definition of velocity, simply stated, as a ratio of distance to time. *The longer diagonal distance must be divided by a correspondingly longer time interval to yield an unvarying value for the speed of light.* Thus, from our relative position of rest, we measure a longer time interval between ticks when a clock is in motion than when it is at rest. We have considered a light clock in our example, but the same is true of any kind of clock. Moving clocks appear to run slow. This stretching out of time is *time dilation*.

The exact relationship between time intervals in different space-times can be derived from Figure 33.4 with simple geometry and algebra.* The relationship between the time, t_0, in the observer's frame of reference, and the relative time, t, in some other frame of reference is

$$t = \frac{t_0}{\sqrt{1 - v^2/c^2}}$$

in which v represents the velocity of the moving clock as observed from our reference frame, and c represents the velocity of light in a vacuum. The v in this equation is important to understand; it is the relative velocity between the observer and the observed. In this case the observed happens to be a light clock. It may be anything. We can see from the equation that if there is any velocity between the frames of reference that t will be greater than t_0, as should be the case for time dilation. For example, if v is equal to 50 percent the speed of light, we sub-

---

*The light clock is shown in three successive positions in Figure 33.5. The diagonal lines represent the path of the light flash as it starts from the lower mirror at position 1, moves to the upper mirror at position 2, and then back to the lower mirror at position 3. Distances on the diagram are marked ct, vt, and ct_0, which follows from the fact that the distance traveled by a uniformly moving object is equal to its velocity multiplied by the time.

The symbol t represents the time it takes for the flash to move from one mirror to the other as measured from a frame of reference at rest relative to the moving light clock. Since the velocity of the flash is c, and the time of travel from the lower mirror at position 1 to the upper mirror at position 2 is t, the distance traveled is ct. During this same time t, the clock (which travels at velocity v) moves a horizontal distance vt from position 1 to position 2.

The symbol t_0 represents the time it takes for the flash to move between the mirrors as measured from a frame of reference fixed to the light clock. The velocity of light is also c in this frame of reference where the path of light is seen to move a vertical distance ct_0. This is the distance between mirrors, which is the same in both reference frames, since the relative motion of the light clock is entirely horizontal.

These three distances make up a right triangle in the figure, in which ct is the hypotenuse, and ct_0 and vt are legs. A well-known theorem of geometry (the Pythagorean theorem) states that the square of the hypotenuse is equal to the sum of the squares of the other two sides. Applying this to the figure we obtain:

Fig. 33.5 Mathematical detail of Fig. 33.4b.

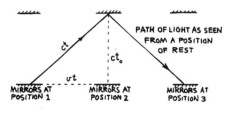

PATH OF LIGHT AS SEEN FROM A POSITION OF REST

MIRRORS AT POSITION 1
MIRRORS AT POSITION 2
MIRRORS AT POSITION 3

$$c^2 t^2 = c^2 t_0^2 + v^2 t^2$$

$$c^2 t^2 - v^2 t^2 = c^2 t_0^2$$

$$t^2(1 - v^2/c^2) = t_0^2$$

$$t^2 = \frac{t_0^2}{(1 - v^2/c^2)}$$

$$t = \frac{t_0}{\sqrt{1 - v^2/c^2}}$$

stitute $0.5c$ for v in the equation and find after some arithmetic that $t = 1.15t_0$, which means that if we viewed the clock on a space ship traveling at half the speed of light, we would see the second hand take 1.15 minutes to make a revolution whereas if it were at rest we would see it takes 1 minute. If the space ship passes us at 87 percent the speed of light, $t = 2t_0$ and we would measure time events on the space ship taking twice the usual intervals. It would appear as if events on the ship were in slow motion. At 99.5 percent the speed of light, $t = 10t_0$, and we would see the second hand of the space ship's clock take 10 minutes to sweep through a revolution requiring 1 minute on our clock.

To put these figures another way, at 99.5 percent c, the moving clock would appear to run a tenth our rate, and would move only 6 seconds while our clock moves 60 seconds. At 87 percent c, the moving clock ticks at half rate and shows 30 seconds to our 60 seconds; at 50 percent c, the moving clock ticks $1/1.15$ as fast and ticks 52 seconds to our 60 seconds. A comparison of rates at different speeds between the seconds ticked off in a moving clock and a 60-second interval for a clock at relative rest is shown graphically in Figure 33.6.

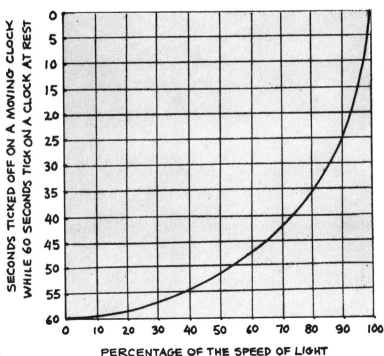

Fig. 33.6   Time dilation.

Nothing is unusual about a moving clock itself; it is simply measuring a different time. The faster a clock moves, the slower it appears to run as viewed from an observer not moving with the clock. If it were possible for an observer to watch a clock pass by at the speed of light, it would not appear to be running at all. The interval between ticks would be infinite if measured by the observer. The clock would be ageless! If our observer were moving with the clock, however, the clock would not show any slowing down of time. To him the clock would be operating normally. This is because there would be no motion between the observer and the observed. The v in the time-dilation equation would then be zero and $t = t_0$—they share the same space-time. If the person checked a clock in our space-time, however, he would find our clock to be running as slowly as we find his to be. We each see each other's clocks running slow. There is really no contradiction here, for it is physically impossible for two observers moving at different velocities to refer to one and the same realm of space-time. Each is in a different space-time. The measurements made in one realm of space-time need not agree with the measurements made in another realm of space-time. The measurement they will always agree on, however, is the velocity of light.

Time dilation has been experimentally observed in studies of cosmic ray "fragments" known as muons. A muon is an elementary particle of matter similar to an electron with a larger mass. A muon is produced when an atomic nucleus undergoes a violent change, much as a spark is produced when two pieces of metal are banged together. Many muons are produced in the upper atmosphere when cosmic rays bombard the nuclei of atoms in the air. They streak downward toward the earth at speeds approaching the speed of light. Being radioactive, most muons decay into other particles while descending. Measurements of muons at rest (or nearly so) in the laboratory show that half the original number decay within two-millionths of a second. But muons produced at the top of the atmosphere traveling at 99.5 percent the speed of light require twenty-millionths of a second to reach sea level. By that time (our time, that is) muons would not make it—nearly all of them would have decayed along the way, half of them decaying during the first two-millionths of a second. But detectors at sea level do catch muons, and plenty of them—half as many as are caught in high-altitude rockets and balloons! For the average muon, there *is* enough time to make the trip. At 99.5 percent c, the muon has ten times as

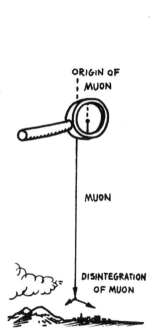

ORIGIN OF
MUON

MUON

DISINTEGRATION
OF MUON

Fig. 33.7 Time dilation for a muon.

much time, or twenty-millionths of a second, to live; the muon's "clock" is running ten times slower than our clocks, allowing sufficient time to make the trip.

This interpretation has been confirmed in the laboratory with atomic-particle accelerators. The lifetimes of fast-moving radio-active particles increase as the speed goes up—and the amount of increase is just what Einstein's equation predicts.

This all seems very strange to us only because it is not our common experience to deal with measurements made at relativistic speeds. The theory of relativity does not make common sense. But common sense, according to Einstein, is that layer of prejudices laid down in the mind prior to the age of eighteen. If we spent our youths zapping through the universe in high-speed space ships, we would probably be quite comfortable with the results of relativity.

Space Travel   One of the arguments advanced against the possibility of inter-stellar travel by man has been that his life span is too short to permit such travel—at least for the distant stars. It was argued, for example, that the nearest star (after the sun), Alpha Centauri, was four light-years* away and a round trip even at the speed of light would require eight years. The center of our galaxy is some 30,000 light-years away, so it has been reasoned that a man traveling even at the speed of light would require a lifetime of 30,000 years to make such a voyage. But these arguments fail to take into account time dilation. Time for a person on earth and time for a person in a high-speed rocket ship are not the same.

Astronauts traveling at 99 percent the speed of light could go to the star Procyon (10.4 light-years distant) and back in 21 years. It would take light itself 20.8 years to make the same round trip. Because of time dilation, it would seem that only three years had gone by to the astronauts. This is what all their clocks would tell them—and biologically they would be only three years older. The space officials to greet them on their return, though, would be 21 years older!

Suppose we wish to take a longer trip and one as biologically comfortable as possible. The most comfortable acceleration is g, that which we are experiencing right now. If we were to travel in a spaceship that maintained a constant acceleration of g, we would feel the ship pushing against our feet just as hard as the

---

*A light-year is the distance light travels in one year, about 6×10^{12} miles.

earth seems to push against us normally. We would be right at home at such an acceleration, and would soon attain very respectable velocities, very close to the velocity of light. Suppose we start off from earth with an acceleration g for a period of 10 years of our lives. We then reverse the direction of our rockets and subject ourselves to the same acceleration but in the opposite direction, and decelerate for another 10 years. After this time we find ourselves at rest relative to our distant starting point. To return to earth we reverse our rockets again and accelerate toward earth for another 10 years; then we reverse rockets again and decelerate toward earth for the remaining 10 years of our journey, where we finally end up at rest on earth. We will have aged 40 years during this journey.

Although our clocks and time-measuring devices kept normal time during this trip, to observers on earth they were running extremely slow, for we would have been traveling at almost the speed of light most of the time. In fact, as observers on earth see it, the farthest point reached in our travels turns out to be 24,000 light-years from earth! The observers to greet us (?) are not the observers who bid us farewell, for the earth has aged 48,004 years during our 40-year trip! In 20 years we can travel 24,000 light-years! At higher accelerations we can travel even farther.

Such journeys are impossible by present-day technology standards. Radiation is the greatest problem. A ship traveling at speeds close to the speed of light would encounter interstellar particles just as if it were on the launching pad and a steady stream of particles shot by an atomic accelerator were incident upon it. No way of shielding such intense particle bombardment for prolonged periods of time is presently known. And if somehow a way were devised to solve this problem, there would be the problem of energy and fuel. Spaceships traveling at relativistic speeds would require billions of times the energy used to put Armstrong and Aldrin on the moon. A possible solution here, however, might be some kind of "interstellar ramjet"—a jet that would scoop up the hydrogen that exists in outer space and burn it in a fusion reactor.

If and when these problems are overcome, and space travel is a routine experience, people will have the option of taking a trip and returning to any future century of their choosing. For example, one might depart from earth in a high-speed ship in the year 2050 and travel for 5 years or so and return in the year 2500. One could live among the earthlings of that period for a while and depart again and try out the year 3000 for style. A person could keep jumping into the future with some expense of his own time, but he could not trip into the past. He could never return to the same era on earth that he bids farewell to. Time, as we know it, travels one way—forward. Here on earth we move constantly into the future at the steady rate of 24 hours per day.

We can see into the past, but we cannot go into the past. For example, we experience the past when we look at the night skies. The starlight impinging on our eyes left those stars dozens, hundreds, even millions of years ago. What we see is the stars as they were long ago. We are thus eyewitnesses to ancient history—and have no idea what may have happened to the stars in the interim.

If we are looking at light that left a star, say, 100 years ago, then it follows that any civilized beings in that solar system are seeing us by light that left *here* 100 years ago—and that, further, if they possessed supertelescopes, they might very well be able to eyewitness earthly events of a century ago—the Civil War, for instance.

Many physicists have not ruled out the possibility that time might just as well move backward into the past as forward into the future. In fact, the whole question of "time reversal" is discussed in great mathematical detail, and is being studied in a number of exquisite and elaborate experiments with subatomic particles. It is hypothesized that particles which move faster than light and backward in time, called "tachyons," may in fact exist. Experiments to detect them have proved unpromising to date. Nearly all physicists conclude that the direction of time is only forward.

This conclusion is blithely ignored in a limerick that is a favorite with scientist types:

> There was a young lady
>   named Bright
> Who traveled much faster
>   than light.
> She departed one day
> In an Einsteinian way
> And returned on the
>   previous night.

We can get our heads fairly well into relativity yet still unconsciously cling to the idea that there is an absolute time and compare all these relativistic effects to it; recognizing that time changes this way and that way for this speed and that speed, yet feeling that there still is some basic or absolute time. We may tend to think of the time we experience on earth as fundamental, and other times differing from it. This is understandable; we're earthlings. But the idea is confining. To observers elsewhere in the universe we are moving at relativistic speeds from their points of view and they see us moving in slow motion. They see us living lifetimes a hundredfold theirs, just as with supertelescopes we would see them living lifetimes a hundredfold ours. There is no universally standard time. None.

We think of time and then we think of the universe. We think of the universe and we wonder about what went on before the universe began and about what will happen if the universe ceases to exist in time. But the concept of time applies to events and entities within the universe—not to the universe as a whole. Time is "in" the universe; the universe is not "in" time. Without the universe, there is no time; no before, no after. Likewise, space is "in" the universe; the universe is not "in" a region of space. There is no space "outside" the universe. Space-time exists within the universe.

Think about that.

Length Contraction

As objects move through space-time, space as well as time undergoes changes in measurement. The lengths of objects appear to be contracted when they move by us at relativistic speeds. This contraction was first proposed by Fitzgerald and mathematically expressed by Lorentz. It is referred to as the Lorentz-Fitzgerald contraction. Mathematically it is:

$$L = L_0 \sqrt{1 - \frac{v^2}{c^2}}$$

where v is the relative velocity between the observed object and the observer, c is the velocity of light, L is the measured length of the moving object, and L_0 is the measured length of the object at rest. Suppose that an object is at rest and $v = 0$. Upon substitution of $v = 0$ in the equation, we find $L = L_0$, as we would expect. At 87 percent the speed of light, an object would appear to be contracted to half its original length. At 99.5 percent the speed of light, contraction would be to one-tenth its original length. If the object moved at c, its length would be zero. This is one of the reasons we say that the velocity of light is the upper limit for the velocity of any moving object. Another ditty popular with science heads is:

> There was a young fencer
>   named Fisk,
> Whose thrust was
>   exceedingly brisk.
> So fast was his action
> The Lorentz-Fitzgerald contraction
> Reduced his rapier
>   to a disk.

As Figure 33.8 indicates, contraction takes place only in the direction of motion. If an object is moving horizontally, no contraction takes place vertically.

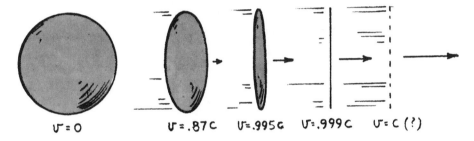

$\upsilon = 0$ $\upsilon = .87c$ $\upsilon = .995c$ $\upsilon = .999c$ $\upsilon = c\ (?)$

Fig. 33.8   The Lorentz-Fitzgerald contraction.

Do objects *really* contract at relativistic speeds? Well, if we attempt to check this out (in principle) and travel alongside the moving object with a yardstick, we note nothing at all unusual about the length of the object. An observer at rest watching this experiment would report that the reason we don't measure the contraction, which is obvious to him, is because our yardstick is shortened as well. But to us, moving with the object, there is no contraction. This is because our relative velocity with respect to the object being measured is zero. The v in the Lorentz-Fitzgerald equation refers to the relative velocity between the observed and the observer. And that is zero, so $L = L_0$. It is important to stress this point, for many of the misconceptions regarding relativity have their basis on this point. The object doesn't contract. A measure of the object from another reference frame contracts. We are simply measuring the distortion of space when we measure such a contraction, just as we measure the distortion of time itself when we find clocks running slow. The distortions are of space and time between different space-times, not of objects and events within individual realms of space-time.

The Increase of Mass with Speed

If we push on an object it will accelerate. If we maintain a steady push it will accelerate to higher and higher speeds. If we push with a greater and greater force, the acceleration in turn will increase and the speeds attained should seemingly increase without limit. But there is a speed limit in the universe—c. In fact, we cannot accelerate any material object enough to reach the speed of light, let alone surpass it.

Why this is so can be understood from Newton's Second Law. Recall that the acceleration of an object depends not only on the impressed force, but on the mass as well, $a = \dfrac{F}{m}$. And the mass of an object, according to Einstein, increases with increasing velocity—so an impressed force produces less and less acceleration as velocity increases. The relationship between mass and velocity is given by

$$m = \frac{m_0}{\sqrt{1 - \dfrac{v^2}{c^2}}}$$

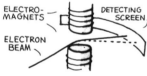

Fig. 33.9 If the mass of the electrons did not increase with speed, the beam would follow the path shown by the dashed line. But because of its increased inertia, the high-speed beam is not deflected as much.

Here m represents the measured mass of an object at any speed v. The symbol m_0 is the *rest mass*, the mass the object would have at rest. Again, v represents the relative velocity between the observer and the observed.

The faster a particle goes, the greater its mass increases, thereby resulting in less and less response to the accelerating force. An investigation of the relativistic mass equation shows that as v approaches c, m approaches infinity! A particle pushed to the speed of light would have infinite mass and would require an infinite force, which is clearly impossible. Therefore we say that no material particle can be accelerated to the speed of light.

Atomic particles have been accelerated to speeds in excess of 99 percent the speed of light, however. Their masses increase thousandsfold, as evidenced when a beam of particles, usually electrons or protons, are directed into a deflecting magnetic field. The more massive particles do not bend as readily as rest-mass particles would, Figure 33.9. They strike their targets at positions predicted by the relativistic equation. This mass increase must be compensated for in circular accelerators like cyclotrons and bevatrons, where mass dictates the radius of curvature. A principal advantage of the linear accelerator is that the particle beam travels in a straight path and mass changes do not produce deviations from a straight-line path. Mass increase with velocity is an everyday fact of life to physicists working with high-energy particles.

The Mass-Energy Equivalence

The most remarkable result in special relativity is Einstein's law of the equivalence of mass and energy. Since the kinetic energy of a body depends on its mass and its velocity, and since there is an upper limit to the velocity, it follows that if the energy of a body is increased indefinitely by the continued application of a force, its mass must be increased also. Energy takes the form of mass. Einstein deduced that mass and energy are different aspects of the same thing. The relationship between mass and energy is given by what might well be called the equation of the twentieth century:

$$E = mc^2$$

Owing to the large magnitude of c, the velocity of light, a small mass corresponds to a fantastically huge quantity of energy. For example, the energy equivalent of a single gram of any matter is greater than the energy used daily by the populations of our largest cities.

The interchange between mass and energy is a common phenomenon and occurs for *all* changes of energy. The change in mass is ordinarily so slight that it has not been detected until recent times. When we strike a match, for example, the chemical reaction that is set off is accompanied by a tiny bit of mass converting to energy. That's where the energy comes from! When the phosphorus atoms in the match head rearrange themselves and combine with oxygen in the air to form new molecules, the resulting molecules are a very slight bit less massive than the masses of the separate phosphorus and oxygen molecules. From a mass standpoint, the whole is slightly less than the sum of its parts. But not very much. The slight decrease in mass goes off in the energy of heat. For all chemical reactions, the mass difference is so tiny that it is not of much practical importance. But atomic nuclear reactions are accompanied with mass differences of appreciable size. For example, when hydrogen nuclei (bare protons) combine to form helium nuclei, almost 1 percent of their mass is released in the form of energy. This happens in the stars. The mass of the sun decreases at the rate of $4\frac{1}{2}$ million tons each second. It is this decrease in mass that bathes the solar system with radiant energy and permits life to exist. This rate of decreasing mass may seem alarming at first, but the sun is mighty big. At the end of one million years, only one ten-millionth of the sun's mass will have been converted to energy. It's comforting to have so big a sun!

The equation $E = mc^2$ is not restricted to chemical and nuclear reactions. *Any* change in energy corresponds to a change in mass. The increased kinetic energy of a golf ball is accompanied by an increase in mass. A light-bulb filament energized with electricity is more massive than when it is turned off. A hot cup of coffee is more massive than the same cup of coffee when cold. But these examples involve small energy changes, and therefore correspond to incredibly small mass changes. For large energy changes, the effect is more noticeable. Electric energy affords a good example. Work is required to bring together electrically charged particles of the same sign. A fantastically huge amount of work would be required to confine a single gram of bare electrons in a small region because of electrical repulsion. One gram of electrons confined to a sphere of diameter 5 inches would have a mass of 10 million tons!

The first direct proof that energy could be converted to mass was found in 1932 in a photograph emulsion that was being used to catch cosmic rays. C. D. Anderson, an American physicist, found that a photon of gamma radiation that had entered the emulsion had changed into a pair of particles. One of the particles was an electron. The other particle, which had the same mass as an electron, but had a *positive* charge rather than a negative charge, was given the name of *positron*. A positron is the *antiparticle* of an electron. When a gamma ray changes from energy to mass, a pair of particles is produced. One of the particles is the antiparticle of the other, having the same mass and spin, but opposite charge. The antiparticle doesn't last long. It soon encounters a particle which is its antiparticle, and the pair is annihilated, sending out a gamma ray in the process.*

Energy in any form has a mass equivalent—that is, it has the property of inertia. A photon, although "massless," has some measure of inertia that responds to a gravitational field. Light is bent slightly as it passes a massive star. We think of mass as congealed energy—and rest-energy is that which we call mass. Just as electricity and magnetism are aspects of

---

*For more information about antiparticles, read Hannes Alfven's short book *Worlds-Antiworlds—Antimatter in Cosmology*, San Francisco, Freeman, 1966.

"electromagnetism," and space and time are aspects of "space-time," energy and mass are aspects of "mass-energy."

Einstein's mass-energy relationship is valid only insofar as the transformation equations for mass, length, and time are valid. Before any new theory can be accepted, it must satisfy the correspondence principle. Recall from the previous chapter that this principle states that any new theory or any new description of nature must agree with the old where the old is known to be correct. If the equations of special relativity are valid, they must reduce to those of classical mechanics when velocities much less than the velocity of light are considered.

The relativity equations do in fact conform to the correspondence principle. If v is very small compared to c, the ratio v^2/c^2 is extremely small. For the velocities we ordinarily experience this ratio may be taken to be zero, and the relativity equations become

$$t = \frac{t_0}{\sqrt{1-0}} = t_0$$

$$L = L_0 \sqrt{1-0} = L_0$$

$$m = \frac{m_0}{\sqrt{1-0}} = m_0$$

So for "everyday" velocities, the time, length, and mass of moving objects is essentially unchanged. The equations of special relativity hold for all velocities, although they are significant only for velocities near the speed of light.

The Special Theory of Relativity is concerned with the relationships between space and time and with the physics of uniform motion, of frames of reference moving at constant velocities with respect to one another. But what about the more general cases of accelerated frames of reference, of curved motion and the like? These cases are treated in Einstein's General Theory of Relativity, which explores the relationships between gravitation and time, and between space-time geometry and gravitation. In this theory the phenomenon of gravity is a consequence of the geometrical warping of space-time. We will not go into the General Theory of Relativity.

Einstein's theories of relativity have raised many philosophical questions. For example, why does time seem to move in one direction? Has it always moved *forward*? Are there other parts of the universe, elsewhere or even here, where time moves *backward*? Is it possible that our three-dimensional perception of a four-dimensional world is only a beginning? Could there be a fifth dimension? A sixth dimension? A seventh dimension? And if so, what would the nature of these dimensions be? Perhaps these unanswered questions will be answered by the scientists of tomorrow. How exciting!

Summary of Terms

Frame of reference. A vantage point (usually a set of coordinate axes) with respect to which the position and motion of a body may be described.

Postulates of the Special Theory of Relativity. (1) All laws of nature are the same in all uniformly moving frames of reference.

(2) The velocity of light in free space will be found to have the same value regardless of the motion of the source or the motion of the observer; that is, the velocity of light is invariant.

Space-time. The four-dimensional continuum in which all things exist; three dimensions being the coordinates of space, and the other of time.

Time dilation. The apparent slowing down of time of a body moving at relativistic speeds.

Length contraction. The apparent shrinking of a body moving at relativistic speeds.

Mass-energy equivalence. The relationship between mass and energy as given by the equation $E = mc^2$.

Suggested Reading

Bondi, Hermann, *Relativity and Common Sense* (Science Study Series), Garden City, N. Y., Doubleday (Anchor), 1964. An excellent paperback.

Durell, Clement V., *Readable Relativity*, New York, Harper Torchbook, 1960.

Gamow, George, *Mr. Tompkins in Wonderland*, New York, Macmillan, 1940. An excellent and very interesting little book.

Questions

1. A person riding on the roof of a freight train car fires a gun in the direction in which the train is traveling. Does the bullet travel faster than it would if he had fired it while standing at rest on the ground?

2. Suppose instead that the person riding on top of the freight car shines a searchlight beam in the direction in which the train is traveling. Does the light beam travel faster across the ground than it would if he had shone it while standing at rest on the ground? Explain.

3. Could a human being who has a life expectancy of 70 years possibly make a round-trip journey to a part of the universe thousands of light years distant? Explain.

4. Is it possible for a son or daughter to be chronologically older than his or her parents? Explain.

5. We might think of the speed of light as a kind of speed limit in the universe. No material particle can attain or surpass this limit even when a continuous, unyielding force is exerted upon it. Why is this so?

6. If you were in a rocket ship traveling away from the earth at a speed close to the speed of light, what changes would you note in your pulse? In your mass? In your volume? Explain.

7. If you were on earth observing a person in a rocket ship traveling away from the earth at a speed close to the speed of light, what changes would you note in his pulse? In his mass? In his volume? Explain.

8. How might the principle of correspondence be used to establish the validity of theories outside the domain of physical science?

9. What does the equation $E = mc^2$ mean?

10. One of the fads of the future might be "century hopping," where occupants of high-speed space ships would depart from the earth for several years and return centuries later. What are the present-day obstacles to such a practice?

Courtesy of Lawrence Radiation Laboratory.

PART 7

Nuclear Physics

34

Radioactivity

X-rays

The Greek word *atom* means "cannot be broken apart." Atoms, however, *can* be broken apart. We have discussed one way that atoms are broken, or at least chipped, and that is by *ionization*—the removal (or addition) of some of the electrons that surround the nucleus. But the very nucleus can be broken apart. The spontaneous breaking apart of atomic nuclei is called *radioactivity*. The story of the discovery of radioactivity begins with another discovery—X-rays.

Before the turn of the century it was discovered that a beam of electrons directed against a metal plate produced radiation that could pass through solid materials. These rays were called *X-rays*. X-rays are simply high-frequency electromagnetic waves emitted by the excitation of the innermost orbital electrons of atoms. Whereas the electron current in a fluorescent lamp excites the outer electrons of atoms and produces visible photons, a more energetic beam of electrons excites the innermost electrons and produces higher-frequency photons of X-radiation.

Because X-ray photons have a high energy they can pass through many layers of atoms before being absorbed. In this way X-rays can pass through you and take pictures of the inside of your body, Figure 34.1.

In 1896 the French physicist Henri Becquerel was trying to find whether any elements emitted X-rays. To do this he wrapped a photographic plate in black paper to keep out the light, and then put pieces of various elements against the wrapped plate. He thought that if these materials emitted X-rays, the rays would go through the paper and blacken the plate. He found that although most elements produced no effect, the mineral pitchblende did give out rays. It was soon discovered that similar rays are emitted by other elements, such as thorium, actinium, and by two new elements discovered by Pierre and Marie Curie, polonium, and radium. The emission of these rays was evidence of a much more drastic breaking apart of the atom than ionization. These rays were the result of a breaking apart and disintegration of the central core of the atom—radioactivity.

491

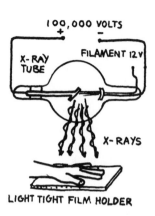
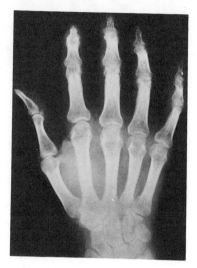

Fig. 34.1   X-rays emitted by excited metallic atoms in the electrode pass through the hand and expose the film. (Photo by New York Hospital.)

Alpha, Beta, and Gamma Rays   The radioactive elements emit three distinct types of rays, called by the first three letters of the Greek alphabet, α, β, and γ, pronounced *alpha*, *beta*, and *gamma*, respectively. Alpha rays have a positive electrical charge, beta rays have a negative charge, and gamma rays have no charge at all. The three rays are separated by putting a magnetic field across their path, Figure 34.2. Further investigation has shown that an alpha ray is a stream of helium nuclei, a beta ray is a stream of electrons, and a gamma ray is electromagnetic radiation (a stream of photons) whose frequency is higher than that of X-rays.

The Nucleus   Study of these rays, together with much other research, indicates that the atom consists of a tiny nucleus surrounded by a number of electrons moving in circular or elliptical orbits, as described in earlier chapters. The atomic nucleus occupies only one-trillionth the volume of the atom. Thus the atom is mostly empty space. The nucleus is composed of *protons* and *neutrons*. Both have about the same mass, the neutron being slightly greater. They are nearly 2000 times heavier than the electrons, so the weight of an atom is practically equal to the weight of its nucleus. The proton is positively charged. Its positive charge is the same in magnitude as the negative charge of the electron. The neutron has no charge, as the name indicates. Since these

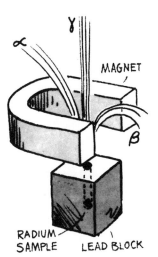

Fig. 34.2 The bending of a narrow beam of rays in a magnetic field. The beam comes from a radioactive source placed at the bottom of a hole drilled in a lead block.

two particles make up the nuclei, they are known collectively as *nucleons*.

Facts about the size, shape, and inner structure of the nucleus are presently being gathered at a rapid rate. Nuclear radii range from about 10^{-13} cm for hydrogen to about six times as large for uranium. The shapes of nuclei vary from ball-shapes to disk-shapes. The surfaces of some nuclei are vibrating in standing waves. It is known that a "skin" of neutrons makes up the outer portion of the heavier nuclei. Just as there are energy levels for the orbital electrons of an atom, there are energy levels within the nucleus. Whereas electrons falling to lower orbits emit photons of light, nucleons within the nucleus falling to lower energy states emit photons of gamma radiation. The emission of alpha particles can be understood from the viewpoint of quantum mechanics. Just as orbital electrons form a probability cloud about the nucleus, inside the radioactive nucleus there is a similar probability cloud for alpha particles (and other particles as well). Probability is extremely high that the alpha particle will be inside the nucleus, but if the probability wave extends outside there is a finite chance that the alpha particle will be outside. Once outside it is hurled violently away by the electric field of the nucleus.

In addition to alpha, beta, and gamma rays, various other kinds of particles have been detected coming out of the nucleus, which are the so-called elementary particles. We do not think of these as buried within the nucleus and then popping out just as we do not think of a spark buried in a match before it is struck. They come into being when the nucleus is disrupted. A great deal of information is known about nuclear structure and elementary particles, but there is much more that needs to be known before we have a complete understanding of the atom. This is the frontier of knowledge, and the area of much current research.

Isotopes   The nucleus of a hydrogen atom consists of a single proton. Helium has two protons, lithium has three, and so forth. In neutral atoms, there are as many protons in the nucleus as there are electrons outside the nucleus. The number of protons in the nucleus is the same as the atomic number. Every succeeding element in the list of elements has one more proton than the preceding element.

The number of neutrons in the nucleus does not follow as simple a rule, however. In a given element, the number of neutrons may vary somewhat. For example, every atom of chlorine has 17 protons, and hence 17 orbital electrons that determine what chemical compounds it can make. Not all atoms of chlorine, however, have the same number of neutrons. Atoms that have like numbers of protons but unlike numbers of neutrons are called *isotopes*. The two chief types of chlorine isotopes have 35 and 37 times the mass of a single nucleon. We denote these by $_{17}Cl^{35}$ and $_{17}Cl^{37}$, where the numbers refer to the atomic number and the *atomic mass*. The atomic mass is also called the atomic weight. The atomic-mass number corresponds to the total number of nucleons in the nucleus. Since for both isotopes 17 of these are protons, the lighter isotope has $35 - 17 = 18$ neutrons, and the heavier isotope has $37 - 17 = 20$ neutrons. In nature the isotopes of chlorine are found mixed, with three times as many $_{17}Cl^{35}$ atoms as there are $_{17}Cl^{37}$ atoms, so the average atomic mass of naturally occurring chlorine is about 35.5. Chlorine is only one of many elements found in nature that consist of two or more stable isotopes. Even hydrogen, the lightest element, has three known isotopes, Figure 34.3. The

Fig. 34.3   Three isotopes of hydrogen. Each nucleus has a single proton, which holds a single orbital electron which in turn determines the chemical properties of the atom. The different number of neutrons changes the mass of the atom, but not its chemical properties.

double-weight hydrogen isotope, H^2, is called *deuterium*. "Heavy water" is the name usually given to H_2O in which the H's are deuterium atoms. The triple-weight hydrogen isotope, H^3, is called *tritium*. Some elements have several isotopes—tin, for example, having no fewer than twelve. At present, over 1300 distinct isotopes are known.

Why Atoms Are Radioactive

The positively charged and closely spaced protons in a nucleus have huge electrical forces of repulsion between them. Why don't they fly apart because of this huge repulsive force? Because there is an even more formidable force within the nucleus—the nuclear force. Both neutrons and protons are bound together by this awesome attractive force. The nuclear force is much more complicated than the electrical force and is still not completely understood. It is known that the nuclear force between nucleons depends on the distance between them and on their velocities and spins. It is a short-range force. Electrical forces weaken with the inverse square of the distance, while nuclear forces weaken much more quickly—probably as the inverse fifth or sixth power of distance. So, while doubling the distance between two protons causes the electrical repulsion to fall to $\frac{1}{4}$ its strength, the nuclear attraction falls to about $\frac{1}{64}$ its strength. As long as protons are close together, as in small nuclei, the nuclear force easily overcomes the electrical force of repulsion. But for distant protons, like those on opposite edges of a large nucleus, the attractive nuclear force may be small in comparison to the repulsive electric force. Hence a larger nucleus is not as stable as a smaller nucleus.

The presence of the neutrons also plays a large role in nuclear stability. Although protons both attract and repel, neutrons only attract, and therefore may be considered a sort of "nuclear cement." Many of the first twenty or so elements have equal numbers of neutrons and protons. Apparently this equal number for the lighter elements is needed to counterbalance the repulsive forces of the protons.

Even more "nuclear cement" is needed by the heavier elements. In fact, most of the mass of the heavier elements is composed of neutrons. For example, in U-238, which has 92 protons, there are 146 (238 − 92) neutrons. If the uranium nucleus were to have equal numbers of protons and neutrons, 119 protons and 119 neutrons, it would fly apart at once because of the electrical repulsion forces. Relative stability is found only if 27 of these protons are replaced by neutrons. This greater number of neutrons is required to compensate for the

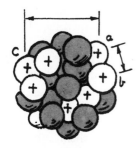

Fig. 34.4 Proton *a* both attracts and repels proton *b*, but only repels proton *c*. The greater the distance between *a* and *c*, the more unstable the nucleus.

repulsion between distant protons. Even so, the U-238 nucleus is still unstable because of the electrical forces.

To put the matter in another way: There is an electrical repulsion between *every pair* of protons in the nucleus, but there is not a nuclear attractive force between every pair, Figure 34.4. Every proton in the uranium nucleus exerts a repulsion on each of the 91 protons—those near and those far. However, each proton (and neutron) exerts an appreciable nuclear attraction on only those nucleons that happen to be near it.

We find that all nuclei having 83 or more protons are unstable. In this unstable environment alpha and beta emission takes place. The actual mechanism of the emission process goes beyond electric repulsion and involves a quantum-mechanical explanation beyond the scope of this book.

Half-life

The radioactive decay rate of an element is measured in terms of a characteristic time, the *half-life*. The half-life of a radioactive material is the time needed for half of the active atoms of any given quantity to decay. Radium, for example, has a half-life of 1620 years. This means that half of any given specimen of radium will be converted into some other element by the end of 1620 years. In the next 1620 years, half of the remaining radium will decay, leaving only one-fourth the original number of radium atoms. The other three-fourths are converted, by a

Fig. 34.5 Every 1620 years the amount of radium decreases by half, but some always remains.

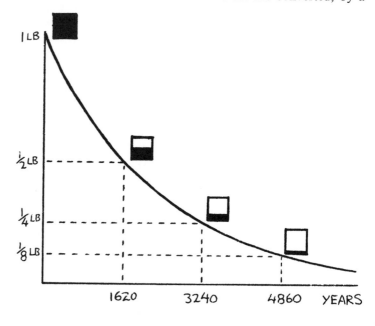

succession of disintegrations, to lead. The isotopes of some elements have a half-life of less than a second, while uranium, for example, has a half-life of $4\frac{1}{2}$ billion years. Each radioactive element has its own characteristic half-life.

The rates of radioactive decay are remarkably constant and are not affected by any external conditions, however drastic. Wide temperature and pressure extremes, strong electric and magnetic fields, and even violent chemical reactions have no detectable effect on the rate of decay of a given element. Any of these stresses, although severe by ordinary standards, are far too mild to affect the nucleus in the deep interior of the atom.

How do we measure half-lives? Certainly not by observing a specimen and waiting until half of it has decayed. The half-life of a radioactive substance is related to its rate of disintegration. In general, the shorter the half-life of an element, the faster is the rate of disintegration and the more active is the element. From the rate of disintegration, which can be measured in the laboratory, the half-life is easily computed.

Half-lives can also be calculated with the use of quantum mechanics. The kinetic energy of an emerging alpha particle tells us its wavelength, which in turn gives its probability of leaking from the nucleus. This information enables the prediction of the half-life of the parent nucleus with some success.

Radiation Detectors   Ordinary thermal motions of atoms in a gas or liquid jostling against one another are not energetic enough to dislodge electrons —and the atoms remain neutral. But when an energetic particle such as an alpha or beta particle shoots through a fluid, electrons one after another are knocked from the target atoms, leaving a trail of freed electrons and positively charged ions. This ionization process is responsible for the harmful effects of high-energy radiation in living cells. It also makes it relatively easy to trace the paths of high-energy particles. We will briefly discuss four radiation detection devices.

Geiger Counter. A *Geiger counter* consists of a central wire in a hollow metal cylinder filled with a gas. An electrical voltage is applied across the cylinder and wire so that the wire is at a higher potential than the cylinder. The voltage distorts the atoms in the gas so that they are *almost* ionized. If radiation enters the tube and ionizes an atom in the gas, the freed electron is attracted to the positively charged central wire. This electron collides with other atoms and knocks out more electrons, re-

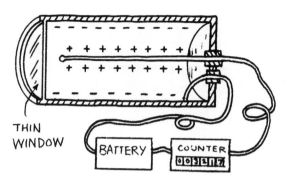

Fig. 34.6   A cutaway view
of a Geiger tube.

THIN
WINDOW

sulting in a cascade of electrons moving toward the wire. This
makes a short pulse of electric current which activates a counting
device connected to the tube.

Fig.   34.7   The   cloud
chamber.

Cloud Chamber. A *cloud chamber* shows a visible path of ionizing
radiation in the form of fog trails. It consists of a cylindrical
glass chamber closed at the upper end by a glass window, and
at the lower end by a movable piston. Water vapor or alcohol
vapor in the chamber can be saturated by adjusting the piston.

The radioactive sample is placed inside the chamber as shown
in Figure 34.7, or it can be placed outside the thin glass window.
When radiation passes through the chamber, ions are produced
along their paths. If the saturated air in the chamber is then
suddenly cooled, tiny droplets of moisture condense about these
ions and form vapor trails showing the paths of the radiation.
These are the atomic versions of the ice-crystals trails left in the
sky by jet planes.

The cooling of the chamber is accomplished by moving the
piston downward suddenly, which results in a sudden expansion
of the air in the chamber. The fog tracks that form are illuminated
with a lamp and may be seen or photographed through the glass
top. The chamber may be placed in a strong electric or magnetic
field which will bend the paths in a manner that provides information about the charge and mass of the radiation particles.
Positively and negatively charged particles will bend in opposite
directions.

Bubble Chamber. The particle trails seen in a *bubble chamber* are
gas bubbles in a liquid rather than liquid droplets in a gas.
Liquid hydrogen is heated under pressure in a glass chamber

Fig. 34.8 The 72-inch hydrogen bubble chamber at the Lawrence Radiation Laboratory. Liquid hydrogen fills the bottom of the chamber. The rays to be studied enter the chamber through a window. (Courtesy of Lawrence Radiation Laboratory, University of California at Berkeley.)

to a point just short of boiling. If the pressure in the chamber is suddenly released at the moment an ion-producing particle enters, a thin line of boiling liquid forms along the particle's path. The boiling quickly spreads throughout the chamber; but in the few thousandths of a second before this happens, it is possible to photograph the particle's trail. Like the cloud chamber, the bubble chamber reveals the charge and relative mass of the particles being studied.

Scintillation Counter. A *scintillation counter* utilizes the fact that certain substances are easily excited and emit light when charged particles impinge upon them. Tiny flashes of light or scintillations

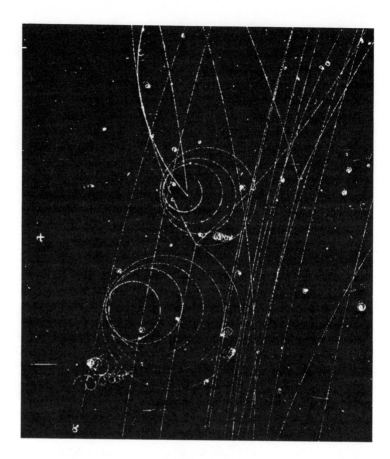

Fig. 34.9 Tracks of elementary particles in a bubble chamber—two particles were destroyed where the spirals emanate, and four others created in the collision. (Courtesy of Lawrence Radiation Laboratory, University of California at Berkeley.)

are converted into electric signals by means of special photomultiplier tubes. A scintillation counter is much more sensitive than the Geiger counter.

Natural Transmutation of the Elements

When an alpha or beta particle is emitted from a nucleus, a different element is formed. The changing of one chemical element to another is called *transmutation*. Consider uranium, for example. Uranium has 92 protons. When an alpha particle is ejected, the nucleus is reduced by two protons and two neutrons (an alpha particle is a helium nucleus consisting of two protons and two neutrons). The 90 protons and 144 neutrons left behind are then the nucleus of a new element. This element is thorium. Letting a proton be represented as $\oplus$ and a neutron as $\bullet$, we can express this reaction as:

$$_{92}U^{238} \rightarrow {_{90}}Th^{234} + {_2}He^4$$

An arrow is used here to show that the U^{238} changes into the other elements. When this happens energy is released, partly in the form of gamma radiation, partly in the kinetic energy of the alpha particle ($_2He^4$), and partly in the kinetic energy of the thorium atom. In this equation, notice that the mass numbers at the top balance ($238 = 234 + 4$), and that the atomic numbers at the bottom also balance ($92 = 90 + 2$). Since this is a nuclear reaction we ignore numbers referring to the orbiting electrons.

Thorium-234, the product of the foregoing reaction, is also radioactive. When it decays, it emits a beta particle. Recall that a beta particle is an electron, not an orbital electron, but one from the nucleus. How can this happen when the nucleus contains only protons and neutrons? The answer is that it comes from one of the neutrons. In a loose sense, we can think of a neutron as a combined proton and electron. When the neutron emits an electron it becomes a proton. A neutron is ordinarily stable when it is locked in the nucleus of an atom, but a free neutron is radioactive, and has a half-life of 16 minutes. It decays into a proton by beta emission.* So in the case of thorium, which has 90 protons, beta emission leaves it with one less neutron and one more proton. The new nucleus then has 91 protons and is no longer thorium, but the element protactinium. Although the atomic number has increased by 1 in this process, the mass number (protons + neutrons) remains the same. The nuclear equation is:

$$_{90}Th^{234} \rightarrow {_{91}}Pa^{234} + {_{-1}}e^0$$

An electron is written as $_{-1}e^0$. The 0 indicates that it has no significant mass. Only protons and neutrons contribute to the

---

*Beta emission is also always accompanied by the emission of a neutrino, a neutral particle with about zero mass. The neutrino (little neutron) was predicted from theoretical calculations by Wolfgang Pauli in 1921, and detected in 1956.

mass number of a nucleus. The -1 is the charge of the electron. Remember that this electron comes from the nucleus and not from the orbital electrons.

From the previous two examples, we can see that when an element ejects an alpha particle from its nucleus, its atomic number *decreases* by 2. The atom is changed to a lower atom in the periodic table. When an element ejects a beta particle (electron) from its nucleus, its atomic number *increases* by 1. The atom is changed to a higher atom in the periodic table. Hence radioactive elements can decay *up* or *down* the periodic table.*

The radioactive decay of $_{92}U^{238}$ to $_{82}Pb^{206}$, an isotope of lead, is shown in Figure 34.10. The steps in the decay process are shown in the diagram, where each nucleus that plays a part in the series is shown by a burst. The vertical column containing the burst shows its atomic number, and the horizontal column shows its mass number. Each arrow that slants downward toward the left shows an alpha decay, and each arrow that points to the right shows a beta decay. Notice that some of the nuclei in the series can decay in both ways. This is but one of many similar radioactive series that occur in nature.

Artificial Transmutation of the Elements

The alchemists of old tried vainly for over two thousand years to cause the transmutation of one element to another. Despite their fervent efforts and rituals, they never came close to succeeding, for their most elaborate experiments were nothing more than ordinary chemical reactions. Atomic transmutation cannot be accomplished by chemical means. The deep interior of the atom, the nucleus, is immune to the most violent of chemical reactions, where only the outermost orbital shells of atoms are altered. To change an element, the nucleus must be changed. In order to change lead to gold, for example, three positive charges must be extracted from the nucleus. Ironically enough, nuclear transmutations were constantly going on around the alchemists. The radioactive decay of uranium and other minerals had been going on in the rocks since their formation. This was not detected by the alchemists and even if they did detect it they would not have recognized it as a transmutation process. They lacked an adequate theory to guide them.

The alchemists did not know about the tiny central nucleus and its whirling electrons. These orbital electrons provide a sort

---

*Sometimes a nucleus emits a *positron*, which is the "antiparticle" of an electron. In this case, a proton becomes a neutron and the atomic number is decreased.

of atomic skin similar to the apparent disk formed by an electric fan. Only a high-speed particle can penetrate the electron cloud to reach deep within the atom, just as a high-speed bullet might

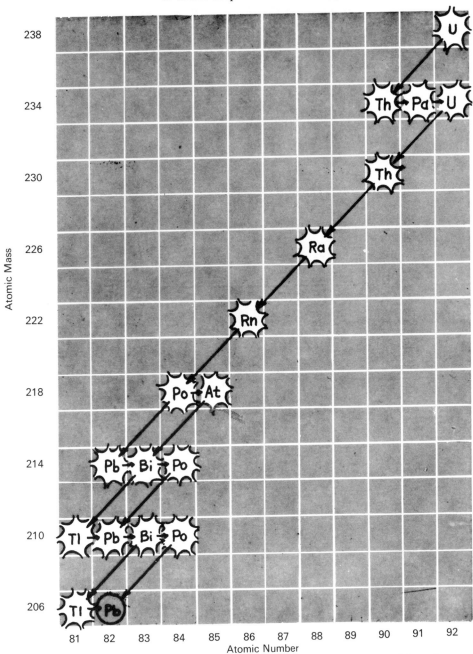

Fig. 34.10 Uranium-238 decays to lead-206 through a series of alpha and beta decays.

pass between the blades of a fan. A slow particle drifting toward an atom is turned back, much as a marble tossed slowly at a spinning fan is batted back. Had the alchemists used the high-speed particles ejected from radioactive ores as bullets, they would have succeeded in transmuting some of the atoms in a substance. But the atoms so transmuted would most likely have escaped their notice.

Rutherford, in 1919, was the first of many investigators to succeed in transmuting a chemical element. He bombarded nitrogen nuclei with alpha particles and succeeded in transmuting nitrogen into oxygen.

$$_7N^{14} + {_2}He^4 \rightarrow {_8}O^{17} + {_1}H^1$$

His source of alpha particles was a radioactive piece of ore. From a quarter of a million cloud-chamber tracks photographed on movie film, he showed seven examples of atomic transmutation. Tracks bent by a strong external magnetic field showed that when an alpha particle collided with a nitrogen atom, a proton bounced out and a heavy atom recoiled a short distance. The alpha particle was seen no more. The alpha particle was absorbed in the process, transforming nitrogen to oxygen.

Since Rutherford's announcement in 1919, we have made many such nuclear reactions, first with natural bombarding projectiles from radioactive ores and then with still more energetic projectiles, protons and electrons, hurled by giant atom-smashing accelerators. Artificial transmutation has been used to produce the hitherto unknown elements from atomic number 93 to 105—*neptunium, plutonium, americium, curium, berkelium, californium, einsteinium, fermium, mendelevium, nobelium, law-rencium, rutherfordium,* and *hahnium.** All of these artificially made elements have short half-lives. If they ever existed naturally on earth they have long since decayed.

Radioactive Isotopes

All elements have isotopes. Some of the isotopes of a given element may be radioactively stable, while others are quite radioactive. Most elements, in fact, have more radioactive iso-

---

*The names *rutherfordium* and *hahnium* for elements 104 and 105 are unofficial as this book goes to press.

topes than stable isotopes. Sodium, for example, has 6 radioactive isotopes, cobalt has 10, and iodine has 21. Radioactive
isotopes of all the elements have been made by bombardment
with neutrons and other particles. As such isotopes have become
available and inexpensive, their uses in scientific research and
industry have grown tremendously.

A small amount of radioactive isotopes can be mixed with
fertilizer before being applied to growing plants. Once the plants
are growing, we can easily measure how much fertilizer they have
taken up, by using a Geiger counter which detects the radiation
given off by the absorbed isotopes. From such measurements
the farmer knows the proper amount of fertilizer to use. Used
in this way, radioactive isotopes are called *tracers*.

Tracers are widely used in medicine to study the process of
digestion and the way in which chemical substances move about
in the body. Food containing a small amount of radioactive
isotopes is fed to a patient and traced through the body with a
Geiger counter. The same method can be used to study the
circulation of the blood.

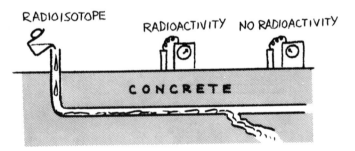

Fig. 34.11   Tracking pipe
leaks with radioactive isotopes.

Large amounts of radioactive iodine taken into the body are
used to combat cancer of the thyroid gland. Since iodine tends
to collect in the thyroid gland, the radioactive isotopes lodge
where they can destroy the malignant cells. Radioactive isotopes
are more and more becoming a powerful tool for the modern
biologist and physician.

Engineers can study how the parts of an automobile engine
wear away during use by making the pistons radioactive. While
the engine is running, the surface of the pistons rub against the
cylinder walls. The tiny particles of radioactive metal that are
worn away fall into the lubricating oil where they can be
measured with a Geiger counter. By repeating this test with
different oils, the oil giving the least wear and longest life to the
engine can be determined.

Tire manufacturers also make use of radioactive isotopes. If a known fraction of the carbon atoms used in an automobile tire are radioactive, the amount of rubber left on the road when the car is braked can be estimated through a count of the radioactive atoms. There are hundreds more examples of the use of radioactive isotopes. The important thing is that this technique provides a means of detecting and counting atoms in samples of materials too small to be seen with a microscope.

Carbon Dating   A continuous bombardment of cosmic rays upon the earth's atmosphere results in the nuclear decay of many atoms in the upper atmosphere. Protons and neutrons are scattered throughout the atmosphere. Most of the protons are quickly absorbed in the upper atmosphere, but the neutrons keep going for long distances because they have no charge and therefore do not interact electrically with matter. Sooner or later many of them collide with the nuclei of atoms in the lower atmosphere. If they are captured by the nucleus of a nitrogen atom, the following reaction takes place:

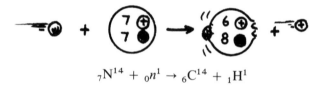

$$_7N^{14} + {_0}n^1 \rightarrow {_6}C^{14} + {_1}H^1$$

The nitrogen nucleus breaks up into an isotope of carbon by emitting a proton, $_1H^1$. Most of the carbon that exists is the stable carbon-12, $_6C^{12}$. Because of the cosmic-ray bombardment, about one-millionth of 1 percent of the carbon in the atmosphere is carbon-14. Atmospheric carbon is in the form of carbon dioxide, which is breathed by plants. Hence all plants have a tiny bit of radioactive carbon-14 in them. All animals eat plants (or eat plant-eating animals), and therefore have a little carbon-14 in them. All living things contain some carbon-14.

Carbon-14 is a beta emitter and decays back into nitrogen by the following reaction:

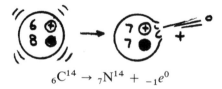

$$_6C^{14} \rightarrow {_7}N^{14} + {_{-1}}e^0$$

So the carbon-14 in living things changes into stable nitrogen. But because living things breathe, this decay is accompanied by a replenishment of carbon-14, and a radioactive equilibrium is reached where there is a fixed ratio of carbon-14 to carbon-12. When a plant or animal dies, however, replenishment stops. The percentage of carbon-14 steadily decreases—at a known rate. The half-life of carbon-14 is about 5770 years, which means that half the carbon-14 atoms decay in that time. Half the remaining carbon-14 atoms decay in the following 5770 years and so forth. The radioactivity of living things therefore gradually decreases at a steady rate after they die.

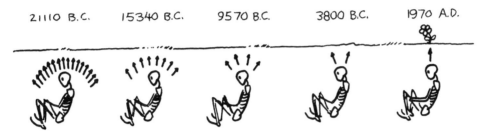

21110 B.C.   15340 B.C.   9570 B.C.   3800 B.C.   1970 A.D.

Fig. 34.12   The radioactive carbon isotopes in the skeleton diminish by one-half every 5770 years.

Since we know the radioactivity of plants and animals today, and have no evidence of any variation in cosmic-ray intensity for the last few thousand years, we are able to determine the ages of ancient objects by measuring their radioactivity. If we extract a small, but precise, quantity of carbon from an ancient wooden ax handle, for example, and find it has one-half as much radioactivity as an equal quantity of carbon extracted from a living tree, then the old wood must have come from a tree that was cut down 5770 years ago. In this way, we can probe into the past as much as twenty-thousand years to find out such things as the age of ancient civilizations or the times of the ice ages that covered the earth.

Uranium Dating   The dating of older, but nonliving, things is accomplished with radioactive minerals, such as uranium. Uranium-238, 235, and 234, which are the naturally occurring isotopes, decay very slowly. U^{238} decays to Th^{234}, and finally to lead, Pb^{206}. U^{235} decays to Pb^{207}. For this reason, a sample of rock containing uranium also contains these lead isotopes. They are not the common lead isotopes, Pb^{208}. All the lead isotopes 206 and 207 which exist were at one time uranium. The longer the uranium has been in the rocks, the higher is the percentage of these isotopes of lead in the rock. After determining the percentage of each isotope in a rock and knowing the half-lives of the original uranium isotopes, we can calculate the time the uranium in the rock first started to decay. In this way the ages of rocks have been found to be as much as 3.5 billion years old. Samples from the moon which have undergone less erosion and fewer physical changes have been dated at 4.6 billion years, which is about the presumed time of Earth's origin.

Summary of Terms

Alpha ray. Streams of helium nuclei ejected by certain radioactive nuclei.

Beta ray. Streams of fast-moving electrons ejected from radioactive nuclei.

Gamma ray. High-frequency electromagnetic radiation emitted by the nuclei of radioactive atoms.

Nucleon. A nuclear proton or neutron; the collective name for either or both.

Isotopes. Atoms whose nuclei have the same number of protons but different numbers of neutrons.

Atomic number. The number associated with an atom which is the same as the number of protons in the nucleus, or the same as the number of extranuclear electrons.

Atomic-mass number. The number associated with an atom which is the same as the number of nucleons in the nucleus.

Half-life. The time required for half the atoms of a radioactive element to decay.

Transmutation. The conversion of an atomic nucleus of one element into an atomic nucleus of another element through a loss or gain in the number of protons.

Suggested Reading

Cohen, Bernard L., *The Heart of the Atom* (Science Study Series), Garden City, N. Y., Doubleday (Anchor), 1967.

Weisskopf, Victor F., "The Three Spectroscopies," *Scientific American,* May, 1968.

Questions

1. Is it at all possible for a hydrogen isotope to emit an alpha particle?

2. Why are alpha and beta rays deflected in opposite directions in a magnetic field? Why are gamma rays undeflected?

3. Will radioactive material which has a short half-life or long half-life give a higher reading on a Geiger counter?

4. If a sample of radioactive isotopes has a half-life of one day, how much of the original sample will be left at the end of the second day?

5. From Figure 34.10, how many alpha and beta particles are emitted in the radioactive decay of a uranium-238 atom to lead-206?

6. When the element polonium, atomic number 84, atomic mass 218, emits a beta particle, it transforms into a new element. What is the atomic number and atomic mass of this new element? Suppose instead that it emits an alpha particle?

7. State the numbers of neutrons and protons in each of the following nuclei: $_1H^1$, $_6C^{14}$, $_{26}Fe^{56}$, $_{79}Au^{197}$, $_{92}U^{238}$.

8. How is it possible for an element to decay up the periodic table?

9. Elements above uranium do not exist in nature because they have short half-lives. Yet there are several elements with equally as short half-lives below uranium in atomic number that *do* exist in nature. How can you account for this?

10. An archeologist extracts a gram of carbon from an ancient ax handle and finds it one-fourth as radioactive as a gram of carbon extracted from a freshly cut tree branch. How old is the ax handle?

35

Nuclear Fission and Fusion

Nuclear Fission

THE GREATER FORCE IS NUCLEAR

CRITICAL DEFORMATION

THE GREATER FORCE IS ELECTRICAL

Fig. 35.1 Nuclear deformation may result in repulsive electrical forces exceeding attractive nuclear forces, in which case fission occurs.

In 1939 two German scientists, Otto Hahn and Fritz Strassmann, made an accidental discovery that was to change the world. While bombarding a sample of uranium with neutrons in the hope of creating heavier elements—a common pastime of atomic research in those days—they found to their surprise that the resulting mixture actually contained barium, an element about half the size of uranium. The mystery was unraveled by Lise Meitner and Otto Frisch, then refugees from Nazism working in Sweden. They showed that the uranium nucleus had split into lighter elements. Lise Meitner named the process *fission*, after the similar process of cell division in biology.

Fission is related to the delicate balance, within the nucleus, between the attraction of nuclear forces and the repulsion of electrical forces. In nearly all nuclei the nuclear forces dominate. In uranium, however, this domination is tenuous. If the uranium nucleus is stretched into an elongated shape, Figure 35.1, the electrical forces may push it into an even more elongated shape. If the elongation passes a critical point, nuclear forces give way to electrical ones, and the nucleus separates. This is fission.

The absorption of a neutron by a uranium atom is apparently enough to cause such an elongation. The resultant fission process may produce any of several combinations of smaller nuclei. A typical example recorded in cloud chambers is:

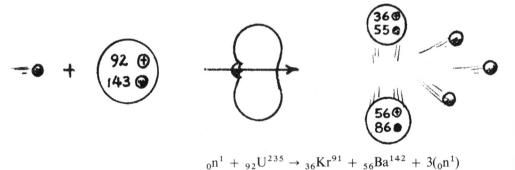

$$_0n^1 + \;_{92}U^{235} \rightarrow \;_{36}Kr^{91} + \;_{56}Ba^{142} + 3(_0n^1)$$

510

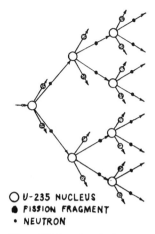

○ U-235 NUCLEUS
● FISSION FRAGMENT
• NEUTRON

Fig. 35.2 A chain reaction.

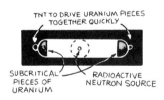

TNT TO DRIVE URANIUM PIECES
TOGETHER QUICKLY

SUBCRITICAL
PIECES OF
URANIUM

RADIOACTIVE
NEUTRON SOURCE

Fig. 35.3 Diagram of a simple atomic bomb.

This reaction has an energy release of about 200,000,000 eV.* (The explosion of the TNT molecule releases 30 eV.) The combined mass of the fission fragments is less than the mass of the uranium nucleus. The tiny amount of missing mass is converted to an awesome amount of energy, according to the relation $E = mc^2$. The scientific world was jolted—not only because of the enormous energy release, but also because of the extra neutrons liberated in the process. A typical fission reaction releases, on the average, between 2 and 3 neutrons. These new neutrons can in turn cause the fissioning of 2 or 3 other atoms, releasing more energy and a total of from 4 to 9 more neutrons. If each of these succeeds in splitting just one atom, the next step in the reaction will produce between 8 and 27 neutrons, and so on. Thus a whole *chain reaction* can proceed at an ever-accelerating rate.

If a chain reaction began in a tiny piece of pure fissionable material, the number of neutrons escaping from the surface, without being captured, might be so numerous that a growing chain reaction would not occur. Recall from Chapter 10 that small objects have a disproportionately large surface area—the greater the surface area, the greater the number of neutrons escaping. In a large piece of fissionable material, where the surface area is less in proportion to size, the results would be explosive. The size of the material that will sustain a chain reaction is called the *critical size*, the mass of which is called the *critical mass*. If the mass of fissionable material is greater than the critical mass, an explosion takes place.

Consider a large quantity of U-235 in units smaller than the critical size, and separated a short distance, Figure 35.3. Because of the relatively large surface area of each unit, neutrons readily escape and a chain reaction cannot develop. If the pieces are suddenly driven together, the relative surface area is decreased. If the combined mass is greater than critical, a violent explosion takes place. Such a device is an atomic bomb.

The uranium used in the Hiroshima blast was about the size of a baseball. We often think of atom bombs as associated with huge intercontinental missiles, but an atom bomb could be carried anywhere inconspicuously in an attaché case. When rapidly driven together, subcritical pieces of fissionable uranium or plutonium at the far ends of the case constitute a bomb.

---

*The eV (electron volt) is defined as the amount of energy an electron acquires in accelerating through a potential difference of 1 volt.

(Have you noticed any suspicious-looking people carrying attaché cases lately?)

Why then, doesn't a chain reaction occur in naturally occurring uranium deposits? The answer is that fission occurs mainly for the rare isotope U-235, which makes up only 0.7 percent of the uranium in pure uranium metal. The more common isotope U-238 absorbs neutrons but does not fission. Hence any chain reaction is quickly extinguished by the neutron-absorbing U-238 nuclei. Naturally occurring uranium is too "impure," from a fission point of view, to undergo spontaneous fission.

The separation of U-235 isotopes was one of the difficult tasks of the secret Manhattan project during World War II. Project scientists used two methods. One method depended on the fact that the lighter U-235 moves on the average slightly faster than U-238 at the same temperature. In gaseous form the faster isotope therefore has a higher rate of diffusion through a thin membrane or small opening, resulting in a slightly enriched U-235 gas on the other side. Diffusion through thousands of chambers ultimately produced a sufficiently enriched sample of U-235. The other, and less successful, method consisted of shooting uranium ions into a magnetic field. The smaller mass U-235 ions were deflected more by the magnetic field than U-238 ions, and were collected atom by atom through a slit positioned to catch them. After a couple of years both methods netted a few kilograms of U-235.

Uranium-isotope separation today is more easily accomplished with a gas centrifuge. Uranium is mixed with fluorine and the uranium hexafluoride gas is whirled in a drum at tremendously high rim speeds (on the order of 1000 miles per hour). Under centrifugal force, the heavier U-238 gravitates to the outside like milk in a dairy separator and gas rich in the lighter U-235 is extracted from the center. Engineering difficulties, only very recently overcome, prevented the utilization of this method in the Manhattan Project.

A chain reaction cannot ordinarily take place in *pure* natural uranium, since it is mostly U-238. The neutrons released by fissioning U-235 atoms are fast neutrons, readily captured by U-238. A crucial experimental fact is that slow neutrons are far more likely to be captured by U-235 than U-238.* If neutrons

---

*This is similar to the selective absorption of different frequencies of light. Just as there are characteristic electron-energy levels in an atom, there are similar energy levels within the nucleus.

A salute in bronze for Fermi The bronze plaque to the right, at Chicago's Stagg Field, commemorates Dr. Enrico Fermi's historic fission chain reaction. Fermi, criticized in Italy for not giving the Fascist salute when presented with the 1938 Nobel Prize, never returned to Italy, and became an American citizen in 1945. (Courtesy of University of Chicago.)

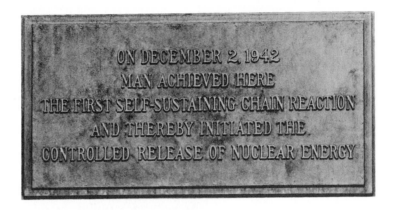

ON DECEMBER 2, 1942
MAN ACHIEVED HERE
THE FIRST SELF-SUSTAINING CHAIN REACTION
AND THEREBY INITIATED THE
CONTROLLED RELEASE OF NUCLEAR ENERGY

Cradle of an age The picture at the left shows the now-demolished stands of the University of Chicago's Stagg Field as they looked in 1942 when, in the racquets court beneath them, a small group of scientists inaugurated the atomic age. They toasted in solemn silence by sipping wine from paper cups. (Courtesy of Argonne National Laboratory.)

can be slowed down there is an increased chance that a neutron released by fission will cause fission in another U-235 atom, even amidst the more plentiful and otherwise neutron-absorbing U-238 atoms. This increase may be enough to allow a chain reaction to take place.

The Italian physicist Enrico Fermi reasoned that a chain reaction with ordinary uranium metal might be possible if the uranium were broken up into small lumps and separated by a material that would slow neutrons. Fermi and his co-workers constructed the first atomic reactor—or atomic pile, as it was then called—in the racquets court underneath the grandstands of the University of Chicago's Stagg Field. They achieved the first self-sustaining controlled release of nuclear energy on December 2, 1942.

A neutron has three possible fates in ordinary uranium metal. It may (1) cause fission of a U-235 atom; (2) escape from the metal into nonfissionable surroundings; or (3) be absorbed by U-238 without causing fission. To make the first fate more probable, the uranium was divided into discrete parcels and buried at regular intervals in nearly 400 tons of graphite, a familiar form of carbon. A simple analogy clarifies the function of the graphite: If a golf ball rebounds from a massive wall it loses hardly any speed; but if it rebounds from a baseball, it loses considerable speed. The case of the neutron is similar. If a neutron rebounds from a heavy nucleus, it loses hardly any speed; but if it rebounds from a lighter carbon nucleus, it loses considerable speed. The graphite was said to "moderate" the neutrons.* The whole apparatus was called a *reactor*.

Now an uncontrolled reactor would not be a reactor, but a bomb. A runaway chain reaction is prevented by control rods made of cadmium or boron metal which easily absorb neutrons. The control rods are inserted into the reactor and absorb a selected fraction of the neutrons such as to maintain a steady rate of energy release. When fully inserted into the reactor, they halt the chain reaction. If fully removed, the reaction could build

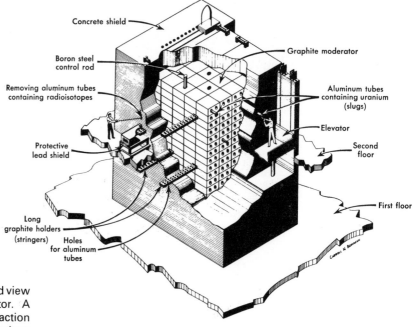

Concrete shield

Graphite moderator

Boron steel control rod

Removing aluminum tubes containing radioisotopes

Aluminum tubes containing uranium (slugs)

Elevator

Protective lead shield

Second floor

First floor

Long graphite holders (stringers)

Holes for aluminum tubes

Fig. 35.4   A detailed view of an atomic reactor. A controlled chain reaction occurs in the uranium slugs embedded in the graphite. (Courtesy of U. S. Atomic Energy Commission.)

Heavy water, which is composed of the heavy hydrogen isotope, deuterium, is also a good moderator.

up to an explosive level or at least to a level capable of melting the reactor.

The principal use of Fermi's atomic pile was the production of the synthetic element plutonium. Plutonium-239, like U-235, will fission. The atomic bomb exploded over Nagasaki was a plutonium bomb. This element does not occur in nature, but is manufactured synthetically from U-238. When U-238 captures a neutron, it emits a beta particle and becomes the first synthetic element, neptunium. Neptunium, in turn, emits a beta particle and becomes plutonium, Figure 35.5. The half-life of neptunium is only 2.3 days, while the half-life of plutonium is about 24,000 years. Since plutonium is an element distinct from uranium, it can be separated from uranium in the pile by ordinary chemical methods. Consequently, the pile provides a process for making pure fissionable material far more easily than by separating the U-235 from natural uranium.

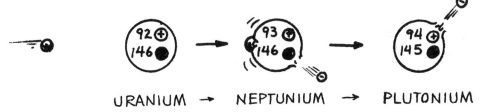

URANIUM → NEPTUNIUM → PLUTONIUM

Fig. 35.5 When uranium-238 absorbs a neutron, it emits a beta particle, resulting in a neutron becoming a proton. The atom is no longer uranium, but neptunium. The neptunium atom in turn emits a beta particle and becomes plutonium.

Although the process is simple in theory, it is very difficult in practice. Not only is plutonium produced in a reactor, but large quantities of radioactive fission products are formed. The radioactivity becomes so intense that the materials in the pile begin to fall apart physically. As a result, the pile has to be shut down after only a few grams of plutonium have been produced. The separation of plutonium from the uranium must be done by remote control to protect the personnel against deadly radiation.

A *breeder reactor* breeds more fuel than it consumes. If U-238 or Th-232 is mixed with plutonium, the fissioning of plutonium liberates neutrons that convert the relatively abundant uranium and thorium into the fissionable isotopes plutonium-239 and uranium-233. For about every two fissionable isotopes put into the reactor, three new fissionable isotopes are produced. This is like filling your gas tank with water, adding some gasoline, then driving your car and having more gasoline after your trip than

Fig. 35.6   A nuclear power plant. (Courtesy of Southern California Edison Co.)

you started with! After the initial expense of building a reactor, this is a very economical method of producing vast amounts of energy. With a breeder reactor a power utility can, after a few years of operation, breed twice as much as its original fuel.

In 1970 fifteen nuclear reactors designed for the production of electric power were in operation in the United States, with some eighty more scheduled for production. There is presently a large-scale effort by the U.S. Atomic Energy Commission, the nuclear industry, and the electric utilities to develop the technology whereby it will be possible to have breeder reactors generating electric power on a commercial scale in the mid-1980s.

Despite their association with atomic bombs and radioactive fallout, nuclear power reactors have been far less hazardous to local populations than conventional fossil-fueled power plants. The drawbacks to nuclear power plants are excessive heat (thermal pollution), low-level release of radioactivity into the air and ground waters, and mainly, the risk of an accidental release of large amounts of radioactivity.

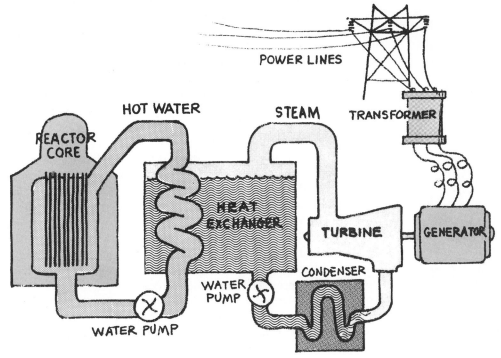

Fig. 35.7   Diagram of a nuclear power plant.

The benefits of nuclear power are low-cost electricity and, increasingly more important, the conservation of our finite reserves of coal, oil, and gas (which in the long term will be far more precious as sources of organic molecules than as sources of heat), and the elimination of the air pollution caused by the burning of these fuels. Nuclear power can produce the large amounts of energy required to run the many kinds of purification plants that will be needed to clean up the air and water and to recycle wastes. Autos may soon be powered with batteries rechargeable at "electric stations."

The benefits of nuclear reactors seem to greatly outweigh the drawbacks.

Radioactive Waste Products

A certain amount of radioactivity is always present in our environment from natural radioactive materials and cosmic rays. This amount was present as humans evolved—you might say our design takes it into account. Our design, however, doesn't allow for radioactivity much beyond these natural levels, and such radioactivity has in recent times increased. Radioactivity produced by atomic reactors has been negligible, far below the natural background radioactivity—the culprit has been the detonation of nuclear bombs. Scattered into the atmosphere by the explosions of nuclear bombs, waste products circulate over the whole earth. Settling to the earth's surface, usually in rain or snow, they become part of the air we breathe, the water we drink, and the food we eat. They are incorporated into our very bodies.

Most of these radioactive products are short-lived and decay into products that are harmless or relatively harmless. A few products, however, are unusually detrimental, notably cesium-137 and strontium-90. Strontium-90 is chemically similar to calcium and concentrates in milk and similar products containing calcium. When taken internally, it concentrates in the bones. Since it has a half-life of nearly 25 years, it continues to emit radioactivity for the life span of the individual. The radioactive rays destroy the material of the bone marrow and the red cells produced in the bone marrow.

A greater hazard is the long-range danger from the effect of the rays on the inheritance genes. Radioactivity, from within the body and from outside, causes mutations and results in stillbirths or malformed, monstrous children. To protect yourself from these dangerous radiations, begin by constructing your home with three-foot-thick slabs of lead. Then for food . . . or air to breathe . . .

Mass-Energy Equivalence

From Einstein's mass-energy equivalence, $E = mc^2$, we can think of mass as congealed energy. The more energy a particle has, the greater is the mass of the particle. The mass of a nucleon is greater when it is outside a nucleus than when it is inside a nucleus. We say it has more mass-energy outside a nucleus than inside. We can understand this by considering the work that would be required to separate the nucleons from a nucleus. Recall that work, which is energy, is equal to the product of force and distance. Then think of the magnitude of force required to pull nucleons apart through a sufficient distance to overcome the attractive nuclear force. Tremendous work would be required. The work we would have to put into such an endeavor would be manifest in the energy of the protons and neutrons. They would have more energy outside the nucleus. This extra energy would be equal to the energy or work required to separate them. This energy, in turn, would be manifest in mass. Hence the mass of nucleons outside a nucleus is greater than the mass of the same nucleons when locked inside a nucleus.

The experimental verification of this conclusion is one of the triumphs of modern physics. The masses of nucleons and the isotopes of the various elements can be measured with an accuracy of one part per million or better. One means of doing this is with the *mass spectrograph*, Figure 35.8.

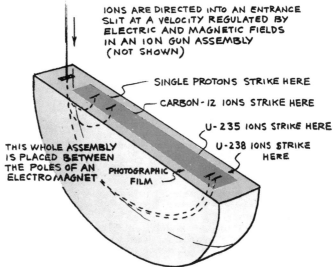

IONS ARE DIRECTED INTO AN ENTRANCE SLIT AT A VELOCITY REGULATED BY ELECTRIC AND MAGNETIC FIELDS IN AN ION GUN ASSEMBLY (NOT SHOWN)

SINGLE PROTONS STRIKE HERE

CARBON-12 IONS STRIKE HERE

U-235 IONS STRIKE HERE

U-238 IONS STRIKE HERE

THIS WHOLE ASSEMBLY IS PLACED BETWEEN THE POLES OF AN ELECTROMAGNET

PHOTOGRAPHIC FILM

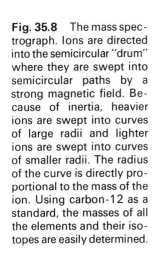

Fig. 35.8 The mass spectrograph. Ions are directed into the semicircular "drum" where they are swept into semicircular paths by a strong magnetic field. Because of inertia, heavier ions are swept into curves of large radii and lighter ions are swept into curves of smaller radii. The radius of the curve is directly proportional to the mass of the ion. Using carbon-12 as a standard, the masses of all the elements and their isotopes are easily determined.

Charged ions directed into a magnetic field are deflected into circular arcs. The greater the inertia of the ion, the more it resists deflection, and the greater is the radius of its curved path. Heavier ions are swept into larger arcs, while lighter ions are swept into shorter arcs by the magnetic force. The ions strike exit slits where they may be collected, or photographic film where they may be simply detected.

An isotope is chosen as a standard and its position on the film of the mass spectrograph is used as a reference point. The standard is the common isotope of carbon, C^{12}. The mass of carbon-12 nucleus is assigned the value of 12 atomic-mass units. The atomic-mass unit (amu) is defined to be precisely one-twelfth the mass of the common carbon-12 atom. With this reference, the amu's of the other atomic nuclei are measured. The masses of the proton and neutron are greater alone than when in a nucleus. They are 1.00728 and 1.00866 amu respectively.

A plot of the nuclear masses for the elements from hydrogen through uranium is shown in Figure 35.9. The curve slopes upward with increasing atomic number as expected—elements are more massive with increasing atomic number. A more inter-

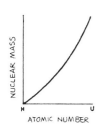

NUCLEAR MASS

ATOMIC NUMBER

H   U

Fig. 35.9 The plot shows how nuclear mass increases with increasing atomic number.

esting curve results if we plot the nuclear mass *per nucleon* from hydrogen through uranium, Figure 35.10. To obtain the nuclear mass per nucleon, we simply divide the nuclear mass by the number of nucleons in the particular nucleus. We find that the masses of protons and neutrons are different when combined in different nuclei. The mass of a proton is greatest as the nucleus of the hydrogen atom, and becomes successively less and less massive as it occurs in atoms of increasing atomic number. The proton is least massive when in the iron atom. Beyond iron, the process reverses itself. Protons (and neutrons) become successively more and more massive with increasing atomic number, all the way to uranium.

Fig. 35.10 The plot shows that the mass of a particular nucleon depends on the atomic number of the nucleus it is a part of. Individual nucleons are most massive in the lightest nuclei, least massive in the iron nucleus, and intermediate in the heaviest nuclei. When light nuclei fuse, the product nucleus is less massive than the sum of its parts; when the heaviest nuclei fission, the parts have less mass than the original nucleus. The mass defect, in both cases, is converted to energy.

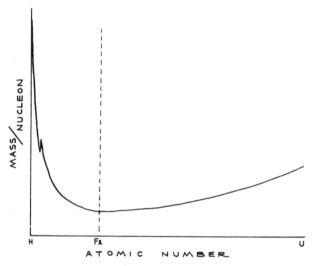

From the plot we can see why energy is released when a uranium nucleus is split into nuclei of lower atomic number. The masses of protons and neutrons in the fission fragments are *less than* the masses of the same protons and neutrons when combined in the uranium nucleus. The nucleons decrease in mass. This mass difference is manifest in the form of energy, the 200,000,000 electron volts yielded by each uranium nucleus undergoing fission.

We can think of the mass-per-nucleon curve as an energy hill, which starts at hydrogen, the highest point, and slopes steeply to the lowest point, iron, then up the more gradual slope to uranium. Iron is at the bottom of the energy hill and is the most stable nucleus. It is also the strongest nucleus—more energy is required to pull each proton or neutron from the iron nucleus than any other.

How about the left side of the hill? We can also gain energy by going from hydrogen toward iron. But to go in this direction is to *combine* or *fuse* nuclei. And this is fusion. Energy is released in fusing the light elements and fissioning the heavy elements. In both cases there is a decrease in the mass per nucleon, giving rise to a huge energy release. From the curve we see that any atom to the left or right of iron is a source of energy. The higher we are on the hill, to either the left or right, and the farther the distance we "roll down the hill," the greater is the amount of energy. No energy can be released by the iron nucleus. If we split it, the total mass of the fragments is greater than the mass of the iron before splitting. If we fuse two or more iron nuclei, the mass of the resulting nucleus is greater than the masses before fusing. In this special case, energy would have to be put into either the fissioning or fusing of iron—no energy would be liberated.

Fig. 35.11 Fictitious example: The "hydrogen magnets" weigh more when apart than when together. (Adapted from Albert V. Baez, *The New College Physics: A Spiral Approach*, San Francisco, Freeman, 1967.)

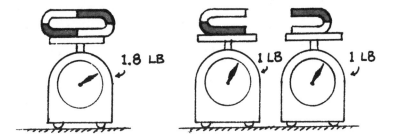

We can see by the curve that elements above iron cannot give off energy if fused. The mass of the fused nuclei would be greater than the sum of the masses before fusion. This would *require* energy, rather than *liberate* it. Likewise, elements below iron would yield no energy if fissioned. The sum of the masses of the fission fragments would be greater than that of the original nucleus, again requiring energy rather than liberating it. Energy is given off only when there is a decrease in mass.

In both fission and fusion reactions, the amount of mass that is converted to energy is less than 1 percent. This is true whether the process takes place in bombs or in the stars.

Nuclear Fusion   In the process of fusing hydrogen isotopes to form helium nuclei, the "shrinking" mass of the nucleons involved produces about 26,700,000 eV of energy. Although this is less energy per reaction of individual atoms than the fissioning of individual uranium atoms, pound for pound it is several times more energy producing than the fission process. This is, of course, because there are more hydrogen atoms in a pound of hydrogen than there are heavier uranium atoms in a pound of uranium.

For a fusion reaction to take place, the nuclei must collide at very high speeds in order to overcome their mutual electrical repulsion. The required speeds correspond to the extremely high temperatures found in the sun and stars. We call fusion reactions in the sun and other stars *thermonuclear* reactions—that is, the welding together of atomic nuclei by high temperature. In the high temperatures of the sun, approximately 657 million tons of hydrogen are converted into 653 million tons of helium each second. The missing 4 million tons are discharged as energy. Such reactions are, quite literally, nuclear burning. Thermonuclear reactions are very much analogous to ordinary chemical combustion. In both chemical and nuclear burning, high temperature starts the reaction, and the release of energy by the reaction maintains a high enough temperature to spread the fire. The net result of the chemical reaction is a combination of atoms into more tightly bound molecules. In nuclear burning the high temperature starts a reaction or series of reactions with the net result of producing more tightly bound nuclei. The difference between chemical and nuclear burning is essentially one of scale.

Prior to the atomic bomb, the temperatures required to initiate nuclear fusion on earth were unattainable. When it was found that the temperature inside an exploding atom bomb is four to five times the temperature at the center of the sun, the thermonuclear bomb was but a step away. This first hydrogen bomb was detonated in 1954. Whereas the critical mass of fissionable material limits the size of atomic bombs, no such limit is imposed on a thermonuclear or hydrogen bomb. Just as there is no limit to the size of an oil-storage depot, there is no theoretical limit to the size of a thermonuclear bomb. Like the oil-storage depot, any amount of nuclear fuel can be stored with safety until it is ignited. Although a match is sufficient to set an oil depot ablaze, nothing less than a fission bomb can ignite a thermonuclear bomb. We can see that it is impossible to have a "baby" hydrogen bomb. It cannot be less energetic than its fuse, which is an atomic bomb.

The destructive potential of thermonuclear weapons is so huge that they are rated in megatons (million tons of TNT). A 100-megaton bomb, for example, has the destructive power of

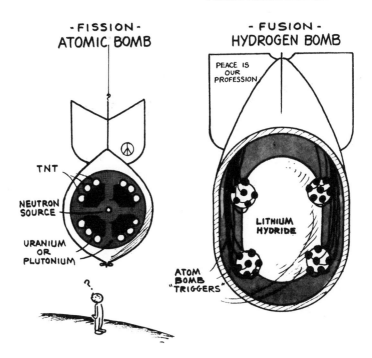

-FISSION-
ATOMIC BOMB

- FUSION -
HYDROGEN BOMB

PEACE IS
OUR
PROFESSION

TNT

NEUTRON
SOURCE

URANIUM
OR
PLUTONIUM

LITHIUM
HYDRIDE

ATOM
BOMB
"TRIGGERS"

Fig. 35.12

100,000,000 tons of concentrated TNT! The hydrogen bomb is another example of a new discovery being applied first to destructive rather than constructive purposes. The constructive side of the picture is the controlled release of vast amounts of energy.

To carry out fusion reactions under controlled conditions, temperatures of millions of degrees are required. The production and sustaining of such high temperatures is the object of much current research. High temperatures are obtained in electric arcs, where injected gases are ionized and become plasmas. Further heating is accomplished by compressing the plasma.

To contain the plasma, the problem arises as to what kind of material can be used to hold it. The container must be able to withstand the tremendous temperatures and pressures that develop. No such material is available, for all known materials melt and vaporize below 4000°C. The situation is not hopeless, however. A magnetic field is nonmaterial and can exist at any temperature and can exert powerful forces on charged particles in motion. "Magnetic bottles" of sufficient strength have been designed to contain plasmas in a kind of magnetic straitjacket.

The magnetic fields can be regulated to constrict the plasma (called the *pinch effect*) which produces fusion temperatures. Fusion has been achieved but instabilities in the plasma current have thus far prevented a sustained reaction. One of the most difficult problems has been to devise a field system that will hold the plasma in a stable position long enough for all the atoms to fuse.

Many approaches to fusion reactors are presently being pursued. One of the most promising is the Tokamak reactor, first developed at the Kurchatov Institute in Moscow. Figure 35.13 shows a Tokamak type device at Princeton University. Another approach to fusion, which bypasses heating by magnetic pinching, utilizes high-power laser beams. When present engineering difficulties can be surmounted and a successful fusion reactor is built, the problem of energy production on the earth will be solved—and ideally, for, unlike fission, there is no radioactive waste problem in the fusion process. Fusion produces clean nonradioactive helium (good for children's balloons). Fusion reactors are also inherently incapable of a "runaway" accident, for there is no "critical mass" required for fusion. Furthermore, the problem of thermal pollution, characterized by reactors that

Fig. 35.13 A fusion research device in Tokamak geometry located at the Princeton University Plasma Physics Laboratory, sponsored by the U. S. Atomic Energy Commission.

Fig. 35.14 Closed materials economy could be achieved with the aid of the fusion torch. In contrast to present systems, which are based on inherently wasteful linear materials economies (*top*), such a stationary-state system would be able to recycle the limited supply of material resources (*bottom*), thus alleviating most of the environmental pollution associated with present methods of energy utilization. (Redrawn from *Scientific American*, February, 1971).

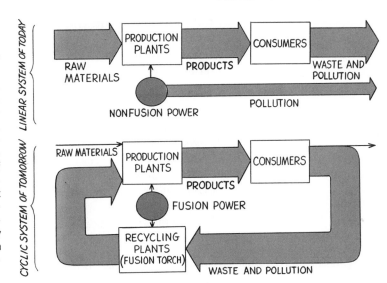

heat water to produce steam to drive conventional steam-generator plants, can be avoided by fusion reactors utilizing charged-particle fuel cycles that employ a direct energy conversion.

In addition to supplying abundant electrical energy, high-temperature plasmas can be used as a *fusion torch* to vaporize urban and industrial wastes. All waste materials, whether liquid or solid, would be reduced to their constituent atoms and separated by a mass-spectrograph-type device into various bins ranging from hydrogen to uranium. In this way, a single fusion plant could in principle not only dispose of thousands of tons of solid wastes per day, but also provide a continuous supply of fresh raw material—thereby closing the cycle from use to reuse, Figure 35.14. Another application is the use of the fusion torch to heat bulk fluids radiantly, thereby providing entirely new approaches to such goals as the conversion of sea water into fresh drinking water.

The fuel for nuclear fusion is hydrogen, the most plentiful element in the universe. The simplest reaction is the fusion of the hydrogen isotopes deuterium ($_1H^2$) and tritium ($_1H^3$), both of which are found in ordinary water. Eight gallons of sea water, for example, contain 1 gram of deuterium, which when fused releases as much energy as 2500 gallons of gasoline or 80 tons of TNT. Natural tritium is much scarcer, but given enough to get started, a controlled thermonuclear reactor will breed it from deuterium in ample quantities. Because of the abundance of fusion fuel, the amount of energy that can be released in a controlled manner is virtually unlimited. There is little doubt that this energy, which will have a profound impact on almost every aspect of human society, will be available in the not too distant future.

Summary of Terms

Nuclear fission. The splitting of the nucleus of a heavy atom, such as uranium-235, into two main parts, accompanied by the release of much energy.

Chain reaction. A self-sustaining reaction which, once started, steadily provides the energy and matter necessary to continue the reaction.

Critical mass. The minimum quantity of radioactive material in a reactor or nuclear bomb that will sustain a chain reaction.

Nuclear fusion. The combination of the nuclei of light atoms to form heavier nuclei, with the release of much energy.

Suggested Reading

Gough, William C., and Bernard J. Eastlund, "The Prospects of Fusion Power," *Scientific American*, February, 1971.

Lubin, Moshe J., and Arthur P. Fraas, "Fusion by Laser," *Scientific American*, June 1971.

Seaborg, Glenn T., and Justin L. Bloom, "Fast Breeder Reactors," *Scientific American*, November, 1970.

Questions

1. Why does a neutron make a better nuclear bullet than a proton or electron?

2. Why don't natural deposits of uranium ore undergo chain reactions?

3. Is the mass of an atomic nucleus greater or less than the masses of the particles composing it?

4. Fission and fusion are opposite processes, yet each releases energy. Isn't this contradictory? Explain.

5. Which process would release energy from gold, fission or fusion? From carbon? From iron?

6. List at least two major advantages of power production by fusion rather than by fission.

7. Discuss and make a comparison of pollution by conventional fossil-fuel power plants and nuclear power plants.

8. What effect on the mining industry can you foresee in the disposal of urban waste by a fusion torch coupled with a mass spectrograph?

9. The world was never the same after the discovery of electromagnetic induction and its applications to electric motors and generators. Speculate and list some of the worldwide changes that are likely to follow the advent of successful fusion reactors.

Epilogue

We approach the twenty-first century with mixed feelings about the role of science in shaping our future. This is because we see many of our present problems stemming from short-sighted use of the findings of science. Progress in technology has not always been measured in terms of its benefit to humanity —it has too often been used to serve some men at the expense of most men; to serve a few in one generation at the expense of many in the next generation. The misuses of science and technology in the past, and the potential today for the total destruction of civilization, have caused many to feel that science should be constrained—some even feel that research and development should be brought completely to a halt.

The answer, however, does not lie in constraining or abandoning science. Science is an indispensable resource. In fact, only wise applications of science can repair the damage already done by our unwise applications. Pollution, for example, would not be lessened by curtailing scientific research, but by finding better methods of monitoring the uses of air, water, and land. Man must also eat. Food production is not optimized by constraining or abandoning science, but by utilizing it. Without scientific methods applied to agriculture, famine would be inevitable. Solutions to problems of our environment—food production, pollution, and population control—all require a fundamental knowledge of science. With this knowledge we can better evaluate the validity of one proposal over another and bring about the social, political, and economic interactions necessary for constructive change.

Both the changes in the physical sciences that characterized the early twentieth century and those today in the social sciences, will more than likely be dwarfed by the changes that will follow the impending breakthroughs in biological science. The present adage, "You can't change human nature" may soon be akin to the older adage, "Man will never fly." Man may soon have a direct hand in guiding and even controlling his own evolution. These advents may produce a nightmare—or mark the beginning of a more beautiful and humane world. What kind of world is in store tomorrow?

The answer to this question will depend on the goals and values that man shapes for himself, and will not be provided by scientists and technologists—it is not the province of science to define goals and values. The answer will be provided by people like the readers of this book, nonscience college students—prospective managers, teachers, economists, anthropologists, poets, and artists. These are the people who will have the largest share in forming policy, creating new values and institutions, and ultimately, new man. In doing so the nonscientist will need a knowledge of science, for the methods of science are the best means to achieve defined goals, and scientific knowledge of the possible and probable is indispensable in defining these goals.

It is difficult to see the beginnings of a better world while we are daily deluged with news about the social disintegration going on about us. These beginnings are nevertheless evident in the concerns of today's students who have the responsibility of choosing the direction of tomorrow's world. My experience with students indicates we can expect humanitarian goals and wise applications of science. I feel the grounds for gloom is going out with the "fraternities, football, and fun" mentality. Today holds much promise for a more loving and beautiful world.

Paul Hewitt

Appendix I
Systems of
Measurement

Two major systems of measurement prevail in the world today: the *English* system and the *metric* system. Each system has its own standards of length, mass, and time. The units of length, mass, and time are sometimes called the *fundamental units* because, once they are selected, all other mechanical quantities can be measured in terms of them.

English System   Developed in England, this system of measurement is used in the United States for many commercial and engineering purposes. It uses the foot as the unit of length, the pound as the unit of weight or force, and the second as the unit of time. It is called the foot-pound-second, or fps, system.

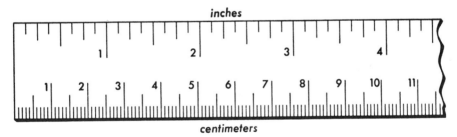

Fig. 1

Metric System   French scientists originated this system of measurement after the French revolution, in 1791. Its simplicity and orderliness make it useful for scientific work, and it is used the world over by scientists. The metric system is subdivided into two systems of units. In one of these the unit of length is the centimeter, the unit of mass is the gram, and the unit of time is the second. This is called the centimeter-gram-second system, usually abbreviated cgs. In the other system of units, the meter is the unit of length, the kilogram is the unit of mass, and the second is again the unit of time. This system is called the meter-kilogram-second, or the mks, system. The cgs and mks units are related to each other as follows: 100 centimeters equal one meter; 1000 grams equal one kilogram. The table in Figure 2 shows how several units of length relate to each other.

	Km	m	cm	in.	ft	mi
1 kilometer =	1	1000	100,000	39,370	3280.83	0.62140
1 meter =	0.00100	1	100	39.370	3.28083	6.21×10^{-4}
1 centimeter =	1.0×10^{-5}	0.0100	1	0.39370	0.032808	6.21×10^{-6}
1 inch =	2.54×10^{-5}	0.02540	2.5400	1	0.08333	1.58×10^{-5}
1 foot =	3.05×10^{-4}	0.30480	30.480	12	1	1.89×10^{-4}
1 mile =	1.60934	1609.34	160,934	63,360	5280	1

Fig. 2   Table of conversions between different units of length.

One major advantage of the metric system is that it uses the decimal system. Thus any unit is related to larger or smaller units in the metric system by powers of ten. The prefixes shown in Figure 3 are commonly used to show the relationships between units.

Micro- means one-millionth. A microsecond is one millionth of a second.
Milli- means one-thousandth. A milligram is one thousandth of a gram.
Centi- means one-hundredth. A centimeter is one hundredth of a meter.
Kilo- means one thousand. A kilogram is one thousand grams.
Mega- means one million. A megacycle is one million cycles.

Fig. 3   Some prefixes.

The Meter   The standard of length for the metric system originally was defined in terms of the distance from the north pole to the equator. This distance is close to (or was thought to be at the time) 10,000 kilometers. One ten-millionth of this, the meter, was carefully determined and marked off by means of scratches on a bar of

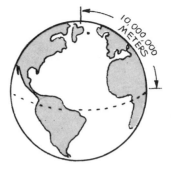

Fig. 4

platinum-iridium alloy. This bar is kept at the International Bureau of Weights and Measures in France. The standard meter in France since has been calibrated in terms of the wavelength of light. The meter is now defined to be 1,650,763.73 times the wavelength of orange light emitted by the atoms of the gas krypton-86.

The Kilogram

The standard unit of mass, the kilogram, is a block of platinum, also preserved at the International Bureau of Weights and Measures near Paris. The kilogram equals 1000 grams. A gram is the mass of one cubic centimeter (cc) of water at a temperature of 4° Celsius. (The standard pound is defined in terms of the standard kilogram; the mass of one pound is equal to 0.4536 kilogram).

Fig. 5   Standard kilogram.

The Second   The official unit of time for both the English and metric systems of measurement is the second. Until 1956 it was defined in terms of the mean solar day, which was divided into 24 hours. Each hour was divided into 60 minutes and each minute into 60 seconds. Thus there were 86,400 seconds per day and the second was defined as 1/86,400 of the mean solar day. This proved unsatisfactory because the rate of rotation of the earth is gradually becoming slower. In 1956 the mean solar day of the year 1900 was chosen as the standard from which to base the second. Further defined in 1964, the second is now officially defined as the time taken by a cesium-133 atom to make 9,192,631,770 vibrations.

Area   The unit of area is a square having a standard unit of length as a side. In the English system it is a square whose sides are each one foot in length. It is called one square foot and written 1 ft^2. In the metric system it is a square whose sides are either one meter or one centimeter in length. In the mks system the unit of area is 1 m^2, and in the cgs system it is 1 cm^2. The number of square feet, square meters, or square centimeters that fit into a given surface is a measure of the area of that surface.

The area of a rectangle equals the base times the height, when both are expressed in the same units. The area of a circle is equal to πr^2, where $\pi = 3.14$ and r is the radius of the circle. Formulas for the surfaces of other objects can be found in geometry textbooks.

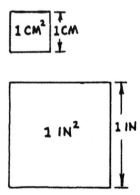

Fig. 6   Unit squares.

Volume   The volume of a body refers to the space it occupies. The unit of volume is the space occupied by a cube having the standard unit of length for its edge. In the English system it is the space

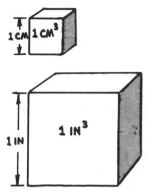

Fig. 7   Unit volumes.

occupied by a cube one foot on an edge and is called one cubic foot, written 1 ft³. In the metric system it is the space occupied by a cube whose sides are one meter (mks) or one centimeter (cgs). It is written 1 m³ or 1 cm³ (or cc). The number of cubic feet, cubic meters, or cubic centimeters that fit into a given space is a measure of the volume of that space.

In the English system, volumes are measured in quarts, gallons, and cubic inches, as well as cubic feet. There are 1728 (12 × 12 × 12) cubic inches in 1 ft³. A U.S. gallon is a volume of 231 in³. Four quarts equal one gallon.

In the metric system, volumes are often measured in liters. A liter is a volume slightly larger than 1000 cm³. For most purposes a liter may be considered equal to 1000 cm³.

Scientific Notation

It is convenient to use a mathematical abbreviation for large and small numbers. The number 50,000,000 can be obtained by multiplying 5 by 10, and again by 10, and again by 10, and so on until 10 has been used as a multiplier seven times. The short way of showing this is to write the number as 5×10^7. The number 0.0005 can be obtained from 5 by using 10 as a divisor four times. The short way of showing this is to write 5×10^{-4} for 0.0005. Thus 3×10^5 means $3 \times 10 \times 10 \times 10 \times 10 \times 10$, or 300,000; and 6×10^{-3} means $6/(10 \times 10 \times 10)$, or 0.006. Numbers expressed in this shorthand manner are said to be in scientific notation.

$$1,000,000 = 10 \times 10 \times 10 \times 10 \times 10 \times 10 = 10^6$$
$$100,000 = 10 \times 10 \times 10 \times 10 \times 10 = 10^5$$
$$10,000 = 10 \times 10 \times 10 \times 10 = 10^4$$
$$1000 = 10 \times 10 \times 10 = 10^3$$
$$100 = 10 \times 10 = 10^2$$
$$10 = 10 = 10^1$$
$$1 = 1 = 10^0$$
$$0.1 = 1/10 = 10^{-1}$$
$$0.01 = 1/100 = 1/10^2 = 10^{-2}$$
$$0.001 = 1/1000 = 1/10^3 = 10^{-3}$$
$$0.0001 = 1/10,000 = 1/10^4 = 10^{-4}$$
$$0.00001 = 1/100,000 = 1/10^5 = 10^{-5}$$
$$0.000001 = 1/1,000,000 = 1/10^6 = 10^{-6}$$

Fig. 8   Powers of ten.

Appendix II
More About Motion

Rule for Computing Distance When Motion Is Uniform

Objects traveling at constant speed along a straight line (constant velocity) travel equal distances in equal intervals of time. We can say

$$\text{Distance traveled} = \text{velocity} \times \text{time}$$

or, in shorthand notation,

$$d = vt$$

If, for example, we are in a car traveling at a constant velocity of 60 miles per hour for a time of one hour, we will have traveled 60 miles. (It is customary to omit the multiplication sign, $\times$, when expressing relationships in mathematical form. When two symbols are written together, such as the vt in this case, it is understood that they are multiplied.)

Rule for Computing Velocity Gained When Acceleration Is Constant

In the case of a falling body where the acceleration is constant, the body gains a velocity each second of 32 feet per second. Hence the speed at the end of the first second of a body falling from rest is 32 feet per second. At the end of the second second, the speed will be the gain per second multiplied by two seconds or

Speed at end of 2nd second = $32 \times 2 = 64$ feet per second

Speed at end of 3rd second = $32 \times 3 = 96$ feet per second

Speed at end of 4th second = $32 \times 4 = 128$ feet per second

It should be clear from this that a general rule follows:

$$\text{Velocity acquired} = \text{acceleration} \times \text{time}$$

or, expressed in symbols,

$$v = at$$

Examples

1. How much velocity will a baseball released from rest acquire in $\frac{1}{2}$ second? *Solution*: Since the ball gains each second a velocity of 32 feet per second, in $\frac{1}{2}$ second the velocity acquired is equal to $32 \times \frac{1}{2} = 16$ feet per second.

2. If it takes 4 seconds for an object to fall to the water when released from Golden Gate Bridge, how fast is the object traveling upon impact? Neglect the effects of air resistance. *Solution*: The velocity acquired is equal to the acceleration (32 ft/sec²) multiplied by 4 seconds, or 32 × 4 = 128 feet per second.

Rule for Computing Distance Traveled When Acceleration Is Constant

How far will an object released from rest fall in a given time? To answer this question let us consider the case in which it falls freely for 3 seconds, starting at rest. Neglecting air resistance, the object will have a constant acceleration of 32 feet per second per second.

Velocity at the *beginning* = 0 feet per second

Velocity at the *end* of 3 seconds = (32 × 3) feet per second

Average velocity = $\frac{1}{2}$ the sum of these two speeds

$$= \frac{1}{2} \times (0 + 32 \times 3) \text{ feet per second}$$

$$= \frac{1}{2} \times 32 \times 3 = 48 \text{ feet per second}$$

Distance traveled = average velocity × time

$$= (\frac{1}{2} \times 32 \times 3) \times 3$$

$$= \frac{1}{2} \times 32 \times 3^2 = 144 \text{ feet}$$

If the meanings of the numbers in the preceding equation are used, the equation may be written

Distance traveled = $\frac{1}{2}$ × acceleration × square of time

This equation is true not only for a body falling for 3 seconds, but for any length of time. If we let d stand for the distance traveled, a for the acceleration, and t for the time, the rule may be written, in shorthand notation,

$$d = \tfrac{1}{2}at^2$$

This relationship was first deduced by Galileo. He reasoned that if a body falls for say twice the time, it will fall with *twice the average speed*. Since it falls for *twice* as long at *twice* the average speed, it will fall *four* times as far. Similarly, if a body falls for *three* times as long, it will have an average speed *three* times as great and will fall *nine* times as far. Galileo reasoned that the total distance fallen should be proportional to the *square* of the time.

In the case of falling bodies it is customary to use the letter g to represent the acceleration instead of the letter a (g is used for the symbol because the acceleration is due to *gravity*). While the value of g varies slightly in different parts of the world, it is approximately equal to 32 feet per second per second. If we use g for the acceleration of a freely falling body, the equations for falling bodies simply become

$$v = gt$$

$$d = \tfrac{1}{2}gt^2$$

Examples   1. An auto starting from rest has a constant acceleration of 4 feet per second per second. How far will it go in 5 seconds? *Solution*: Distance $= \tfrac{1}{2} \times 4 \times 5^2 = 50$ feet.

2. How far will an object released from rest fall in 1 second? In this case the acceleration is $g = 32$ feet per second per second. *Solution*: Distance $= \tfrac{1}{2} \times 32 \times 1^2 = 16$ feet.

3. If it takes 4 seconds for an object to fall to the water when released from Golden Gate Bridge, how high is the bridge? *Solution*: Distance $= \tfrac{1}{2} \times 32 \times 4^2 = 256$ feet. Notice that the units of measurement when multiplied give the proper units of feet for distance:

$$d = \tfrac{1}{2} \times 32 \,\frac{\text{feet}}{\text{sec}^2} \times 16 \,\text{sec}^2 = 256 \text{ feet}$$

Appendix III
More About Torque

In Chapter 5 we defined torque as the product of force and lever-arm distance. We say lever-arm distance to distinguish this from the distance in which the force acts. Recall from Chapter 6 that the product of force and the distance through which the force acts is called work, or the expenditure of energy. The lever-arm distance is always perpendicular to the applied force, which then produces rotation.

In Chapter 5 we discussed the case of two boys sitting on a seesaw, Figure 1. The seesaw is in equilibrium because the torques about the fulcrum provided by the weight of the boys balance each other. It is easy to see that the lever-arm distance for the larger boy is 3 feet, and the lever-arm distance for the smaller boy is 6 feet.

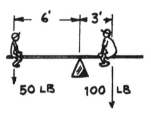

Fig. 1

Suppose that the seesaw is elevated and that the 50-pound boy is suspended from an 8-foot rope hanging from his end of the seesaw. His distance from the fulcrum is now 10 feet. Will the seesaw still be balanced? The answer is yes. An experiment would show that moving the 50-pound boy to this position would have no effect on the balance. Therefore it is *not* the distance from the fulcrum to the point at which the force is applied that is important; rather, it is the *perpendicular* distance from the fulcrum to the extended line along which the force acts. This is the lever-arm distance. *The lever arm for any point of rotation is the perpendicular distance from the point to the line along which the force acts.* This will always be the shortest distance between the point of rotation and the line along which the force acts.

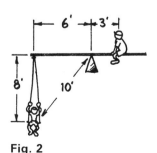

Fig. 2

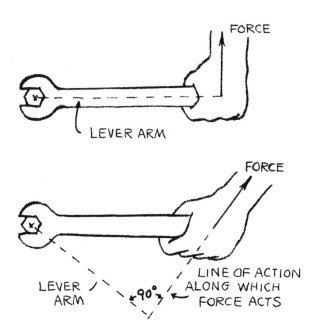

Fig. 3

This is why the stubborn bolt shown in Figure 3 is more likely to turn when the applied force is perpendicular to the handle as shown in the top figure, rather than at an oblique angle as shown in the bottom figure. In the top figure the lever arm is equal to the length of the wrench handle. In the bottom figure the lever arm is shown by the dotted line, and is less than the length of the wrench handle.

Consider the operation of a bicycle. If we push down on the pedal with our full weight, the rotational effect produced depends on the location of the pedal. If the pedal is in the position shown in Figure 4, maximum rotational effect is produced because the

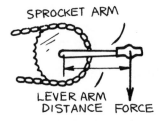

Fig. 4

torque at this position is maximum, being equal to the weight exerted on the pedal multiplied by the full length of the sprocket arm.

When the pedal is in the position shown in Figure 5, the torque is zero and no rotational effect is produced. This is because the lever-arm distance is zero. There is no distance between the line of action of the applied force and the axis about which the sprocket rotates.

Fig. 5   FORCE

When the pedal is in some intermediary position, Figure 6, the torque is less than maximum and greater than zero. This is because the lever-arm distance is less than the full length of the sprocket arm.

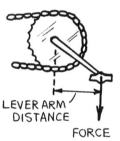

LEVER ARM
DISTANCE

Fig. 6   FORCE

The idea of torque provides a way for determining the center of mass of objects. For example, consider the two spheres shown in Figure 7, which for simplicity are joined by a rigid rod

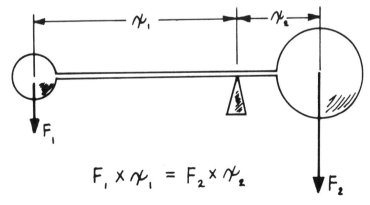

$$F_1 \times \varkappa_1 = F_2 \times \varkappa_2$$

Fig. 7

of negligible mass. The center of mass is located at a point be-tween the spheres such that the product of weight times lever arm on one side of the fulcrum equals the product of weight times lever arm on the other side.

The center of mass of our earth-moon system is found in this way. We can consider the earth and moon to be parts of a dumb-bell connected by a massless rod. The distance between the centers of earth and moon is about 240,000 miles. The earth is 80 times more massive than the moon, so for the torques to balance each other, the lever arm from the moon to the "fulcrum" (center of mass of the earth-moon system) must be 80 times longer than the lever-arm distance from the fulcrum to the earth.

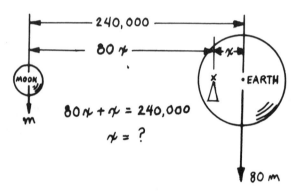

Fig. 8

Simple algebra shows that the center of mass of the earth-moon system is about 3000 miles from the center of the earth. Since the radius of the earth is about 4000 miles, this point is about 1000 miles beneath the earth's surface! (It is the center of mass of our earth-moon system, not any other point, that follows a smooth orbital path about the sun.) Both earth and moon wobble about this point.

Appendix IV
The Universal Gravi-
tational Constant, G

We have expressed Newton's law of gravity as a proportion, namely

$$F \sim \frac{mm'}{d^2}$$

Proportionalities are difficult to deal with, so we can write it as an equality by including a *constant of proportionality*. For example, the circumference of a circle is proportional to the diameter:

$$C \sim D$$

If we divide the circumference of any circle by its diameter we find a constant proportion of 3.14 or

$$\frac{C}{D} = \pi$$

We can therefore be more specific than the proportionality $C \sim D$ by including the constant of proportionality and write it as an equation:

$$C = \pi D$$

The value of π tells us something about a circle. Similarly, the constant of proportionality in the equation that expresses the law of gravitation is G, and it tells us something about the strength of the gravitational force. The law of universal gravitation is written as:

$$F = G\frac{mm'}{d^2}$$

G was first measured by Cavendish in the eighteenth century. He used a torsion balance in which two spheres of mass m

are attached to the end of a light rod which is suspended by a long wire so that it can turn easily, Figure 1. When two massive lead balls are introduced, the attraction between the light and heavy balls causes a displacement in the balance. Knowing the force necessary to cause such a displacement, Cavendish was able to calculate the ratio G.

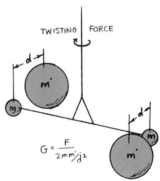

Fig. 1

A simpler method was developed by Jolly. A spherical vessel of mercury was attached to one arm of a sensitive balance, and the balance put in equilibrium, Figure 2. Then a 6-ton lead sphere was rolled beneath the mercury flask. The gravitational force between the two masses was equal to the weight that had to be placed on the opposite end of the balance to restore equilibrium. All the quantities m, m', F, and d were known, from which the value of G was calculated. In the metric system of units, $G = 6.67 \times 10^{-11}$ m^3/kg sec^2, and in the English system of units, $G = 3.44 \times 10^{-8}$ ft^4/lb sec^4.

Once the value of G is known, the mass of the earth can be calculated. The force which the earth exerts on a mass of 1 kilogram at its surface is equal to 9.8 newtons. The distance between the 1-kilogram mass and the center of mass of the earth is the earth's radius, 6.4×10^6 meters. Therefore, from $F = G\dfrac{mm'}{d^2}$ where we let m' be the mass of the earth,

$$9.8 \text{ newtons} = 6.67 \times 10^{-11} \frac{\text{meter}^3}{\text{kg sec}^2} \frac{1 \text{ kg} \times m'}{(6.4 \times 10^6 \text{ meter})^2}$$

$$(\text{where 1 newton} = 1 \text{ kg} \frac{\text{meter}}{\text{sec}^2})$$

from which the mass of the earth, $m' = 6 \times 10^{24}$ kilograms (equivalent to the mass of 6.6×10^{21} tons)!

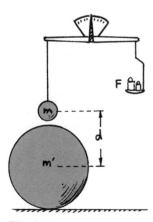

Fig. 2

Glossary

Aberration: A distortion in an image resulting from defects in the lens that produces the image.

Absolute humidity: A measure of the amount of water vapor in a sample of air.

Absolute temperature scale: A temperature scale that has its zero point at $-273.16°C$. Temperatures in the absolute scale are designated in degrees Kelvin, $°K$. *Absolute zero* is $0°K$; $0°C$ is $273.16°K$.

Absolute zero: The lowest possible temperature that a substance may have—the temperature at which the molecules of a substance have their minimum kinetic energy.

Absorption spectra: A continuous spectrum, like that of white light, interrupted by dark lines or bands that result from the absorption of certain frequencies of light by a substance through which the radiation passes.

Acceleration: The acceleration of a body is the rate at which its velocity changes with time; the change in velocity may be in magnitude or direction or both.

Acceleration of gravity (g):   The acceleration of a freely falling body. Its value near the earth's surface is about 32 ft/sec^2.

Alpha particle: The nuclei of a helium atom, which consist of two neutrons and two protons, ejected by certain radioactive elements.

Alpha ray: Streams of helium nuclei ejected by certain radioactive nuclei.

Alternating current (ac):   Electric current that rapidly reverses in direction. The electric charges vibrate about relatively fixed points, usually at the vibrational rate of 60 cycles per second.

Ampere: The unit of electric current equal to a flow of one coulomb of charge per second.

Amplitude: For a body undergoing simple harmonic motion, the amplitude is the maximum displacement on either side of its equilibrium position. For a wave the amplitude is the maximum value of the wave variable (displacement for a transverse or longitudinal wave in a solid, pressure for a wave in a liquid or gas, electric and magnetic field intensity for an electromagnetic wave, etc., depending on the nature of the wave).

Angstrom: A unit of length equal to 10^{-8} (0.00000001) centimeter. Atoms have a radius of one to two angstroms.

Angular acceleration: The rate of change of direction for a body following a circular path; expressed $a = v^2/r$, where v is the speed and r the radius of the path.

Archimedes' Principle: An immersed body is buoyed up by a force equal to the weight of the volume of fluid it displaces.

Archimedes' Principle for air: An object surrounded by air is buoyed up with a force equal to the weight of displaced air.

Atmospheric pressure: The pressure exerted against bodies immersed in the atmosphere, resulting from the weight and motion of molecules of atmospheric gases. At sea level atmospheric pressure is about 14.7 pounds per square inch.

Atom: The smallest particle of an element that has all of its chemical properties.

Atomic bonding: The linking together of atoms to form solids. The different kinds of bonding are *ionic, covalent, metallic* bonding and *Van der Waals forces.*

Atomic-mass number: The number associated with an atom which is the same as the number of nucleons in the nucleus.

Atomic-mass unit (amu):   The standard unit of atomic mass which is equal to one-twelfth the mass of an atom of carbon-12, arbitrarily given the value of exactly 12.

Atomic nucleus: The core of an atom, consisting of two basic building blocks—protons and neutrons. The protons have a positive electric charge, giving the nucleus a positive electric charge; the neutrons have no electrical charge.

Atomic number: The number associated with an atom which is the same as the number of protons in the nucleus, or the same as the number of extranuclear electrons.

Avogadro's Principle: Equal volumes of all gases at the same temperature and pressure contain the same number of molecules.

Barometer: Any device that measures atmospheric pressure.

Beats: A series of alternate reinforcements and cancellations produced by the interference of two sets of superimposed waves of different frequencies; heard as a throbbing effect in sound waves.

Beta particle: An electron (or positron) emitted during the radioactive decay of a nucleus.

Beta ray: Streams of fast-moving electrons ejected from radioactive nuclei.

Boiling: A rapid state of evaporation that takes place within the liquid as well as at its surface. As in evaporation, cooling of the liquid results.

Bow wave: The V-shaped wave made by an object moving across a liquid surface at a speed greater than the wave velocity.

Brownian motion: The haphazard movement of tiny particles suspended in a gas or liquid which results from bombardment by the fast-moving molecules of the gas or liquid.

Buoyant force: The net force that a fluid exerts on an immersed object.

Capillarity: The rise or fall of a liquid in a fine hollow tube or in narrow spaces.

Carbon dating: The process of determining the age of organic materials by measuring the radioactivity of carbon-14 isotopes remaining in the material.

Celsius temperature scale: The centigrade temperature scale having the freezing point of water assigned the value 0°C and the boiling point of water the value 100°C.

Center of gravity: The average position of weight, or the single point associated with a body where the force of gravity can be considered to act.

Center of mass: The average position of mass, or the single point associated with a body where all its mass can be considered to be concentrated.

Centrifugal force: The reaction to centripetal force, which is an outward force.

Centripetal force: A center-seeking force that causes an object to follow a circular path.

Chain reaction: A self-sustaining reaction which, once started, steadily provides the energy and matter necessary to continue the reaction.

Charge polarization: The spacial separation of positive and negative charges by the electrical alignment of molecules.

Charging by contact: The transfer of charge from one body to another by physical contact between the bodies.

Charging by induction: The redistribution of charge in an object which is caused by the electrical influence of a charged body close by, but not in contact.

Chemical reaction: A process in which rearrangement of atoms from one molecule to another occurs.

Complementary colors: Any two colors that, when added, produce white light.

Component: The parts into which a vector can be separated, and which act in a different direction than the vector.

Condensation: The change of state from vapor to liquid; the opposite of evaporation. Warming of the liquid results.

Conduction: The transfer and distribution of thermal energy from molecule to molecule within a body.

Conductor: Any material through which charge easily flows when subject to an impressed electrical force.

Conservation of energy: Energy cannot be created or destroyed; it may be transformed from one form into another, but the total amount of energy never changes. In machines the work output cannot exceed the work input. In an ideal machine, where no energy is transformed into heat,

$$\text{Work input} = \text{work output}$$

$$F \times d_{(input)} = F \times d_{(output)}$$

Convection: The transfer of thermal energy in a gas or liquid by means of currents in the heated fluid.

Converging lens: A lens that is thicker in the middle than at the edges and refracts parallel rays passing through it to a focus.

Correspondence principle: The rule that a new theory is valid only if it overlaps and agrees with the verified results of the old theory.

Coulomb's Law: The relationship between electric force, charge, and distance:

$$F \sim \frac{qq'}{d^2}$$

If the charges are alike in sign, the force is repulsive; if the charges are unlike, the force is attractive.

Critical mass: The minimum quantity of radioactive material in a reactor or nuclear bomb that will sustain a chain reaction.

De Broglie matter waves: All particles of matter have associated wave properties. The wavelength of a particle wave is related to its momentum and Planck's constant h by the relationship:

$$\text{Wavelength} = \frac{h}{\text{momentum}}$$

Density: The mass of a substance per unit volume:

$$\text{Density} = \frac{\text{mass}}{\text{volume}}$$

Diffraction: The bending of light around an obstacle or through a narrow slit in such a way that parallel fringes of light and dark or colored bands are produced.

Direct current (dc): An electric current flowing in one direction only.

Dispersion: The splitting up of a beam of light into its component frequencies by passage through an object such as a prism.

Diverging lens: A lens that is thinner in the middle than at the edges, causing parallel rays passing through it to diverge.

Doppler effect: The change in frequency or pitch of sound waves, heard when the source of sound and/or the listener are moving toward or away from each other.

Elasticity: The property of a material by which it experiences a change in shape when a deforming force acts upon it and by which it returns to its original shape when the deforming force is removed.

Electric current: The flow of electric charge which transports energy from one place to another. Measured in amperes, where one ampere is the flow of $6\frac{1}{4}$ billion-billion electrons (or protons) per second.

Electric field: The energetic region of space surrounding a charged body; about a charged point the field decreases with distance according to the inverse-square law, as does the gravitational field. Between oppositely charged parallel plates the electric field is uniform. A charged object placed in the region of an electric field experiences a force.

Electric potential: The electrical potential energy per unit of charge, measured in volts, and often called "voltage,"

$$\text{Voltage} = \frac{\text{electrical energy}}{\text{unit of charge}}$$

Electric power: The rate of energy transfer, or the rate of doing work; the ratio of energy per time which can be measured by the product of current and voltage:

$$\text{Power} = \text{current} \times \text{voltage}$$

Measured in watts (or kilowatts) where 1 ampere $\times$ 1 volt $=$ 1 watt.

Electric resistance: The property of a material that resists the flow of an electric current through it; measured in ohms.

Electromagnetic induction: The induction of voltage when a magnetic field changes with time. If the magnetic field within a closed loop changes in any way, a voltage is induced in the loop.

$$\text{Voltage induced} = -(\text{number of loops}) \times \frac{\text{magnetic field change}}{\text{time}}$$

which is called Faraday's Law. The induction of voltage is actually the result of a more fundamental phenomenon: the induction of an electric *field*. See Faraday's Law for this more general case.

Electromotive force (emf):   An energy source that maintains a potential difference across an electric circuit; the source of voltage, measured in volts.

Electron: The negatively charged part of the atom that orbits the nucleus.

Element: A substance composed of atoms all of which have the same atomic number and therefore the same chemical properties.

Emission spectra: A continuous or partial spectrum of colors resulting from the dispersion of light from a luminous source.

Equilibrium: The state of a body when not acted upon by a net force or net torque. A body in equilibrium may be at rest or moving at uniform velocity; that is, it is not accelerating.

Ether: A hypothetical medium supposedly required for the propagation of electromagnetic waves.

Evaporation: The change of state at the surface of a liquid as it passes to vapor. This results from the random motion of molecules that occasionally escape from the liquid surface. Cooling of the liquid results.

Excitation: The process of boosting one or more electrons in an atom or molecule from a lower to a higher energy level. An atom in an excited state will usually decay (de-excite) rapidly into a lower state by the emission of radiation. The frequency and energy of emitted radiation are related by:

$$E = hf$$

Fahrenheit temperature scale: The temperature scale having the freezing point of water assigned the value $32°F$ and the boiling point of water the value of $212°F$.

Faraday's Law: An electric field is induced in any region of space in which a magnetic field is changing with time. The magnitude of the induced electric field is proportional to the rate at which the magnetic field changes. The direction of the induced field is at right angles to the changing magnetic field.

Fluorescence: The property of absorbing radiation of one frequency and re-emitting radiation of a lower frequency. Part of the absorbed radiation goes into heat and the other part into excitation; hence the emitted radiation has a lower energy, and therefore lower frequency, than the absorbed radiation.

Focal length: The distance between the center of a converging lens and the point at which parallel rays of incident light converge; or the distance between the center of a diverging lens and the point from which parallel rays of light appear to diverge.

Force: Any influence that can cause a body to be accelerated, commonly measured in pounds (in *newtons* in the metric system).

Forced vibration: The setting up of vibrations in a body, at frequencies other than the body's natural vibrating frequency, by a vibrating force.

Fourier analysis: A mathematical method that will resolve any waveform into a series of simple sine waves.

Frame of reference: A vantage point (usually a set of coordinate axes) with respect to which the position and motion of a body may be described.

Freezing: The change of state from the liquid to the solid form; opposite of melting. Energy is released by the substance undergoing freezing.

Frequency: For a body undergoing simple harmonic motion, frequency is the number of vibrations it makes per unit time. For a wave the frequency of a series of waves is the number of waves that pass a particular point per unit time.

Friction: The resistive forces that arise to oppose the motion of a body past another with which it is in contact.

Gamma ray: High-frequency electromagnetic radiation emitted by the nuclei of radioactive atoms.

Greenhouse effect: Glass enclosures, such as florist's greenhouses, transmit radiant energy in the visible region of the electromagnetic spectrum, but are opaque to lower-frequency infrared radiation. Consequently, energy in the form of light passes into such an enclosure, is absorbed by matter within, and much of it is reradiated—but not as visible light. It is emitted as infrared radiation, for the frequency of emitted radiation is proportional to the temperature of the emitter (which is hardly the temperature of the sun that produced the visible frequencies). Infrared cannot go through the glass, so energy is trapped within the enclosure.

Half-life: The time required for half the atoms of a radioactive element to decay.

Heat: The thermal energy that flows from a body of higher temperature to a body of lower temperature, commonly measured in calories (or Btu's).

Impulse: The product of the force acting on a body and the time during which it acts. Impulse is equal to the change in the momentum of that which the impulse acts upon. In symbol notation:

$$Ft = \text{change in } mv$$

Incandescence: The state of glowing while at a high temperature, caused by electrons in vibrating atoms and molecules that are shaken in and out of their stable energy levels, emitting radiation in the process. Radiation of many frequencies is emitted; the peak frequency is proportional to the mean kinetic energy of the vibrating atoms and molecules. Therefore the peak frequency of radiation is proportional to the absolute temperature of the heated substance:

$$\bar{f} \sim T$$

Inertia: The sluggishness or apparent resistance a body offers to changes in its state of motion.

Insulator: Any material through which charge resists flow when subject to an impressed electrical force.

Interference: The superposition of waves producing regions of reinforcement and regions of cancellation. Constructive interference refers to regions of reinforcement; destructive interference refers to regions of cancellation. The interference of selected wavelengths of light produces colors, known as interference colors.

Isotopes: Atoms whose nuclei have the same number of protons but different numbers of neutrons.

Kepler's laws of planetary motion: *Law I.* Each planet moves in an elliptical orbit with the sun at one focus.

Law II. The line from the sun to any planet sweeps out equal areas of space in equal time intervals.

Law III. The squares of the times of revolution (or years) of the planets are proportional to the cubes of their average distances from the sun. ($R^3 \sim T^2$ for all planets.)

Kinetic energy: Energy of motion, described by the relationship:

$$\text{Kinetic energy} = \tfrac{1}{2}mv^2$$

Laser: (*l*ight *a*mplification by *s*timulated *e*mission of *r*adiation). An optical instrument which produces a beam of coherent monochromatic light.

Length contraction: The apparent shrinking of a body moving at relativistic speeds.

Light: The visible part of the electromagnetic spectrum.

Linear motion: Motion along a straight-line path.

Liquid: The state of matter possessing a definite volume in the same sense as a solid, but having no definite shape—it takes on the shape of its container.

Longitudinal wave: A wave in which the individual particles of a medium vibrate back and forth in the direction in which the wave travels. Sound consists of longitudinal waves.

Mach number: The ratio of the speed of an object to the speed of sound. For example, an aircraft traveling at the speed of sound is rated Mach 1.0; at twice the speed of sound, Mach 2.0, etc.

Magnetic domains: Clustered regions of aligned magnetic atoms. When these regions themselves are aligned with each other, the substance containing them is a magnet.

Magnetic field: The region of "altered space" that will interact with the magnetic properties of a magnet. It is located mainly between the opposite poles of a magnet, or in the energetic space about an electric charge in motion.

Magnetic force: (1) Between magnets it is the attraction of unlike magnetic poles for each other and the repelling between like magnetic poles. (2) Between a magnetic field and a moving charge—a moving charge is deflected from its path in the region of a magnetic field; the deflecting force is perpendicular to the motion of the charge and perpendicular to the magnetic field lines. This force is maximum when the charge moves perpendicular to the field lines, and is minimum (zero) when moving parallel to the field lines.

Mass: The quantity of matter in a body. More specifically, it is the measurement of the inertia or sluggishness that a body, in the absence of friction, exhibits in response to any effort made to start it, stop it, or change in any way its state of motion.

Mass-energy equivalence: The relationship between mass and energy as given by the equation

$$E = mc^2$$

Maxwell's counterpart to Faraday's Law: A magnetic field is induced in any region of space in which an electric field is changing with time. The magnitude of the induced magnetic field is proportional to the rate at which the electric field changes. The direction of the induced magnetic field is at right angles to the changing electric field.

Melting: The change of state from the solid to liquid form. Energy is absorbed by the substance that is melting.

Molecule: The smallest particle of a substance that has all its chemical and physical properties; atoms combine to form molecules.

Momentum: The product of the mass of a body and its velocity.

Neutrino: A massless, uncharged particle that is emitted along with an electron during beta decay. It can possess energy, momentum, and angular momentum.

Newton's laws of motion: Law 1. Every body continues in its state of rest, or of uniform motion in a straight line, unless it is compelled to change that state by forces impressed upon it.

Law 2. The acceleration of a body is directly proportional to the net force acting on the body and inversely proportional to the mass of the body.

Law 3. To every action force there is an equal and opposite reaction force.

Nonlinear motion: Any motion not along a straight-line path.

Nuclear fission: The splitting of the nucleus of a heavy atom, such as uranium-235, into two main parts, accompanied by the release of much energy.

Nuclear fusion: The combination of the nuclei of light atoms to form heavier nuclei, with the release of much energy.

Nucleon: A nuclear proton or neutron; the collective name for either or both.

Nucleus: The positively charged core of an atom.

Ohm's Law: The statement that the current in a circuit varies in direct proportion to the potential difference of emf, and in inverse proportion to resistance:

$$\text{Current} = \frac{\text{voltage}}{\text{resistance}}$$

A potential difference of 1 volt across a resistance of 1 ohm produces a current of 1 ampere.

Overtones: Tones produced by vibrations which are multiples of the lowest or fundamental vibrating frequency.

Parabola: The curved path followed by a projectile.

Parallel circuit: An electric circuit having two or more resistances arranged in such a way that any single one completes the circuit independently of all the others.

Pascal's Principle: The pressure applied to a fluid confined in a container is transmitted undiminished throughout the fluid and acts in all directions.

Phosphorescence: A type of light emission that is the same as fluorescence except for a delay between excitation and de-excitation, which provides an afterglow. The delay is caused by atoms being excited to energy levels that do not decay rapidly. The afterglow may last from fractions of a second to hours, or even days, depending on the type of material, temperature, and other factors.

Photoelectric effect: The emission of electrons from a metal surface when light is shined on it.

Photon: A light corpuscle, or the basic packet of electromagnetic radiation. Just as matter is composed of atoms, light is composed of photons (quanta).

Pitch: The "highness" or "lowness" of a tone, as on a musical scale, which is governed by frequency. A high-frequency vibrating source produces a sound of high pitch; a low-frequency vibrating source produces a sound of low pitch.

Planck's constant: A fundamental constant h which relates the energy and the frequency of light quanta. $h = 6.6 \times 10^{-34}$ joule-second.

Plasma: Hot gases composed of electrically charged particles. Most of the matter in the universe is in the plasma state.

Polarization: The alignment of the electric vectors comprising electromagnetic radiation. Such waves of aligned vibrations are said to be polarized.

Positron: The antiparticle of an electron; a positively charged electron.

Postulates of the Special Theory of Relativity: (1) All laws of nature are the same in all uniformly moving frames of reference.

(2) The velocity of light in free space will be found to have the same value regardless of the motion of the source or the motion of the observer; that is, the velocity of light is invariant.

Potential difference: The difference in voltage between two points, which can be compared to a difference in water level between two containers. If two containers having a different water level are connected by a pipe, water will flow from that with the higher level to that with the lower level until the two levels are equalized. Similarly, if two points with a difference in potential are connected by a conductor, a current will flow from that with the greater potential to that with the smaller potential until the potentials are equalized. Potential difference is measured in volts.

Potential energy: The stored energy that a body possesses because of its position with respect to other bodies.

Power: The time rate of work:

$$\text{Power} = \frac{\text{work}}{\text{time}}$$

Pressure: The ratio of the amount of force per area over which the force is distributed.

$$\text{Pressure} = \frac{\text{force}}{\text{area}}$$

$$\text{Liquid pressure} = \text{density} \times \text{depth}$$

Primary colors: The colors red, blue, and green which, when added in certain proportions, will produce any color in the spectrum.

Principle of flotation: A floating object displaces a weight of fluid equal to its own weight.

Projectile: Any body that is projected by some force and continues in motion by its own inertia.

Quality: The characteristic timbre of a musical sound, governed by the number and relative intensities of the overtones.

Quantum mechanics: The branch of quantum physics that deals with finding the probability amplitudes of matter waves, organized principally by Werner Heisenberg (1925) and Erwin Schrödinger (1926).

Quantum theory: The theory that energy is radiated in definite units called quanta, or photons. Just as matter is composed of atoms, radiant energy is composed of quanta. The theory further states that all material particles have wave properties.

Radiation: The transfer of energy by means of electromagnetic waves.

Real image: An image formed by the actual convergence of light rays upon a screen.

Reflection: The return of light rays from a surface in such a way that the angle at which a given ray is returned is equal to the angle at which it strikes the surface. When the reflecting surface is irregular, light is returned in irregular directions; this is *diffuse reflection.*

Refraction: The bending of an oblique ray of light when it passes from one transparent medium to another. This is caused by a difference in the speed of light in the transparent media. When the change in medium is abrupt (say from air to water), the bending is abrupt; when the change in medium is gradual (say from cool air to warm air), the bending is gradual, accounting for *mirages* and *looming.*

Regelation: The process of melting under pressure and the subsequent refreezing when the pressure is removed.

Relative humidity: The ratio of the amount of water vapor in a sample of air to the amount of water vapor the sample of air is capable of supporting at a given temperature.

Resolution: A method of separating a vector into its component parts.

Resonance: The setting up of vibrations in a body at its natural vibration frequency by a vibrating force or wave having the same (or submultiple) frequency.

Resultant: The geometric sum of two or more vectors.

Reverberation: Re-echoed sound.

Ritz combination principle: The spectral lines of the elements have frequencies that are either the sums or the differences of the frequencies of two other lines.

Rotational inertia: The property of a body that resists any change in its state of rotation— if at rest it tends to remain at rest; if rotating it tends to remain rotating and will continue to do so unless interrupted.

Scalar quantity: A quantity that may be specified by magnitude and without regard to direction. Examples are mass, volume, speed, and temperature.

Scattering: When light falls on a medium, electrons in the medium are set into oscillation by the time-varying electric vector of the incident light. The electrons in turn emit light in every direction, scattering the incident beam from its straight-line path.

Schrödinger wave equation: The fundamental equation of quantum mechanics that interprets the wave nature of material particles in terms of probability wave amplitudes. It is as basic to quantum mechanics as Newton's laws of motion are to classical mechanics.

Semiconductor: A normally insulating material such as crystalline silicon or germanium which becomes conducting when made with certain impurities or when energy is added.

Series circuit: An electrical circuit with resistances arranged such that the electric current flows through all of them in turn.

Shock wave: The cone-shaped wave made by an object moving at supersonic speed through a fluid.

Simple harmonic motion: A vibratory or periodic motion, like that of a pendulum, in which the force acting on the vibrating body is proportional to its displacement from its central equilibrium position and acts toward that position.

Sine curve: The wavelike path traced by an object undergoing simple harmonic motion.

Solid: The state of matter characterized by definite volume and shape.

Sonic boom: The loud sound resulting from the incidence of a shock wave.

Sound: A longitudinal wave phenomenon that consists of successive compressions and rarefactions of the medium through which it travels.

Space-time: The four-dimensional continuum in which all things exist; three dimensions being the coordinates of space, and the other of time.

Special Theory of Relativity: A formulation of the consequences of the absence of a universal frame of reference, developed by Albert Einstein. It has two postulates: (1) All laws of nature are·the same in all uniformly moving frames of reference. (2) The velocity of light in free space will be found to have the same value regardless of the motion of the source or the motion of the observer; that is, the velocity of light is invariant.

Specific heat: The quantity of heat per unit mass required to raise the temperature of a substance by one degree centigrade; measured in units calories per gram Celsius degree (or Btu's per pound Fahrenheit degree).

Spectroscope: An optical instrument that separates light into its constituent frequencies in the form of spectral lines.

Speed: The rate at which distance is covered by a moving body with time.

Standing wave: Stationary wave patterns formed in a medium when two sets of identical waves pass through the medium in opposite directions.

Sublimation: The direct conversion of a substance from the solid to the vapor state, or vice versa, without passing through the liquid state.

Superfluidity: The term used to describe the resistanceless flow of material near the absolute zero of temperature.

Surface tension: The tendency of the surface of a liquid to contract in area and thus behave like a stretched rubber membrane.

Technology: A method and means of solving practical problems by implementing the findings of science.

Temperature: A measure of the average kinetic energy per molecule in a body, measured in degrees Celsius, Fahrenheit, or Kelvin.

Time dilation: The apparent slowing down of time of a body moving at relativistic speeds.

Torque: The product of force and lever-arm distance, which tends to produce rotation.

Total internal reflection: The total reflection of light traveling in a medium when it is incident upon the surface of a less dense medium at an angle greater than the critical angle.

Transformer: A device for transforming electrical power from one coil of wire to another, by means of electromagnetic induction. A changing magnetic field in the core of the transformer is provided by alternating current in the primary coil. Voltage in the secondary coil may be stepped up or down according to the relation:

$$\frac{\text{Primary voltage}}{\text{Number of primary loops}} = \frac{\text{secondary voltage}}{\text{number of secondary loops}}$$

If the voltage is stepped up, the current is correspondingly stepped down in such a way that the product of current and voltage (power) is no greater in the secondary coil than in the primary coil; that is,

$$(\text{Voltage} \times \text{current})_{\text{primary}} = (\text{voltage} \times \text{current})_{\text{secondary}}$$

Transmutation: The conversion of an atomic nucleus of one element into an atomic nucleus of another element through a loss or gain in the number of protons.

Transverse wave: A wave in which the individual particles of a medium vibrate from side to side perpendicular (transverse) to the direction in which the wave travels. The vibrations along a stretched string are transverse waves.

Uncertainty principle: The principle formulated by Heisenberg which states that the ultimate accuracy of measurement is given by the magnitude of Planck's constant h. Further, it is not possible to measure exactly both the position and the momentum of a particle at the same time, nor the energy and time of a particle simultaneously.

Universal Law of Gravitation: Every body in the universe attracts every other body with a force that for two bodies is proportional to the masses of the bodies and inversely proportional to the square of the distance separating them.

$$F \sim \frac{mm'}{d^2}$$

Vector: An arrow drawn to scale used to represent a vector quantity.

Vector quantity: A quantity that has both magnitude and direction. Examples are force, velocity, acceleration, torque, and electric and magnetic fields.

Velocity: The specification of the speed of a body and its direction of motion, a vector quantity.

Virtual image: An illusionary image that is seen by an observer through a lens but cannot be projected on a screen.

Volume: The quantity of space a body occupies.

Wavelength: The distance between successive crests, troughs, or identical parts of a wave.

Wave velocity: The speed with which waves pass by a particular point:

$$\text{Wave velocity} = \text{frequency} \times \text{wavelength}$$

Weight: The force of gravitational attraction upon a body.

Work: The product of the net force exerted and the distance through which the force moves:

$$W = F \times d$$

Index